PSYCHOGENIC PSYCHOSES

ENGLAND: BUTTERWORTH & CO. (PUBLISHERS) LTD.
                LONDON: 88 Kingsway, W.C.2

AFRICA: BUTTERWORTH & CO. (AFRICA) LTD.
                DURBAN: 33/35 Beach Grove

AUSTRALIA: BUTTERWORTH & CO. (AUSTRALIA) LTD.
                SYDNEY: 6–8 O'Connell Street
                MELBOURNE: 473 Bourke Street
                BRISBANE: 240 Queen Street

CANADA: BUTTERWORTH & CO. (CANADA) LTD.
                TORONTO: 1367 Danforth Avenue, 6

NEW ZEALAND: BUTTERWORTH & CO. (NEW ZEALAND) LTD
                WELLINGTON: 49/51 Ballance Street
                AUCKLAND: 35 High Street

U.S.A.:   BUTTERWORTH INC.
                WASHINGTON, D.C.: 7235 Wisconsin Avenue,

Psychogenic Psychoses

A Description and Follow-up

of

Psychoses following Psychological Stress

POUL M. FAERGEMAN, M.D.

Senior Physician, Department of Psychiatry, University of Aarhus; State Hospital, Risskov, Denmark

LONDON
BUTTERWORTHS
1963

Printed in Great Britain by
Spottiswoode, Ballantyne & Co., Ltd.
London and Colchester

FOREWORD

During the past few decades psychiatric research has been mainly directed towards elucidation of the mechanisms associated with the causation and perpetuation of mental disorder. Psychoanalysts have devoted themselves to the psychodynamic aspects—those with an organic orientation to the physiodynamics of mental illness. It might appear that the frontiers of the main forms of psychiatric illness can be regarded as clearly delineated, but many of the difficulties in communication experienced by psychiatrists have probably arisen from this assumption, for there is much to suggest that it is erroneous.

In Scandinavian countries, however, nosological as well as genetic problems have continued to receive attention and Dr. Faergeman's monograph has been partly inspired by the previous studies of Wimmer and Strömgren on psychogenic psychoses. The atypical schizophrenias or schizophreniform psychoses which have been studied by Langfeldt and other Scandinavian workers are related to Dr. Faergeman's subject in that psychological stresses impressively related to the onset of the illness are among the features held to differentiate this group of conditions from the nuclear or typical schizophrenias.

Dr. Faergeman's method is empirical. He examines the validity of the concept of psychogenic psychosis by ascertaining the fate of patients with different types of clinical picture fifteen to twenty years after admission to hospital. In a substantial proportion of cases the illness proved on follow-up to have pursued a course that could not be explained in terms of psychogenic factors alone. Thus in more than half the cases with a paranoid syndrome, the psychogenically precipitated illness pursued an unmistakably schizophrenic course. And even among emotional syndromes, the diagnosis of psychogenic psychosis proved to have been erroneous in a third of the cases, more than half of these incorrect diagnoses being accounted for by schizophrenia. Yet in well over half the cases with a disturbance of consciousness in the first attack, follow-up studies confirmed the initial diagnosis of psychogenic psychosis. The concept of psychogenic psychosis thus received some degree of validation. Moreover, Dr. Faergeman's studies shed interesting light on the relative predictive value of the different components of the clinical picture. Thus a strong affective colouring, duration of the illness for less than three months and a 'massive psychic trauma' preceding the onset of symptoms, were all associated with a

v

relatively favourable prognosis as were also the absence of paranoid features and hallucinations. There are some obvious similarities between these pointers and the clinical features which have been described as characteristic of schizophreniform psychosis. The link between the two phenomena clearly invites exploration.

However, the value of Dr. Faergeman's book extends well beyond its contribution to such practical problems of diagnosis, interesting and important though they are. His training both as a psychoanalyst and as a psychiatrist in the orthodox European tradition, and the success with which he has managed to integrate the teaching of both, endow his thought with an unusual range and flexibility. His discerning grasp of the crucial events in the evolution of psychiatric knowledge adds further strength to the bridges he has evidently set out to build to facilitate communication between the organic and psychodynamic worlds of thought and psychiatry.

His book should do something to broaden perspectives all round. On the one hand, the organically orientated psychiatrist generally appreciates that the psychological stresses contribute to the causation of some forms of mental disorder, but the fact that they can be so rarely held to be both necessary and sufficient causes, tends perhaps to make him underestimate their importance. The psychoanalyst on the other hand, is in danger of concluding that any relevant psychological processes that have been defined are of specific importance in the causation of illness, when in fact they may be entitled only to a relatively low place in the hierarchy of causes. Dr. Faergeman's book inevitably leaves many problems unsolved, but it has something to teach both those who seek for the causes of mental disorder with cerebral mechanisms on the one hand, and the vicissitudes of interpersonal relationship in the early years of development on the other. For this effort in bridge building and also for its contribution to the practical problem of diagnosis in the interesting borderlands between the neuroses and psychoses, and between schizophrenia and other forms of mental disorder that appear to engulf the personality, it deserves a warm welcome.

Durham
December 1962

MARTIN ROTH

CONTENTS

CONTENTS

ix

PREFACE

This monograph is based on a thesis (University of Copenhagen), published in Danish in 1945, upon the follow-up study of 170 cases of presumed psychogenic psychoses, that is, mental disorders caused by psychological stress varying from violent external events to conflicts of a purely personal nature. The original diagnoses had been made by the late Professor August Wimmer of the University of Copenhagen, and, upon the suggestion of Professor Erik Strömgren of Aarhus University, I undertook, many years later, to test these diagnoses with the object of obtaining a clearer understanding of psychogenic psychoses and of their differentiation from symptomatologically related mental diseases.

The thesis was oriented along the lines of traditional Continental psychiatric thinking, and, in the present book, which is a freshly written work, special prominence has been given to a discussion of the concept of psychogenesis as it is employed in the two great, and radically different, traditions of psychiatry, the Continental and the Anglo-American. The experience derived from a number of years spent in the United States of America as a practising psychoanalytic psychiatrist has furnished me with additional background for this discussion.

The suggestion that a translation and revision of the thesis might help to bridge the gap between the two traditions came from Professor Martin Roth of the University of Durham and from Professor Erik Strömgren. For their initiative and subsequent encouragement I wish to express my sincere gratitude. I wish also to thank Professor Roth for kindly writing the Foreword. The preparation of the book has been aided by grants from the Rask-Oersted Foundation and the Danish State Research Foundation.

Risskov, Denmark   POUL M. FAERGEMAN
March, 1963

Part I

GENERAL

CHAPTER 1

INTRODUCTORY: AN ATTEMPT AT CLARIFICATION OF THE CONCEPT OF PSYCHOGENESIS*

In this introductory chapter an attempt will be made to list and discuss at least some of the numerous—and often vague and contradictory—definitions of the concept of psychogenesis which are to be found in textbooks and monographs within the fields of psychology and psychiatry. Following this the latter part of the chapter will endeavour to define 'psychogenesis' as it is used in this work.

For conceptual and historical reasons it would seem advantageous in this particular respect to compare the two great traditions in psychiatry, the Continental and the Anglo-American. There are encouraging signs to the effect that in the not too distant future we shall be able to learn more about the Soviet's progress within our field.

The conceptual aspect of the problem will be dealt with primarily in Chapters 1 and 3, the historical aspect mostly in Chapter 2.

The Two Traditions in Psychiatry

The mutual understanding between Continental and Anglo-American psychiatry—and their mutual co-operation—is hampered by a number of factors. One is the German preference for speculative constructions and explanations as contrasted with the English inclination towards objective observation and the American proclivity for pragmatic approaches. Another is due to the simple linguistic fact that Englishmen and Americans usually find German an awkward language—a sentiment that is reciprocated by the Germans so far as non-Teutonic languages are concerned. People belonging to the small West European countries are for obvious reasons in a better position in this respect.

A third factor—undeniably connected with the one just mentioned—is that certain words have completely different meanings in the two psychiatric traditions. A classic example is the word 'amentia'. This

* This chapter is based on a paper read at a meeting of The Royal Medico-Psychological Association at Gloucester on 3 May 1961.

word designates in German–Viennese psychiatry an acute hallu-cinatory confusion of rather mild degree and with 'bewilderment' (*Ratlosigkeit*) as the most striking symptom (Bonhoeffer, 1910); the aetiology is toxic-infective. In England and in the United States it is, on the other hand, synonymous with primary mental deficiency. Mayer-Gross, Slater and Roth (1960) prefer the term 'sub-acute delirious state' for the German meaning of the word.

Psychogenesis and the Two Traditions

A second example which will bring us to our topic is the word 'psychogenesis'—introduced into psychiatry in 1894 by R. Sommer—and the *verbally* kindred, but *conceptually* unrelated 'psychogenetics'. It may prove instructive to compare a number of whole-hearted—and half-hearted—definitions of these words. Strictly speaking, it is not only a question of *definitions* of these terms, but also a matter of different *uses* of them by psychiatrists and psychologists with different conceptual needs. They are not, perhaps, as numerous as the Midianites and the Amalekites and their camels, but we are certainly reminded of Allport's (1937) list of fifty definitions of the word 'personality'. The word 'psychogenic' can, naturally, considering the semantics of its two component parts and completely separating it from all clinical connotations, mean two entirely different things: (1) a condition is psychogenic when it is 'born by the mind', that is, growing out of innate constitutional factors as, for example, the psychopathias, the manic-depressive psychoses and at least some of the 'schizophrenias'. We shall see that this is the connotation usually given it in British–American psychiatry. (2) On the other hand, it can signify psycho-pathological conditions caused by environmental factors with which the organism cannot cope with the employment of the normal defence-mechanisms and discharge-channels. This is the usual meaning of the word in Continental psychiatry. To put it differently: from this linguistic take-off, we can conclude that 'psychogenic' can refer equally well to 'something' caused or produced by the 'psyche' as to some alteration in this 'psyche' due to situational or environmental—particularly interpersonal—factors.

Psychologists have demonstrated an eagerness similar to the psychia-trists' in their use of the word—and with the same sovereign con-tempt for the meanings already attached to it by others. Murray (1938) divides 'needs' into two groups: viscerogenic and psychogenic. To the former (or primary) belong the needs for air, water, food, sex, urination, etc., to the latter (or secondary) belong the needs for acquisi-tion, conservance, order, aggression, abasement, blamavoidance, and

4

many others. The psychogenic needs have, to quote Murray, 'no subjectively localizable bodily origins; hence the term "psychogenic"'. One of the broadest and vaguest definitions is suggested by Drever (1952):

> Psychogenesis: the origin and development of mental phenomena in general, or particular features or peculiarities of mental processes, as manifested in behaviour. Psychogenic: term usually employed of disorders which originate in mental conditions, though they may come to involve physiological changes, as a result of these mental conditions.

Hinsie and Campbell (1960) have the definition:

> The term psychogenesis means, in so far as present knowledge extends, that certain activities of the individual, called psychic activities, may be traced back at least to the psyche.

Adding to the conceptual confusion is the fact that English psychology (Eysenck and colleagues, 1960) has defined 'psychogenetics' as a convenient shorthand term for 'psychological genetics', 'behaviour genetics', or 'genetical psychology'. Kallman (1959) uses the word 'psychogenetics' in a way that conceptually makes it a cousin of Eysenck's notion. It embraces simply all hereditary factors in psychology and psychopathology.

The World Health Organization has in its *International Classification of Diseases* (1957) a group of 'psychogenic disorders' (numbers 314–317, inclusive) which comprises 'psycho-neurosis with somatic symptoms', that is some of the psychosomatic diseases plus 'psychogenic depression'. This implies that the only psychotic condition that can be considered psychogenic according to this system is depression caused by psychic traumatization and sufficiently severe to deserve the adjective 'psychotic'.

This classification is entirely different from the one advocated by the American Psychiatric Association in its *Diagnostic and Statistical Manual* (1952) in which we find a group of 'disorders of psychogenic origin or without clearly defined physical cause or structural change in the brain', to which belong—among others—the 'manic-depressive reactions' and the 'schizophrenic reactions'. But here the psychosomatic illnesses ('psychophysiologic autonomic and visceral disorders') and the 'psychoneurotic disorders' are not listed under the heading 'psychogenic'.

Several Continental classifications (Denmark, Norway, Holland and Germany), and also the classification of the Soviet Union, recognize formally the existence of psychogenic disorders although a clear

distinction between psychoneurotic and psychotic reactions is usually not attempted.*

Laughlin (1956) has these definitions:

Psychogenesis: The emotional or interpersonal origin and development of an emotional illness.

Psychogenic: Of intra-psychic origin. Psychogenic is an adjective referring to the emotional or psychologic origin of a symptom or a condition, as opposed to an organic origin.

This kind of circular definitions does not help us much; also, it is not clear whether the words 'emotional', 'interpersonal', and 'psychologic' are synonymous or are supposed to designate different concepts.

Some authors use the words without even offering a definition. To give but two examples: Noyes (1958) simply uses the concept 'psychogenic schizophrenia' without further ado. Glover (1939) talks—justifiably so—with gloom about 'the muddled state of psychiatric classification and terminology', and at the same time omits to make a clear definition of the word 'psychogenic' himself. It would seem that he uses it synonymously with 'psychological factors'. We can hardly be expected to feel illuminated by such approaches.

Psychoanalysts have, on the whole, shown some scepticism towards the use of the word 'psychogenic'. Margolin (1953) puts it bluntly in this statement: 'I do not believe in "psychogenesis"; that is that a psychophysiological process is initiated *de novo* in the mind. Mental events in both health and disease are but links in the psycho-somatic chain of events.' And in his summing up, Deutsch in the same symposium states that the term 'psychogenic' has become invalidated because 'from the analytic point of view, all biologic functions are continually governed psychodynamically'.

Four Principal Contributions to the Problem of Psychogenesis

Before discussing the contributions of four psychiatrists (Wimmer, Jaspers, Kretschmer, and Gerö) who have made important contributions to the discussion of 'psychogenesis', I should like to mention that I have personal anecdotive evidence for the state of confusion regarding this term. When I visited the Department of Psychiatry at the University of Rochester, New York, recently, I took the opportunity to pose a question to six members of Professor Romano's staff. I suggested that they give me their first association to a stimulus word I would

* An exhaustive survey of the modern psychiatric nosological classifications of several European countries, Great Britain, the U.S.A., the Soviet Union, and Argentina is to be found in the article by Meyer (1961).

6

mention. Four of them looked a bit uneasy. The stimulus word, naturally, was 'psychogenic psychosis'. Four of the subjects in this little experiment with the word association test applied to experienced psychiatrists answered without hesitation: 'Oh—schizophrenia, of course.' The fifth looked thoughtful and answered after a brief pause: 'Has it not something to do with hysteria?' The sixth responded in a charmingly straightforward way: 'Well, I never heard of that one before!'

Wimmer

In 1916 the Danish psychiatrist August Wimmer published his classic monograph on the psychogenic psychoses. In his work, which has, unfortunately, never appeared in a major language, the late Professor of Psychiatry at the University of Copenhagen defined 'psychogenic psychoses' as a group of clinically independent psychoses that are caused by psychic traumatizations in individuals with a psychopathic predisposition. The psychic traumata are responsible for the appearance of the illness, its clinical 'movements', its content, and, very frequently, also for its termination. He stated that the prognosis, on the whole, is favourable and never results in a deterioration of the personality. However, some paranoid psychoses do take a chronic course. With great erudition, Wimmer discussed the literature— particularly the French, of which he was very fond—and defined the two types of psychopathic temperament which offer the best soil for the development of psychogenic psychoses: 'the explosive-emotional' and 'the paranoigenic'. His material consisted of 98 patients (37 men and 61 women) of which 24 representative cases are described in the article. Unfortunately, his descriptions and conclusions are based solely on fresh case material, that is, there are no follow-ups. There is no knowing whether the outcome was as favourable as he had claimed. Indeed, some of his patients seem to have been cases of schizophrenia. Wimmer himself mentioned that among the psychogenic paranoid psychoses ('evolutional paranoias') described in his thesis (1902) there were probably a good many schizophrenias.

This limitation of Wimmer's work prompted Professor Strömgren to suggest that undertake a follow-up study of a fairly large number of psychoses, diagnosed as 'psychogenic' by Wimmer and his staff (at the Psychiatric Department of the Municipal Hospital of Copenhagen) during the three years 1924–6. Altogether 170 patients were diagnosed as suffering from psychogenic psychoses during this period. All except 3 were identified and 98 were re-examined personally. Of the remaining 69 most were dead (53) while 16 were not contacted, mostly for reasons

7

of tact. In passing it can be mentioned that 33 per cent of the patients 15–20 years after the initial diagnosis had been made turned out to be schizophrenics—in the strict Continental sense of the word, that is with autism and deterioration of the personality.

Jaspers

It is obvious that Wimmer's definition of psychogenic psychoses was adopted from Jaspers' (1913) concept of 'genuine reactions' to 'affective shocks' (*Gemütserschütterung*) as contrasted with 'precipitated psychoses' (*bloss ausgelöste Psychosen*) as, for example, the appearance of a catatonic psychosis after the death of a beloved person. Jaspers expressly mentions that *causation, content, course*, and *termination* of the 'genuine reactions' are dependent on the traumatic situation (*Die Psychose bleibt auf das zentrale Erlebnis bezogen*, 3rd ed., 1923). Actually, this is a systematic sharpening of the criteria of 'reactive depressions', already formulated by Reiss (1910).

Jaspers began his career as a psychiatrist. Later he became a philosopher with a bend towards existentialism. He produced the abovementioned clear-cut but not completely satisfactory definition of the concept we are here struggling with. In later editions of his book—for example the fifth from 1948—he expanded his views on the 'reactions' and introduced 'the three-dimensional comprehensibility of psychogenic reactions' (*Die dreifache Richtung der Verstehbarkeit der Reaktionen*). We 'understand' (1) the *intensity* (*Mass*) of the experience as an adequate explanation for the patient's breakdown, (2) the *purpose* (*Sinn*) of the reaction (prison psychoses, compensation neuroses), and finally, (3) the *content* (*Inhalt*) of the reaction from the nature of the traumatic experience.

Theoretically attractive as such conceptualizations are, they fail us often when we are dealing with clinical realities. In my material, for example, it was only possible in a very few cases to demonstrate that the traumatizing situation was reflected in the content of the psychoses. Lewis (1934) in one of his classic papers on depression states bluntly: 'It may as well be said at once that not a single patient was found in whose illness these requirements [Jaspers'] were satisfied.' He found in his material, consisting of 61 patients, the criteria of content, course or termination met in a few cases, 'but in no patient were they all satisfied'. He concludes his paper by agreeing with the stand taken by Schultz (1930):

> The question whether an illness is reactive or endogenous is often put too schematically; it might more sensibly be formulated as: How far are reactive processes, in the widest sense, concerned in this case,

and how far obscure hereditary or somatic determinants of a fateful sort?

The following examples from my material will illustrate this point. What is the 'comprehensible' connection between being in a train accident and developing a clouded state in which the patient believes he is in a different section of Copenhagen than he really is, and that the year is 1872 instead of 1924? (Case 75). Or what is 'understandable' in Case 81 in which the psychosis is triggered by the loss of a child and its content consists of hallucinatory experiences of spiders crawling in the bed and of a fire in the attic? (*Cf.* Chapter 14).

While still discussing the problem of a comprehensible relationship between the traumatic event and the psychotic content it should be mentioned that Freud in *Mourning and Melancholia* (1917) formulated the dictum that in depressions 'the self-accusations are accusations'. He illustrated this by means of a clinical example: a young woman developed a depression in which she accused herself of being a thief. In fact, it was her father who, shortly before, had been sentenced because of a theft. In other words, she identified herself with her father.

With regard to the liquidation of the traumatic situation and the course and termination of the psychotic reaction, experience forces us to conclude that in this respect also the Jaspers–Wimmer criterion is not entirely satisfactory. This study has demonstrated very varying durations of psychogenic reactions. Disturbances of consciousness (*cf.* Chapter 4) are, on the whole, brief, with 60 per cent of the patients recovering from the psychotic state within a week after the onset of the illness. The depressions and the paranoid reactions, on the other hand, tend to persist for weeks or months. However, some disturbances of consciousness continue for months *after* the traumatic situation is eliminated. This was emphasized by Wimmer himself. It seems to be the psychogenic stupors that particularly tend to fall outside this criterion.

So far as the environmental factor as a *causative* agent is concerned there appears to be a more regular and clear-cut connection between experience and reaction. In this material there were only 2 cases out of 79 verified psychogenic psychoses where information about 'psychic trauma', respectively 'inner conflict', was missing. This in contrast to the 'psychogenic psychoses' which the follow-up demonstrated to be schizophrenias: in 12 of the 43 cases information about psychic traumatization had not been forthcoming; on the basis of the clinical material it is much harder to venture an opinion about the presence of severe inner conflicts in these 12 cases.

These facts concerning the Jaspers–Wimmer criteria suggest the existence of two categories of psychogenic psychoses: the '*complete*', in which all criteria are fulfilled, and the *'incomplete'*, fulfilling only partly the demands made by Jaspers.

Gerö

A serious attempt at tackling our problem was made by Gerö (1943). His paper possesses certain merits, mainly in the effort to bring together the traditional Continental point of view and the psychoanalytic approach to this subject. But in his very first paragraph he finds himself in a conceptual quagmire. He starts out by stating: 'By "psychogenesis" we understand a causal chain of psychic phenomena only.' In other words, he accepts the dichotomy: body–soul. Whereupon he hastily adds that 'of course it is not meant that the psyche is an independent entity as we know that psychic and organic form a unity'. In other words, he rejects the body–soul dichotomy. We are apparently facing a basic conceptual dilemma. 'Psychogenic' and 'organic' are words reflecting the traditional thinking in our culture: the dichotomy between 'soul' and 'body', which can be traced back at least to Plato and his unfortunate insistence on the idea of man as consisting of a mortal carcass into which God has put an immortal spirit.

Gerö now proceeds to a critical evaluation of 'psychogenesis' as understood by Wimmer and later by Kretschmer. He praises Wimmer for his insistence that the psychic trauma in psychogenic psychoses does decide not only the triggering of the reaction but also its psychopathology, its symptomatological expression and clinical course, whereas in the pre-Wimmer era psychiatrists tended only to consider the *general* effect of the traumatic situation (shock, insomnia, poor nutrition). Gerö also approves of Wimmer's overcoming of a purely symptomatological approach. Wimmer often made a diagnosis of 'psychogenic psychosis' where other psychiatrists would have said 'schizophrenia'. As already mentioned, a good many of the patients in my material who displayed schizophreniform symptoms in the initial stage actually turned out to be schizophrenic.

Although Wimmer's trauma theory is accepted as a psychopathological sophistication compared with earlier approaches to the problem of psychogenesis, Gerö finds it to be too naïve in its simple and general formulation: these psychoses result from the reaction of an abnormal constitution to a traumatic event. The specific criticism consists of the objection that Wimmer's theory does not give us real psychopathological understanding of the formation of the symptoms. When Wimmer is in trouble, in this respect, he attempts to find a way out by accessory hypotheses such as the temporary heightened psychic vulnerability due to menstruation, malnutrition, insomnia, abuse of alcohol and nicotine, etc.

10

Kretschmer

Gerö's discussion of Kretschmer's theory concerning development of the sensitive paranoid psychoses follows similar lines. Kretschmer, in his classic book *Der sensitive Beziehungswahn* (1918), which will be discussed in more detail in the introduction to Chapter 8, described types of paranoid development, particularly 'sensitive' and 'expansive' forms. He considered them to be the outcome of specific paranoigenic temperaments which are hit by specific 'key-experiences'. There is no paranoia, only paranoics. The individual case has to be, and can be, understood from its specific characterological equipment and the specific environmental stress. To Gerö the idea that, for example, a constitutionally sensitive character structure produces delusions when hit by certain life situations as, for instance, disappointment in love, is too plain. The connection between such character-traits and the situation—usually experienced by the patient to be a shameful one—is not considered by Gerö to be comprehensible. He proposes an extension of Kretschmer's theory: the sensitive patient has a rigid, hyper-moralistic superego that completely rejects the sexual impulses. This intra-psychic conflict the patient attempts to solve by projecting his relentless self-criticism on to other people, that is, developing delusional features.

Gerö thus feels that Wimmer's as well as Kretschmer's concepts of constitution and character are too static and that their whole approach to the problem lacks the conceptual and psychodynamic refinement of psychoanalytic thinking.

The criteria of psychogenic psychoses can now be summarized. Continental psychiatry has the following:

(1) Psychogenic psychoses are reactive and therefore 'reasonable', that is, it is understandable not only that they develop at all, but also their form, content, course, and termination are comprehensible.

(2) They are centred around an emotionally supercharged idea, around a life episode of emphasized affect.

(3) There are no formal disturbances of thinking.

(4) It is always possible to establish contact with the patient, in other words, autism is absent.

Psychoanalysis has added the following three criteria:

(1) Although traumatic events may not be demonstrable a psychosis may be psychogenic; only a detailed knowledge of an individual's personality structure makes it possible to determine why a seemingly innocuous episode had had traumatic effect.

(2) The presence of sexual pathogenic factors point to a psychogenic aetiology.*

(3) The most important criterion is the demonstration of the psychic mechanisms that are responsible for the symptom formation.

Three Factors in Psychogenesis

Three aetiological and pathogenic agents are usually reckoned with: constitution, psychic trauma, and inner-psychic conflict. The constitutional aspects will be discussed in Chapter 3. So far as trauma and conflict are concerned, we find ourselves in conceptual confusion. Should the two words designate entirely different psychophysiological happenings or are they rather to be thought of as naming events that differ quantitatively from each other but belong to the same psychophysiological continuum? Kris (1956) emphasizes '... a continuum characterized by its extremes, by the stress on *endopsychic* and the stress on *environmental* factors.' Let us formulate some questions in our approach to a differential definition. What should be understood by 'psychic trauma'? An earthquake, a brutal rape, seeing one's child being killed by a car, obviously can lead to psychotic reactions, almost always some kind of disturbance of consciousness. Such situations are thus 'psychic traumata'—for some people. Not everybody in an earthquake reacts in a psychotic way, and some women seduce men into raping them and enjoy it,† and some parents seeing their child killed react with mourning rather than a melancholic or an acute delirious state.

What is the proper meaning that should be attached to the words 'inner-psychic conflict'? And are there normal as well as pathological 'inner conflicts'? The impulse to kill an enemy, frustrated by the ego's realistic concern for the consequences and the superego's condemnation of the impulse is an 'inner-psychic conflict'. We can safely say that 'inner-psychic conflicts' are a part of human nature and are to be found in prince as well as pauper. They are ubiquitous because we have —maybe foolishly—abandoned the law of the jungle and accepted the burden of limitation and civilization as it was pointed out by Freud in his *Civilization and its Discontents* (1930). It is nonsense

* Gerö certainly can be challenged here. It was the early Freud who saw sex as the *primum movens* of human behaviour—'normal' and 'pathological'. The older Freud and modern psychoanalysis consider aggressive drives to be even more important than the sexual impulses (*cf.*, for example, Glover, 1931). And are sexual agents less important in schizophrenias than in psychogenic psychoses?

† *Cf.* André Pieyre de Mandiargues' novel (1956): *Le Lis de Mer* (*The Girl Beneath the Lion*).

12

to claim that some antisocial psychopaths are without a super-ego. Greenacre (1945) has pointed this out in her statement:

It has been said that the psychopath has no guilt feelings, no conscience (the potentialities of a conscience have never been internalized and what remains is only a fear of external punishment), and no psychic mechanisms of defense; some descriptions state that he has no anxiety. If all this were true, I believe that the psychopath would not live very long, but would explode from the force of his own primitive aggression.

Definition of Inner-Psychic Conflict and Psychic Trauma

Inner-psychic conflicts thus are the unavoidable state of tension between two or more of the constituents of the personality.

The following proposition may be an approximation to the definition of the term 'psychic trauma': *A 'psychic trauma' is a situation that elicits such quantities of excitation in an organism that they cannot be handled without production of conscious or unconscious anxiety.*

The term 'unconscious anxiety' may seem meaningless to some people. But as Zilboorg (1933) has pointed out, anxiety reactions consist of three components: ideational content, affect, and motoric-secretory activities. The first two may remain repressed while the anxiety manifests itself in acting out, conversion phenomena or neurotic lacrimation, handsweating, etc., etc. The topophobic patient who avoids the trigger situation still suffers from anxiety.

In this context it will be useful to consider Freud's (1926a) distinction between fear or realistic anxiety (*Realangst*) and neurotic anxiety (*Angst*). When I go for a walk in the desert and meet a lion I experience fear. When a woman reacts with panic by walking in the streets she displays anxiety—maybe because of her repressed prostitution fantasies (prostitutes are often referred to as 'street-walkers'). Is there a basic and principal difference between realistic and neurotic anxiety or are they connected in a psychodynamic continuum? The latter is probably the case. Anxiety, generally is, according to Freud's second theory (1926a) about this problem, a *signal* that warns against a danger, in realistic anxiety an external danger, in neurotic anxiety an internal danger. But there is most likely a continuous scale between the two. Freud in the above quoted work wrote:

A danger-situation is a recognized, remembered, expected situation of helplessness. Anxiety is the original reaction to helplessness in the trauma and is reproduced later on in the danger-situation as a signal for help. The ego, which experienced the trauma passively, now repeats it actively in a weakened version, in the hope of being able itself to direct its course. . . . So far we have had no occasion to regard realistic anxiety in any different light from neurotic anxiety. We know what the distinction is. A real danger is a danger which threatens a person from

13

an external object, and a neurotic danger is one which threatens him from an instinctual demand. In so far as the instinctual demand is something real, his neurotic anxiety, too, can be admitted to have a realistic basis. We have seen that the reason why there seems to be a specially close connection between anxiety and neurosis is that the ego defends itself against an instinctual danger with the help of the anxiety reaction just as it does against an external real danger, but that this line of defensive activity eventuates in a neurosis owing to an imperfection of the mental apparatus. We have also come to the conclusion that an instinctual demand often only becomes an (internal) danger because its satisfaction would bring on an external danger—that is, because the internal danger represents an external one.

Bullfighters risk their lives in the arena and wear black trousers because most of them wet their pants before or in the beginning of the fight. This is *Realangst*. Is it fundamentally different from the neurotic anxiety experienced by a woman watching a bull at a relatively safe distance? Who can tell how much *anxiety* is mixed up with *fear* in the bullfighter? May not the bull, besides being a bull, also represent the father he wants to kill or the father he wants to be the woman to in the goring? Certainly, bullfighting is loaded with tremendous unconscious symbolic meanings, to the crowd as well as to the matador.

To take another example from the animal kingdom. Horseback-riding is a noble sport, but not without a real risk. Many people have been killed exercising it—especially in steeple chasing. However, practised in a sensible way, it is not more dangerous than crossing Piccadilly. Obviously, some people have a phobic anxiety attached to the horse because of the different unconscious fantasies it represents, and the resulting projective misunderstanding of the equine reality. It submits to the skilful rider like a woman to the man in the sexual act (*cf.* the bawdy dialogue between the Duke of Orleans and the Dauphin in *King Henry V*, Act III, Scene vii). And, on the other hand, it clearly has a phallic symbolic significance. It is a curious fact that approximately 75 per cent of all young riders (both in Europe and America) are girls.

Thus, one could say that 'inner-psychic conflict', for example the tension between the sado-masochistic impulses towards the father and the superego's frowning on them—and the 'psychic trauma'—for example the matador's anxiety in his deadly dance with the bull—are the stuff human nature is made of. They are two aspects of the same psychophysiological event. An environmental factor can usually not be traumatically operative without the existence of an inner-psychic conflict. The opposite is not necessarily true (see Case 149).

An important implication here is that there cannot be any sharp line

14

of demarcation between 'normality' and 'pathology'. To God we are all neurotics. And probably psychotics too. Glover (1932) writes: 'As for larval psychoses, we are all larval psychotics and have been such since the age of two.'

In criticizing the conventional meaning given to 'psychic trauma', it must be emphasized that it usually means a situation, sufficiently shocking or dramatic according to our 'common sense' to make 'understandable' a 'psychopathological' reaction. This is unsophisticated thinking.

Catathymia and Overindividual Reactions

It will prove helpful here to bring into the discussion the extremely important concept of *catathymia* introduced in 1912 by the Swiss psychiatrist H. W. Maier. By this is understood the specific psychic vulnerability due to earlier, particularly infantile, traumatizations.

> The principle of catathymia can be well demonstrated by the following anecdote; it is said that Freud was very fond of it. Before World War I two young, noble and arrogant Hungarian officers were discussing the problem of will power in the officers' mess. One of them bragged that he possessed that quality to such an extent that he would be able to eat faeces without showing any sign of disgust. A large bet was made and the meal was presently served on a golden platter. The young man ate with perfect dignity. When he had almost finished, his face suddenly contorted in an expression of the most violent loathing. The bet was lost. When the astonished friends who had gathered around the table asked him why in the world he had not been able to gobble up the last bit of his unusual dish, he answered, 'Didn't you see ? There was a hair in it.'

Thus, catathymia is a kind of psychic allergy.* A seemingly insignificant event will precipitate a large amount of excitation, that is, anxiety, only understandable to the observer who has knowledge of the catathymic hypersensitivity. Thus, 'catathymia' bridges the concepts of 'inner-psychic conflict' and 'psychic trauma'.

A traumatic situation is a situation which triggers the catathymic potential. This is the essence of psychogenesis. An example: a young male patient of mine lived in a rented room. The adjoining room was occupied by a young girl who was often visited by her boy friend and they regularly committed the most forgivable of all human sins. This

---

* In this chapter I have deliberately chosen to put the emphasis on the catathymic aspect of the phenomenon of psychogenesis. In Chapter 3 some attention will be paid to the constitutional factors and to Freud's ideas about psychic traumatization and his concept of complementary series. Qualitative as well as quantitative problems obviously are common to both the catathymic and the constitutional aspects of psychogenesis.

evoked in the patient a very intense discomfort (*Unlust*). He had spent the nights of the first six years of his life in his parents' bedroom. The experience of the primal scene had catathymically sensitized him to the sounds of the sexual act. In many persons this situation would cause sexual excitement only.

Another example from the same psychopathological realm. A violent jealous reaction in a man to the adultery of his wife can be due to a catathymic potential originating in especially intense experiences of the mother's unfaithfulness in her intimacy with the father and other offensive separations from her.

Obviously, not all psychogenic reactions can be considered catathymic. Logically, the first 'catathymizing' experience or series of experiences are 'traumatic', but not 'catathymic'. Another immediate objection to the proposition that 'psychogenesis' is synonymous with 'catathymia' would be that certain particularly dramatic happenings need no catathymic point of attack to produce a psychogenic reaction. This may be so in relatively few instances. Certain 'overindividual' or generic situations (early separations from an important person, particularly the mother, foxhole experiences, catastrophes) cause reactions so intense that they must be considered pathologic without presupposing a catathymic readiness to response. However, this idea of 'psychic trauma' must be qualified. One does not have to dwell long on empirical material to see how easily this 'common sense' concept of 'psychic trauma' is being outwitted by the facts (*cf*. Case 158). It is a scientifically valid observation that individuals in the German concentration camps only rarely developed psychoses (Helweg-Larsen and colleagues, 1952; Cohen, 1954). However, after they had been liberated many developed serious psychosomatic symptoms and there were many cases of death from coronary disease even in men under the age of 25 years (Welner, 1960). From my own practice, I can offer the following example. An outstanding intellectual, who was quite neurotic with a variety of psychosomatic symptoms, was an active member of the underground resistance movement. He was arrested by the Gestapo and put into prison. He was not subjected to physical torture. While in prison his symptoms virtually disappeared only to return on his release. I interpret this to mean that the incarceration took over the punitive functions of the patient's superego. In other words, the 'psychic trauma'— imprisonment and the distinct possibility of torture and execution— had a temporarily ameliorating effect.

Other observations that throw a monkey wrench into the works of the naive 'psychic trauma' conception are concerned with brain washing technique and experiments with sensory deprivation. Zweig has,

16

in his beautiful little novel *Schachnovelle* (1943), convincingly accounted for the pathological effects of lack of stimulation. An intellectual victim of the Nazis is being kept prisoner in a hotel room with absolutely no equipment besides his bed. He is being fed regularly by a tongue-tied and deadpanned waiter. Weeks and months go by and the man is only saved from detrimental insanity by his successful attempt, while waiting in an anteroom for a hearing, to steal a book about chess problems which he learns by heart.

Experiments with individuals subjected to a minimum of sensory stimulation, submerged in water of body temperature, with no visual, acoustic, and other stimuli being present (replica of the intra-uterine situation) have proven to result in hallucinations and other psychopathological reactions. Sensory deprivation, thus, must be considered a 'psychic trauma' (for example, Lilly, 1956; Wexler and colleagues, 1958; Miller, 1962).

In this context is may be mentioned that Kraepelin (1915) has described the not infrequent paranoid-hallucinatory psychoses in individuals suffering from deafness. It is noteworthy that the blind only rarely become paranoid even when they suffer from visual hallucinations. Mayer-Gross, Slater and Roth (1960) and Schipkowensky (1960) suggest that this difference may be explained by the fact that deafness has a more disturbing effect than blindness because it is a greater barrier between man and man; blindness chiefly intervenes between man and the inanimate world. Isolation by language from the environment (for example prisoners of war) can be considered a variant of sensory deprivation. Allers (1920), Herschmann (1919), Schneider (1927), Wimmer (1936), and Faergeman (1941) have described benign paranoid psychoses in persons exposed to this particular type of 'psychic trauma'; these psychoses are usually found in intellectually retarded individuals.

Child Analysis and the Concept of Psychic Trauma

Child analysis has greatly attributed to what properly should be understood by 'psychic trauma' and hence to a clarification of the concept of psychogenesis. Kris (1956) has traced events from their actual occurrence in a child's life, through the changes to which they are subjected in the mind, to their reappearance on the surface in analysis. As a result of such comparisons he went so far as to state that the traumatic significance of an event is not laid down from the time of its occurrence but that 'the further course of life seems to determine which experience may gain significance as a traumatic one'. This means that an event may become traumatic long after its occurrence. In the

17

same paper Kris suggests a differentiation between two kinds of traumatic situations—the 'shock trauma' when a single experience in reality powerfully and often suddenly infringes on the child's life and the 'strain trauma' when long-lasting situations cause traumatic effects by the accumulation of frustrating tensions. He points out that we are only rarely able to distinguish with desirable sharpness between the effects of the two kinds of traumatic situations.

Freud (1958) has a wealth of astute clinical observations which convincingly demonstrate the naïveté of the traditional concept of trauma. She points out that biographical material supplied by the parents cannot be used for guidance as to the pathogenic importance of past events. A mother may date her boy's disturbance from a car accident his father has had and which has been traumatic to both parents. The child's analysis, on the other hand, may show that in his mind this event had been completely overshadowed by the departure of a beloved maid, which has occurred at the same time and has proved traumatic for him. Anna Freud further states that where bodily illnesses are concerned the mothers will report those as significant which were dangerous objectively or aroused their own anxiety; the child, on his part, may react pathologically to any minor disturbance of health on the basis of pain, discomfort, anxiety, dietary, and motor restrictions, enforced passivity, etc., which are felt to be intolerable. A similar variance in evaluation exists concerning time: separations may seem short and therefore negligible by adult standards and still be interminable and therefore traumatic for the child, etc.

Analyses of children who have been subjected to war and concentration camp experiences demonstrate the same point. Where one would expect to unearth buried memories of death, destruction, violence, hatred, etc., analysts usually find the traces of separations, motor restrictions, deprivations (of toys, pleasures), together with all the usual emotional upsets which are inseparable from any child's life.

Anna Freud has a particularly striking example from the case of a little girl who, at the age of 4 years, had witnessed her father murdering her mother in a delusional attack of jealous rage. The child's analysis, undertaken six months later, was recorded by her therapist, Mary E. Bergen (1958). In this paper, the author traced in detail the child's attempt to assimilate 'an act of violence which in a few minutes had swept away her home and parents and irrevocably changed the course of her life'. It is the merit of this record, Anna Freud points out, that it illuminates, under the microscope of analysis, how one element of the horrifying event after the other became involved with the child's own fantasy world, thereby receiving weight through emotional cathexis.

Thus, the girl's pre-oedipal sense of frustration, jealousy and rage, and her search for an ideal, 'good' mother, found guilty fulfilment in her move to a new foster home. Her death wishes against three younger siblings served her identification with the violent, but loved, father. On the oedipal level, the murder of the mother gave reality to the guilt-laden wish to remove the rival parent. Actually, all the elements of the oedipal position appeared in full force; love for the father, rivalry with the mother, guilt for wishing to separate the parents and set them quarrelling, the effects of the prolonged witnessing of the primal scene. The latter determined the child's deep involvement with that particular moment of the tragedy when the threatened and frantic woman tried to remove the child from the scene of murder by screaming at her, 'Get out of here!' In the analysis, this detail was shown to symbolize the crowning insult, the mother being experienced as trying to exclude the child angrily from the parents' intimacy.

In other words, we cannot predict from outside observations, and at the time of occurrence, which events will prove important, that is, traumatic, for future pathology. Nor can we know which aspect or element of a given experience will be selected for cathexis and emotional involvement. The infant's capacity to absorb environmental events is limited by the infant's capacity of understanding at the stage at which it happens to be. To paraphrase Goethe's remark in *Faust*: *Ein jeder versteht nur, was er verstehen kann.*

According to psychoanalytic experience, the decisive traumatic event—that is, an anxiety-provoking situation—is separation from a needed person or part of that person. The only really important fact in life is our relationship with others. From this proposition follows the conclusion that object-loss must be the basic insult to human beings. The earlier in life the separation occurs the more traumatic will be its effects. From this assumption we can advance a temporal hierarchy of 'psychic traumata' according to their deleterious effects. The oldest traumatic situation—aside from being born—is the separation from the object that provides instinct gratification, first of all the oral needs and the need for protection against cold. This is what we call 'simple need gratification'. At this early stage of development the object (usually the mother) has no meaning beyond the satisfaction of the need: the object is the breast rather than the mother. In the next phase (occurring in the human around the ninth to twelfth months of life) the trauma is the loss of love of a specific object, again usually the mother. This pre-supposes a permanent relationship to this particular object as a totality. The most important empirical basis for these formulations are the beautiful observations of Anna Freud, and Spitz's (1945, 1946)

19

film-recorded anaclitic depressions in the first year of life in emotionally deprived infants.

Next follows the stage in which the relationship with the loved and permanent object is threatened by the emergence of new needs, the satisfaction of which might cause the parents to withdraw their love. In the anal-sadistic phase this is, among others, the impulse to smear with faeces. Later, in the oedipal period—to take the case of the boy— there exists the risk not only of being castrated by expressing the hostile jealousy for the father but also to lose his love. The boy's oedipus complex has not been understood if his ambivalent attitude towards the father has not been taken into consideration.

The last of the infantile anxiety situations is dependent on the development of the superego, particularly after the liquidation of the oedipus situation, although we know that the origin of this complex structure in the personality precedes the establishment of the oedipus complex. It will be seen that feelings of guilt are here considered to be variants of human anxiety.

Summary

Below I summarize this discussion of 'anxiety', 'catathymia', 'psychic trauma', 'inner-psychic conflict', and 'psychogenesis'.

(1) 'Anxiety' is a state of excitation in the psychophysiological system (the organism). There is a sliding scale between the little 'normal' anxiety of banal everyday events (for instance, when I consider whether to take a shower and feel too lazy) and the big, 'pathological', realistic anxiety in extreme situations (for instance, when meeting the lion in the desert). The matrix for all anxiety is laid down in the first 5–6 years of life by crucial experiences—above all the trauma of the birth and the separation from a needed and, later, loved object—which no being can avoid, but which hit different individuals with different intensity due to different constitutional equipment and circumstances. The crucial experiences are anxiety-provoking because the infant cannot escape them by fight or flight (I *may* escape the lion by running or by shooting it).

(2) The crucial infantile experiences 'catathymize' the organism in such a fashion that experiences in later life acquire the power to trigger the anxiety preparedness (*Angstbereitschaft*).

(3) A 'psychic trauma' is, first of all, the anxious reaction of the organism to a catathymic event. It must be added, however, that certain situations may in themselves be so overwhelming that they are cause for arousal of such intense excitation that they must be considered operative without presupposing a catathymic preparedness. But, 'psychic

20

traumata' are usually not thinkable without taking into consideration the catathymizing effects of earlier, especially infantile, experiences and particularly repeated frustrations.

(4) An 'inner-psychic conflict' is a state of tension between different elements of the personality, for example an id-impulse to kill and the superego's disapproval of the impulse.

(5) 'Psychogenesis' is the all-embracing term that comprises the four previous concepts as they have here been defined. 'Psychogenesis' is a word that connotates the psychophysiological processes in an organism reacting to a situation. Artificially limiting ourselves to the 'psychopathological' use of the term, 'psychogenesis' is:

(*a*) The probably relatively rare cases of 'overindividual' anxiety reactions in organisms exposed to extreme stress or complete lack of sensory stimulation.

(*b*) The production of such quantities of excitation in an organism, prepared to respond in an exaggerated way based on infantile experiences and frustrations that pathological ways of handling the anxiety become mandatory. 'Psychogenesis', in this sense of the word, implies the impossibility of realistically coping with the exciting situations by fight or flight.

CHAPTER 2

PURPOSE AND HISTORICAL SUMMARY

Purpose

As has been emphasized in the preceding chapter the psychogenic psychoses, in the rather brief history of their conceptual existence, have been relatively little subjected to a comprehensive and systematic analysis. This book is an attempt to present a clearer picture of these disorders—and to come to better terms with some of the problems involved in this class of mental disturbances. In exploring the material obtained from the follow-up study, we are particularly interested to see whether the course of the disease has borne out the psychogenic diagnosis, as the psychoses so diagnosed appear to be frequently difficult to distinguish from the incipient stages of other psychoses that are momentarily so conspicuously camouflaged by psychoplastic* mechanisms that only the further course reveals their true, non-psychogenic nature. The principal *raison d'être* of the study, besides revising and defining some basic concepts, is to present as fully as possible the characteristics of those disorders which the course of events verified as psychogenic, and to tackle the problem of differential diagnosis between psychogenic psychoses and other psychoses, particularly the schizophrenias. The material was expressly chosen to include a more representative group of the psychogenic disorders than has so far appeared in order to give a reliable expression of the absolute and relative frequency of the disease in the Copenhagen population of a given period as compared to other hospital admissions with an estimate of the disease expectancy and the distribution by age and sex. I have also investigated the relative frequency with which the various psychogenic syndromes appear, another area that has so far been somewhat murky. The question of prognosis for the different syndromes is dealt with, one problem here being the frequency of relapses and their nature and duration. I also touch upon the lethality of the disease itself and the possibly related post-psychotic death rate. There is some investigation of the problems of heredity and

* Birnbaum (1923) in his *Der Aufbau der Psychose* (*The Structure of the Psychosis*) has introduced the multidimensional diagnosis in which system a distinction is made between predisposing, pathogenetic, precipitating, and pathoplastic (for example, psychoplastic) factors.

22

pre-morbid personality. In Chapter 13 there is a discussion of the relation between the nature of the psychic conflict situation and the form of the psychogenic psychosis. The intricate difficulties of differential diagnosis between psychogenic psychosis and schizophrenia have stimulated an attempt at clarification of the pertinent prognostic signs and symptoms, a matter of the greatest significance as the prognosis in psychogenic psychoses is quite favourable, while that for the schizophrenias is not. The problem is discussed in Chapter 12 (*cf.* Faergeman, 1946).

Historical Summary

The Psychological Era

Historically speaking, the psychogenic psychoses reflect the spirit of the age viewing them. For a fuller account of the historical aspect of the problem of environmental factors as causative agents of mental disease, see Zilboorg (1941). Psychiatrists of the first half of the nineteenth century stressed the psychogenic factors in mental disturbances, and neglected elaboration of the somatic. A typical example is a statement by Prichard (1835):

> Care and anxiety, distress, grief, and mental disturbances, are by far the most productive causes of insanity. A sufficient proof of this remark may be found at once by inspecting the preceding tables drawn up by M. Esquirol.

In the tables to which Prichard refers, Esquirol (1838), taking his material from La Salpêtrière in Paris in the years 1811 and 1812, gives as the causes in 105 cases household vexation, in 46 cases disappointment in love, in 18 cases jealousy, in 16 cases anger, and so forth. Syphilis is named only eight times and alcoholism not at all. Heinroth (1818), whose view of the aetiological question makes a rather odd impression today, put exclusive weight on 'sin' as the cause of mental illness and that without even somatic illness such as alcoholism or cerebral syphilis as instrumental in bringing about the psychic disease. Although primitively and semi-theologically expressed there is a nucleus of truth in Heinroth's puritanical and God-fearing conception of aetiology, which actually brings it rather close to modern and sophisticated thinking of psychoanalytic psychiatry in which the power of the superego is incessantly stressed. Many people, also today, have as severe and harsh a superego as that of Heinroth himself. And it should not be forgotten that the sophisticated freedom with which many people in our time approach the subject of sex, for instance, is only a sham and that the pious superego is wide awake a little beneath

23

the surface. Griesinger also stressed the importance of the psychic causes. In the fourth edition of his textbook (1876; the first edition was published in 1845) he stated:

> We consider the psychic causes to be the most frequent and most productive sources in the manufacturing of mental illness. This is true, not only about the predisposition, but particularly about the immediate triggering of the illness. This point of view is based not only on statistics, namely from the literature, but also on the total impression of many [personal ?] observations. Were we able to know about all the psychic causes—and the most important are often hidden—this impression would probably be even stronger.

Again we have to admit that although the lingo is different some of the old psychiatrists intuitively knew more than is evident at first glance. The last part of Griesinger's statement is actually prophetic. More than fifty years before the appearance of *The Interpretation of Dreams* (1900) and *Three Essays on the Theory of Sexuality* (1905), Griesinger suspected the force with which psychic impulses can operate.

The Somatic Period

Experimental medicine towards the end of the century brought about a pendulum swing to the somatic, and now demonstrable cerebral pathology was preferred in the aetiological thinking, an approach greatly validated by the demonstration in patients suffering from general paresis of the spirochaete in the brain and the Wassermann test at the outset of this century.

It may be historically significant that not long before, the American James (1884, 1890) and the Dane Lange (1885), independently of each other, proposed a theory concerning the nature of emotion. Briefly speaking, the idea advanced by these two men is that our feelings are secondary to physiological processes in our bodies: I do not cry because I feel grief—I experience anguish because I cry. It deserves to be mentioned that already Spinoza in his *Ethica* (1677) formulated this conception of emotion. He wrote:

> By EMOTION (affectus) I understand the modifications of the body by which the power of action in the body is increased or diminished, aided or restrained, and at the same time the ideas of these modifications.

The naïveté of Heinroth and Prichard appears no more peculiar today than the narrow intensity with which the somatically oriented asserted their points of view, emphatically stated in a remark of Westphal to the effect that any psychology in psychiatry is superfluous. Nissl (1899, 1902) was equally anti-psychological in his contention that hysteria as well as the organic psychoses have an organic pathological basis. The predominantly somatic orientation, however, was, during this whole period, protested against by many, and it was Nissl himself who, according to Bumke (1928), coined the ironic term 'brain mythology', thus intimating how hopeless it is to look for man's complicated psychology in a correlation with the brain's gross anatomical and finer histological construction.

Hoche (1902), among the others who protested the purely somatic attitude, asserted with some vehemence that hysteria is definitely without organic pathology and in 1906 he rebutted the prevalent dogma that all psychoses are organic brain diseases. Wernicke (1900), whose main efforts were to understand and systematize mental illness as localized brain disorders, was, nevertheless, far from 'brain mythology' when he introduced the concept of '*überwertige*' ('supervalent') ideas, and his theory of '*zirkumskripte Autopsychosen*' ('circumscribed autopsychoses') and he also stressed the psychogenic nature of certain paranoid psychoses.

The Modern Trend

The predominantly somatic emphasis culminated with the first decade of this century. It was superseded by a fresh influx of psychological approaches, quite different from that of the previous century. The expansion of psychiatric experience and the heightening of interest in the less serious psychic abnormalities were strong influences on current psychiatry. Kraepelin, from the first edition of his textbook in 1883 to the ninth and last, published posthumously in 1927, paid only little attention to neurotic disorders. But the work of Liébeault, Charcot, Bernheim, Janet and many others with hypnosis and with hysteria was an important inspiration in this respect. And Freud and his students were prominent in broadening psychiatric experience of the neuroses. Perhaps most significantly from our point of view, and in contrast to the sterile experimental psychology, they focused attention where it was urgently needed: on the total personality. It is a testament to the impact of Freud's observational power and visionary theorizing that a psychiatrist such as Bleuler, in his famous monograph on schizophrenia in 1911, recognized the necessity of acknowledging his debt to Freudian concepts. Like the Germans, Bleuler remained basically faithful to the conviction of somatic aetiology, yet he confirmed the importance of conflict and the other experiential factors involved. The awakening interest in prison psychoses in the beginning of the century also gave impetus to the further examination of psychogenic mechanisms. And, of course, the two world wars with their mass production of psychogenic reactions have played a formative role in the modern psychological orientation.

Nowadays, the studies of the psychic and somatic causative factors manage to coexist in greater harmony, and study of the one inspires greater efforts in understanding of the other—despite the fact that there are fanatics on both sides of the fence who cannot see eye to eye. This is certainly a favourable development as both trends obviously must be explored. The manic-depressive psychosis, for example, is most likely caused by biological agents. It is an established fact that hereditary factors play a role in it. However, the effect of non-genetic factors also has to be taken into account. It is, for example, a legitimate question whether manic-depressive phases can be provoked by psychological stress. Regarding manic-depressive psychosis, American psychiatry considers psychogenic factors to be much more important as causative, respectively precipitating, factors than is the case in European psychiatry (Rennie, 1942; Arieti, 1959a). Also, many American psychiatrists believe that there is a decline in the frequency in this disease or its very existence is only reluctantly accepted. In a large monograph Engel (1962) refers to this once venerable nosological category as: '... the so-called manic-depressive psychosis.' Fitzgerald's novel *Tender is the Night* (1933) is a fine literary illustration of American psychiatry's emphasis on psychological stress as a causative factor in schizophrenia and on the optimistic notion that many cases within this group of diseases are curable.

On the whole, modern American psychiatry tends to stress the psychological factors more than does Continental psychiatry. British psychiatrists, although on the whole quite conservative, now demonstrate a trend towards the psychological orientation. Typical in this respect is the following quotation from the textbook by Mayer-Gross, Slater and Roth (1960):

> This [that is, that constitutional factors are the most decisive in psychiatric illness] is not to say that sociology is of no interest to the psychiatrist, or that there are no fields in which psychiatrists and sociologists have a common interest. Nor are we unaware that future investigation of the possible *influence of social and environmental factors* on the overall incidence of different kinds of mental disorder may reveal data of importance for preventive psychiatry.

And Roth (1957), referring to Slater's (1953) work on psychotic and neurotic illnesses in twins, emphasizes that environmental factors may be important in promoting or suppressing the manifestation of a disease even where the evidence seems to point to a predominantly genetic cause.

26

One is reminded of Gruhle's apt remark (1932) in reference to theories of schizophrenia: *Ein positives Wissen über Wesen und Ursprung der Schizophrenie besitzen wir nicht*—a pronouncement that, years later, still contains the essential truth.

To digress for a moment, it is well to keep in mind that many clinical problems diverge in both directions and, to be properly handled, must draw on both approaches. To give a clinical-therapeutic example: it is an everyday experience to see a patient suffering from recurrent neuroses. After a detailed case history is taken and the hereditary picture reviewed, the disturbance is revealed as a light endogenous depressive phase with atypical neurotic, for example, obsessive-compulsive, symptomatology. In other words, part of the syndrome is a latent neurosis (unconscious conflicts) with such slight tendency to spontaneous manifestation that it is first activated when the somatic, presumably endocrine-vegetative disturbances (the basis for the cyclic depressive phases), commence operation. Expressed differently, we are here dealing with mild, endogenous phases with pathoplastic features determined by the latent neurosis. The psychiatrist will best be able to handle the somatic aspects of the case; the analytically trained therapist will be the one best able to influence the neurotic mechanisms so that the patient's next depressive phase will have a less neurotic stamp and will, therefore, be actually less painful.

Modern psychiatry has advanced our understanding of psychogenic psychoses in several ways. First it has been established that only the experience that executes a definite influence on the emotional life can have a pathological effect. That an emotional shock is the significant experience now appears quite self-evident, but this understanding signalled decisive progress in comparison with the older concept of psychogenesis—which to a great extent dealt with a purely intellectual psychotic development, a kind of misguided thought processes.

Maier's (1912) concept of catathymia, which has already been introduced in Chapter 1, establishes the emotional relativity of experiences—apart from certain very intense experiences of catastrophe which almost without exception arouse generic reactions in the form of emotional stupor and similar responses (Baelz, 1901; Stierlin 1909, 1911; Kleist, 1918; Wetzel, 1921). In other words, no experience can be considered greater than the effect is has on a particular psyche, which means that without psychological penetration it is often extremely difficult to distinguish the effective internal personality conflicts from the external and more flamboyant experiences and events that trigger the reaction. Wicksell (1934), Gruhle (1940), and Stengel (1958) have emphasized this point with regard to the

27

motives for suicide and suicidal attempts. See also the example of phobia mentioned in Chapter 1, page 15.

In connection with the reference to overindividual reactions it should not be forgotten how incomplete is our knowledge concerning traumatic neuroses in general and neuroses of war in particular. The confused and confusing literature relating to the subject reflects this ignorance. By some authors, for example Bonhoeffer (1911), Oppenheim (1915, 1916) Gerstmann (1920), and Wwedensky (1929) the very intense 'psychic trauma' was thought to have given rise to some specific and irreversible damage to the central nervous system. Although this notion was widely held during and after World War I it was hard to prove. A psychoanalytic attempt to comprehend this group of neuroses was made in the symposium by Ferenczi, Abraham, Simmel, and Jones (1921). More recently Kardiner (1947, 1959) has dealt with the subject.

It should also be mentioned that energetic French efforts with *les dégénérés supérieurs* of the last century, followed by lively German interest, established the significance of predisposition in European psychiatry. 'Degenerative psychoses' are to a certain extent identical with 'psychogenic psychoses', the essential difference between the two terms being whether greater weight is attributed the predisposition on the one hand, or the conflict, respectively the psychic trauma, on the other.

But this distinction was not self-evident a generation ago, and therein, perhaps, lies the explanation for the fact that Birnbaum's insistence (1910a and b, 1911, 1918) on the personal predisposition as the only significant cause for the psychogenic disorders now seems exaggerated. Some years later Birnbaum (1923, 1928a) claimed again that the constitutional predisposition is the crucial factor, the significance of the experience being restricted to serving as a provocation.

Only certain psychopathological syndromes can be considered psychogenic reactions. These have been narrowed down by Schneider (1927) to three basic types: disturbances of consciousness, paranoid and emotional reactions. This classification and its division into subgroups will be discussed in Chapter 4.

The most important contributions are briefly covered here to give the historical flavour and conditioning with which the student customarily approaches his problems. The only other follow-up study of psychogenic psychoses of any appreciable size is that undertaken by Kretschmer on his sensitive paranoics, published in the second (1927) and third (1950) editions of *Der sensitive Beziehungswahn*. These follow-ups are of considerable interest because they seem to have validated Kretschmer's original diagnoses. But in psychiatry one never can tell.

CHAPTER 3

TERMINOLOGY AND FURTHER CONCEPTS

The Concept of Psychosis

There is a regrettable lack of unity in the nomenclature of psycho-pathology, and the concept of psychosis is no exception.

Satisfactory definitions of abnormal psychic life are so difficult to achieve that it is no wonder that a generally accepted basis for distinction between psychosis and neurosis has not yet been reached. This also applies to the difference between neurosis and 'normal' psychic life. Ross (1936) recognizes the difficulty of the formulation of these distinctions in theory and Helweg (1939) feels that concepts of mental illness transcend the limitations of definition to the same extent as empirical concepts of disease in general. Is it abnormal to loathe innocent snakes? Is a subclinical hypothyroidism a pathological state? The concept of normality is interwoven with confusions. Is the person who can love, work and have satisfactory social relationships necessarily 'normal'? The anthropologists, for instance Benedict (1934), tend to adopt pragmatic definitions of normality: normal is that which society has approved. The more philosophically minded prefer to think that:

> ... there are *no* scientific definitions [of normality]. There are only logical and ostensive definitions whose correctness may be matters of scientific fact and which are consequently used by scientists in their work. (McLean, 1959.)

The Three Criteria of Psychosis

There are three criteria on which concepts of psychosis are based: the practical–social, the biological, and the psychological. It is remarkable that the broad sweep of psychiatry has been so easily satisfied with vague practical–social definitions of psychotic mental life. Bleuler (1919) admits this with regret, while Wigert (1939) accepts the impossibility of conciseness. Romano (1947) likewise prefers a sociological and practical distinction between psychotic and non-psychotic states, and emphasizes the fact that 'insanity' is a legal, not a medical, concept.

Representatives of the biological approach contend that it is meaningless to separate concepts of disease from non-biological criteria, as all disease is a biological phenomenon and must therefore be defined with

29

the aid of biological concepts. It remains to be seen how useful the sophisticated approach to the problem of mental disorders (for example, Selye, 1956) by modern organismic biologists will prove to be. It need only be said here that the old linear series of cause-and-effect relationships is now being abandoned by some authors and is being replaced by an approach that, to quote Rome and Robinson (1959):

> . . . emphasizes the significance of interlocking physiological and psychologic patterns in a general-system type of theory [which] holds behavior to be essentially unfractionated and sees it to be adaptive.

These authors use 'biological reaction' synonymously with 'adaptation'.

The third criterion, the psychological, has, until quite recently, scarcely been used by academic psychiatry. It is mainly the psycho-analytically oriented who have attempted to set the boundaries between neurosis and psychosis on the basis of a detailed knowledge of the structure of psychopathological phenomena. Freud paid attention to the problem. In one of his papers (1924a) he stated:

> Neurosis is the result of a conflict between the ego and its id, whereas psychosis is the analogous outcome of a similar disturbance in the relation between the ego and the outer world.

In another paper (1924b) this basic view is elaborated within the same frame of reference. It is succinctly expressed in the cynical joke: The neurotic builds castles in the air, the psychotic moves into them and the psychiatrist collects the rent. The most lucid formulation of it is perhaps to be found in Freud's paper *The Question of Lay Analysis* (1926b) in which he emphasized the intimate psychopathological relationship between neurosis and psychosis. In both conditions the ego—like a harassed ambassador from a small and weak country—strives to serve three mighty powers: the id, the superego and reality. The neurotic, as well as the psychotic, patient is more dominated by id-impulses and fantasies than the 'normal' individual. Freud's opinion was that, very likely, the crucial point so far as the choice between neurosis and psychosis is concerned, lies in the decision of the ego either to join forces with the unrelenting reality and remain neurotic or to capitulate to the overwhelming forces from the id, to disintegrate while being inundated by fantasies from 'down there', and to loosen its hold of external reality. This second alternative means psychosis. See also the conclusion to Case 126.

Ego-Strength

The concept of ego-strength is implied in these deliberations. We cannot measure it objectively, but we can, by an evaluation of the functions of one particular ego, obtain some estimate of its strength. To mention only a few of the criteria: a person has a strong ego if he can establish mature and intense object relationships and if his ego has 'conflict-free areas' (cf. page 33); the more control he has over his impulses, the stronger is his ego; and, finally, a mild degree of regression in the face of adversity or disaster is an indication of ego-strength. Rapaport (1955))has the following terse definition: '. . . a strong ego is measured by its ability to tolerate necessity.'

The Structural Point of View

It is hardly possible fully to appreciate the line of thought expressed in the three papers, if one does not keep in mind that they are all written shortly after Freud's (1920, 1923) decision to replace his old tripartition—the topographic—of the personality (unconscious, preconscious, and conscious) with a new metapsychological category, the structural (id, ego, and superego) which proved to be a much more effective and much more elegant means of paying due justice to the clinical facts. The structural point of view is a working hypothesis concerning the nature of man. It is open-minded and perfectible. Although it lacks the merits of the ideal—and non-existing—personality theory, for example, objective or experimental testing, it has been chosen as one of the basic concepts of this book.

It is consistent with the structural point of view that large areas of the ego and the superego are unconscious. The ego employs its defence-mechanisms without being aware of the process and the superego often has an easy time with a depleted and naïve ego, forcing it, for instance, into self-destructive and masochistic acting out as in the discreet and slow alcoholic suicide. Groddeck (1923) expressed this in the formula that the ego 'is being lived' (gelebt wird) by unknown and uncontrollable forces within us. The psychotic has, temporarily or definitely, moved into those castles in the air—the world of fantasies—which he built when he was still only a neurotic.

This aspect of the problem permits a normal state to grade off into neurosis and neurosis into psychosis which is in accordance with clinical observations. A patient is sometimes seen at his wits' end, fighting a losing battle against an obsessive-compulsive impulse that finally—for minutes, for hours, or for ever—drives him over in psychosis. In this clinical connection it is the paranoid conviction that, for instance, the compulsion to right all the wrong he has done by washing his face in slops is not a morbid ritual, but a deserved punishment meted out by Satan himself.

31

With regard to psychogenic depressions the gradual transition from normal sadness to pathological reaction is particularly striking. Weekends and holidays have a peculiarly depressive effect on many individuals. It is remarkable how people come to life again after the ordeal of Easter holidays. And Christmas is everybody's funeral as someone has said so expressively. The heavy drinking associated with those occasions is not the expression of relaxation and gaiety, but of depression. Ferenczi (1919) and Sterba (1944) have contributed to an analytic understanding of this problem.

Neurosis and Psychosis

I do not believe that in neurosis generally selected functions only suffer while in psychosis the total personality is involved in the disease process. This opinion, held by many, ignores a wealth of clinical facts, for example, that there need be no sharp line of demarcation between compulsion and delusion. A few other examples illustrate this point. Many severely psychoneurotic persons are more preoccupied with their pathological ideas than some ambulatory schizophrenics. Of the latter, many have what E. Bleuler designated a 'double orientation': the same thing has simultaneously both its real meaning and a symbolic significance peculiar to the distorted psychotic experience; is then, we have the right to ask, the *whole* personality affected? An individual can certainly be psychotic in one respect and healthy in all others; a man may be so jealous with regard to a certain woman that he must be considered psychotic in this one particular area of his interpersonal relationships, but otherwise completely without morbid features (*cf.* Wernicke's *Überwertige Ideen*, page 25). Again, would the psychiatrist who is an atheist or an agnostic say that a deeply religious person is the victim of delusions? He ought to.

Turning to the psychoneurotic patient, there is no doubt that his whole personality may be affected. Neurotic fatigue does to a varying degree paralyse all the functions of a person. The most striking example within this area of pathology is to be found in that of the individual who is affected by character neurosis and who cannot discern the nature of his difficulties. It can be just as hard a task to convince such a patient of the morbid nature of his condition as to persuade a paranoid schizophrenic to abandon the conviction that he has created the Milky Way with one mighty splash of his semen.

The Borderline Patient

In this context the 'borderline' patient who has received so much attention in recent years (Hoch and Polatin, 1949; Wolberg 1952, and many others) must be mentioned. The borderline patient borders on normality, on the neuroses, on the psychogenic psychoses, and on psychopathy (Schmideberg, 1959). Schmideberg herself admits that no psychiatric entity is absolutely rigid and that neurotics sometimes do cross the border into psychosis or psychopathy and vice versa. The same is true of the borderline, she says. Case 151 in this material illustrates this clearly. The borderline is the twilight between neurosis and psychosis just as the hypnagogic state is the twilight between being awake and being in the dreams of sleep. It is easy— or hard, as one looks at it—to be a psychiatrist with all the diagnostic labels at our disposal today*: 'normal', psychoneurotic (many subgroups), psychosomatic (innumerable subroups), pre-psychotic, pre-schizophrenic, borderline, pseudo-schizophrenic, symptomatic schizophrenia, process schizophrenia, acute recurrent schizophrenia, schizo-affective psychoses, schizophrenoid psychoses in children, schizophrenic (four subgroups), psychogenically psychotic, manic-depressive, to mention the maybe most important in the area of 'functional' psychoses in vogue today but which need not be in 10, 20, or 100 years hence. The 'borderline' patient and the 'borderline' concept have already become shopworn words bandied about as they have been from one psychiatric tongue to another. The intense preoccupation over the last decade with the 'borderline' has not convincingly supported the view that there exists a hard-and-fast line of distinction between different mental disease 'entities', for example 'neurosis' and 'psychosis'.†

Conflict-Free Areas of the Ego

I believe it would be easier to come to terms with these last mentioned conditions if Hartmann's (1939) concept of conflict-free areas of the ego was generally accepted. We would then consider as psychotic those areas of a personality in which the ego's conflicts are so severe that its capacity for reality testing is compromised to the extent that the ego has joined forces with the id; in all other respects the ego may still function reliably.‡ A neurotic ego would be neurotic only in those

* Actually our psychiatric predecessors had just as many, only they were different. Heinroth (1773–1843) may hold the record by having described 48 different mental diseases, although it should not be forgotten that, concerning the subdivisions, Hall (1914) did not do badly by dividing phobias into 134 categories.

† See also the important contributions by Waelder (1951) and Freeman (1959). Knight (1954) writes: '... the label "borderline state", when used as a diagnosis, conveys more information about the uncertainty and indecision of the psychiatrist than it does about the condition of the patient.'

‡ 'I want to stress that those parts of the personality of the psychotic patient which are not involved in this conflict [that is between urges from the id, and to ego] maintain their cathexis. Accordingly, at times when the conflict is not active, a psychotic patient may behave quite normally.' (Katan, 1960). See also Katan's (1954) earlier paper on the same topic.

areas in which conflicts dominate and impair its proper executive duties; a man can have a severe phobia concerning bridges and yet be the creator of a business empire. Obviously, the extremes are represented too in our daily clinical reality. It is, for instance, obvious that an ego can be so depleted in strength that it is entirely overwhelmed by its id and its superego, the two often forming an alliance (Alexander, 1927), and can hardly be said to exist. This is, for instance, the case in marked mental retardation and in some organic conditions. It is just as obvious that an ego can be so relatively free from conflict that it would be justified to call it 'normal' or only 'slightly neurotic' in some specific respects. We might then assume a psychopathological continuum between neurosis and psychosis (cf. page 12 for a continuum between 'inner-psychic conflict' and 'psychic trauma'). This seems to accord with Freud's (1922) view concerning jealousy, supposing a nucleus of truth even in the genuine delusional forms of this symptom. Also Kretschmer assumes a continuum between the non-paranoid and the sensitive paranoid states and claims the reversibility of the latter. This stand would also enable us to pinpoint such areas of a neurotic or psychotic personality as are relatively conflict-free. Dynamic diagnostics would replace descriptive classification. Cf. the conclusion to Case 74 and also Menninger (1959) on the subject of a continuum of the successfulness of an individual-environment adaptation.

The Schizophrenic Ego

A schizophrenic ego is a different matter. Were we Kraepelinians we should consider the deeply deteriorated dementia praecox patient to be utterly lost and beyond therapeutic hope. But only fifteen years elapsed between the appearance of the fifth edition (1896) of Kraepelin's *Lehrbuch* in which dementia praecox was described as a nosological entity and the publication of Bleuler's monograph (1911) on schizophrenia. His concept of dementia is radically different from that of Kraepelin's. According to Bleuler all the functions of the personality are potentially preserved even in the deteriorated schizophrenic. And the autistic patient often fools us. Bleuler gave an illustration of this in the clinical anecdote about the very schizophrenic old lady who, when a fire broke out in her ward, proved to be far from 'demented'. Bleuler (1953) has written a lively and moving account of his father's intense work with patients suffering from 'dementia praecox' and the resulting crystallization of the concept of schizophrenia. The undiscovered country, from whose bourn no traveller returns, is really only the severe dementias of organic origin.

Constitution and Psychogenesis

In Chapter 1 the concept of catathymia was discussed in some detail. This section of the present chapter will be devoted to other aspects of psychogenesis, namely, the constitutional factor and Freud's ideas concerning psychic trauma and his concept of complementary series.

Constitutional agents are—as has been emphasized earlier—generally as important for the appearance of psychogenic psychoses as situational factors. It must regretfully be admitted that only little is known about them; we acknowledge their existence but lack a satisfactory definition. However, for the very reason that our knowledge is so scant the definitions are so manifold. According to professional upbringing and personal prejudice, the biologist, the constitutionalist, the physician, the psychologist, the psychiatrist, and the psychoanalyst will put the emphasis on different aspects of this many-headed monster 'constitution'. It should be stressed that constitution is not only hard to define, it is also extremely difficult to measure its qualities with any degree of exactness. Considering its predominantly quantitative significance for our purpose one can feel tempted to quote the truism, coined by Ogden Nash in a different context: 'Some fish are minnows, some are whales.' Maybe some day a sophisticated descendant of the electroencephalograph will make possible the accurate measurement of, for instance, the constitutional excitability of parts of the central nervous system.

In this context it would lead too far afield to go into a minute discussion of the many definitions that have been suggested. The reader is referred to the competent article by Ostow (1959) in which mention is made of the most important contributions from the time of Hippocrates to the present-day research programme at the Child Study Center at Yale University and which also offers samples of definitions by a wide variety of eminent scientists. The author himself suggests a fresh and apt definition:

> Constitution . . . is the organizational pattern potential, the selective realization of which, in respect to degree and content, is modified by physical, psychological, and social environment. The constitutional approach assumes all behaviour, variations as well as general tendencies, to have an economy and a significance.

He also lays stress on the important fact that research in constitutional problems is no longer, as it has been for centuries, exclusively typologically oriented, but that a new trend, inspired by dynamic psychology, has emerged quite recently. This approach is aimed at elucidating the role which constitutional factors play in human behaviour and in the dynamic processes by which these factors influence and find expression in clinically observed behaviour and personality. This means that the static and sometimes rather uninspiring labour of classification into somatic and psychological *types*—Kretschmer and Sheldon are the best known exponents of this approach in modern times—is supplemented by the attempt to comprehend dynamically the constitutional basis for human *behaviour*. By far the most ambitious of these endeavours is the so-called 'longitudinal study in child development', initiated by Kris and Senn in 1949. Only preliminary reports (Kris, 1957; Ritvo, 1958) have been published so far. This new trend in constitutional research has abandoned the old controversy of constitution versus environment and, instead, investigates the intimate and continuous interplay between the two.

In the psychogenic psychoses we find a group of clinical phenomena which *par excellence* demonstrates this interaction between a constitutional readiness to respond in an adaptive way and a situational agent ('psychic trauma'). The latter acts on the former, which can be considered a vital store of potential and unrealized behaviour patterns—in the widest sense of the word—in an organism.

Freud's Concepts of Trauma and Complementary Series

Before attempting any general formulations of the most important concepts discussed in this and in the introductory chapter, attention must be paid to Freud's ideas about 'psychic trauma' and 'complementary series'.

In Chapter 1 'psychic trauma' was defined as an anxiety-producing situation. Freud, in many of his earlier papers, considered a trauma to be an event that arrested development (that is, fixation). Subsequent traumata had the effect of reviving the developmental arrest by regression to the fixation points (originally thought to be oral and anal libidinal stations in the course of infantile development). It will be seen that Freud's 'trauma' corresponds with 'catathymizing event' and his subsequent 'traumata' with 'catathymic situations'. Later, in *Beyond the Pleasure Principle* (1920), he went deeper into the matter and postulated the existence of a *Reizschutz*. According to this theory mental pathology is caused by the break-through of a barrier erected as a protection against too powerful stimulation which would set up a great amount of anxiety. Should the *Reizschutz* fail to accomplish its mission an emergency situation arises which can be dealt with in different ways. In neuroses of war and the like the shocking experience may be repeated in anxious dreams, thus allowing a slow and piece-meal discharge of the excess of excitation; or a woman who does not want to be raped and goes through the experience may therapeutically repeat the traumatic situation several times in hypnosis and in this way find relief. In objectively less dramatic circumstances, to which most catathymic situations belong, neurotic defence-mechanisms will go into action and lead to the formation of neurotic structures in the personality. Finally, overindividual respectively catathymic events may mobilize psychotic measures of adaptation to the pathogenic situation.

Psychoanalysts are often charged with overestimating the significance of external events, particularly those of a sexual nature, although many of Freud's papers deal extensively with the constitutional aspect of psychopathology. A good example is *Analysis Terminable and Interminable* (1937) in which constitutional predisposition and experiential factors are seen playing supplementary roles in varying degrees. This is what is meant by 'complementary series'. It seems to have escaped the attention of many that Freud during his long life held the opinion that all our provisional ideas on psychology will some day be based on organic structure.

Summary

We are now in a position, tentatively and schematically, to formulate, however imperfectly, the factors involved in the production of a psychogenic psychosis.

A psychogenic psychosis is the result of the action on a psychogenic potential by a situational agent ('trigger', 'psychic trauma', or 'experiential factor').

The psychogenic potential is characterized by its quantitative and its qualitative readiness to respond, the first mainly being dependent on constitutional factors, the second on catathymic variants. The quantitative variability can be exemplified by comparing the sensitive poet, who reacts to even a tiny little earthquake with a *fugue amnésique* or a stupor while it takes a really bad earthquake to shake a phlegmatic and 'strong' man. An example of how capricious the qualitative variability can be is that of the young man in the anecdote in Chapter 1 (page 15); we may assume him to be constitutionally strong-willed, but there was a chink in his armour: he was catathymically and specifically hypersensitive.

The constitutional variant results from the action of physical agents on the genetic endowment. The physical factors in question can be, to mention only a few among innumerable others: intra-uterine, and intra-partum events, brain injuries, localized and general infections, acute and chronic intoxications, malnutrition, radiation, etc. Concerning the genetic variants, their qualities, changeability and vicissitudes, readers are referred to manuals on the subject.

The catathymic agent has been discussed in the introductory chapter. Suffice it to say here that it results from the interplay between constitutionally determined predispositions and situational factors, particularly those of infancy and childhood.

Finally, there is the trigger which has also been examined in the first chapter. It can be a massive psychic trauma, in the naïve sense of the word, or it can be a highly specific key-experience which hits home only where an elective vulnerability is present.

In the above I have attempted to make some formulations pertinent to the principle of psychogenesis by using a clinical group as a model. It should, however, be kept in mind that psychogenesis, as here understood, is a wider concept embracing pathological as well as normal phenomena. It ranges from the contraction of precapillaries when faced with danger, to intricate mechanisms of identification and projection in the formation of delusions in a situation that wounds a catathymic spot in the self-image. Psychogenesis, in this sense of the word, is a term denoting the adaptive response in an organism to minor or major, overindividual or specific, stress. The applicability of Cannon's (1932) theory of homeostasis of psychological phenomena has been supported by some authorities (*cf.* Menninger, 1959) and questioned by others (*cf.* Toch and Hastorf, 1955).

CHAPTER 4

CLARIFICATION OF DIAGNOSTIC TRENDS

Classification of Psychogenic Disorders

As mentioned in Chapter 2, Schneider's (1927) subdivision of psychogenic disorders has been adopted here. All attempts at clinical-descriptive classification are arbitrary and variegated and Schneider's system is no exception. The classificatory haphazardness is particularly striking in the 'functional' area of psychiatry, functional in the sense of being without demonstrable somatic aetiology and pathogenesis. Therefore, it is necessary to clarify the diagnostic criteria used in the follow-up study. It will only be mentioned in passing that Widlocher (1958) has suggested a different and fully acceptable division of the psychoses here under discussion.

Emotional Syndromes

The emotional syndromes have been divided into depressive syndromes and syndromes of elation. Further, the depressive cases have been subdivided into four groups which are defined and discussed in Chapter 6.

Disturbances of Consciousness

There is great confusion and inconsistency in the terminology used to describe the disturbances of consciousness. It would be better to follow one descriptive set and I have chosen the one suggested by Strömgren (1945), for reasons of clarity. Those reactions, then, are divided into three syndromes: (1) *impairment of consciousness*, as in somnolence, sopor, and coma; (2) *turbid states* as in delirium and confusional states; and finally (3) *dissociations of consciousness* as found in cloudy states, multiple personality, and depersonalization.

Impairment of consciousness is most commonly provoked by organic agents and, in their pure forms, only rarely, if ever, psychogenically. Turbid conditions, whose prototypes are delirium tremens, fever delirium, and amentia (in the Continental sense of the word, *cf.* pages 3–4), are usually also organically determined but some are psychogenic. In dissociations of consciousness we find psychogenic as well as organic forms, for instance Kleist's (1926) *episodische Dämmerzustände* ('episodic twilight states'); these were regarded by Kleist as organic conditions, characterized by clouding of consciousness, which were related to epilepsy.

Thus, psychogenic disturbances of consciousness occur mostly among turbid states and dissociations of consciousness. A distinction is here made between four types.

(1) Those dissociations which clinically most often are seen in temporary cloudy states sometimes combined with fugues.

(2) and (3) Turbidity of the sensorium which shows a multiplicity of symptomatology not seen in impairment and dissociation (chiefly hallucinations, more marked and more labile affect and transient paranoid ideas). Turbid states are divided into those with deliria (2) and those with hallucinations (3); this distinction is vague as hallucinoses are defined as deliria dominated by hallucinations and only slight disturbance in the level of consciousness.

(4) The psychogenic stuporous states, which here are considered as a distinct group, although some of them rather belong to either dissociations or to turbid conditions. In certain cases stuporous states could be included under psychogenic depressions, but for practical reasons I have preferred to group all stuporous cases under disturbances of consciousness.

Paranoid Syndromes

The paranoid syndromes have been divided into those without and those with hallucinations, a grouping that has proved prognostically useful. A discussion of some of the nosological problems pertaining to paranoid conditions will be found in the introductory remarks to Chapter 8.

Differential Diagnosis Between Psychogenic and Non-Psychogenic Psychoses

A few words must be said about the three most important groups of mental disorders from which the psychogenic psychoses in their initial stages often cannot be distinguished: the manic-depressive psychoses, the schizophrenias and the epileptic equivalents.

With regard to *manic-depressive psychoses* I have, in accordance with Lange (1928), considered three qualities as significant: the emotional (syntonic or cyclothymic) personality, pyknic body type, and finally periodicity. Also, unmistakable inhibition is considered a symptom that strongly suggests the endogenous, 'vital' nature of a depression.

Concepts of schizophrenia are among the most elastic in psychiatry. E. Bleuler claimed—as do the majority of American psychiatrists today

—that many psychoses cured without visible defect are schizophrenic, simply because they have certain features which are considered characteristically schizophrenic. In a reaction against this Schneider (1932) has suggested a restoration of the old Kraepelinian concept of dementia praecox with its emphasis on the course of the disease. Zilboorg (1941), on the other hand, argued against the return to a Hippocratic principle, namely, that the course and the prognosis of an illness decide the diagnosis. In the present work a psychosis has only been diagnosed 'schizophrenia' where there has been a demonstrable defect in comparison with the pre-psychotic personality. The testimony of relatives obviously is of particular significance in doubtful cases (cf. for example, Case 88). I have considered the following phenomena supremely characteristic of schizophrenia: autism, 'withdrawal of thoughts', 'pressure of thoughts', 'audible thoughts', experienced without disturbance of consciousness, and finally a marked flatness of affect. But it should be emphasized that it was the course of the disease that was considered the most significant diagnostic factor.

The psychotic epileptic equivalents and the epileptic temperament types also must be clinically and conceptually distinguished from phenomenologically related pathological conditions. The clinical task is often a hard one; the conceptual has become simpler thanks to Strömgren's (1940) coining of the words 'ixophrenic', 'ixoid' and 'ixothymic', the prefix referring to the quality 'viscous'. The three words, of course, are parallels to 'schizophrenic', 'schizoid' and 'schizothymic'. Psychopathologically the common denominator is the proclivity towards perseverance in mood, thought and action. Another characteristic of this psyche is the tendency to dysphoric changes of mood and explosive, sometimes desperate, and criminal actions. These propensities are also observed in some non-epileptic members of epileptic families and occasionally develop in subjects with cerebral pathology, It seems that chronic epidemic encephalitis and head injuries play a particularly important pathogenic role. Ixophrenia is probably a constitutional reaction type and Strömgren considers it to have a definite relation to the athletic habitus. He emphasizes the significance of ixophrenia as the basis for episodic disturbances of consciousness. Cases 101 and 102, in this material, are most likely examples of the ixophrenic syndrome. The epileptic equivalents will only be briefly mentioned here. They have received special attention from Kleist (1926) who described episodic psychoses related to epilepsy. Chronic, usually paranoid conditions associated with epilepsy, have also found mention in the literature. Postictal as well as longer lasting twilight states are well known.

41

Psychogenic and Hysterical

The boundary between psychogenic and hysterical has been the subject of a good deal of discussion in European literature. Without going into too much detail, the most common and practical view is that 'psychogenesis' is the main concept and 'hysteria' the subordinate: hysteria is a special type of psychogenic disturbance. By most German authors hysterical reactions are seen as the expression of a 'tendency' (*Zweckneurose*), 'intention neurosis', Kehrer, 1930). Kretschmer (1923) is also of the opinion that a tendency to flight into illness is of great significance for the understanding of the hysterical reaction, but he further emphasizes that this depends on the phylogenetically determined constitutional reaction tendencies. Here follows his definition of hysteria:

> We designate as hysterical those psychogenic reaction types which employ instinctive, reflex, and other biologically pre-existing mechanisms for the purpose of shamming.

In British psychiatry, also, it is usual to call those conditions hysterical in which some motivation for the symptoms can be discovered. American psychiatrists customarily include manifestations of hysteria under the headings of conversion hysteria and dissociations.

Over the last few thousand years a host of definitory attempts concerning the pathogenesis of hysterical symptom-formation have been made. Already the old Greeks were aware of the significance of sexual factors. A different aspect of the aetiology was emphasized by French clinicians in the last century. To Janet hysteria was the expression of 'a malady of the personal synthesis'. Breuer (although reluctantly) and Freud stressed once more the importance of sexual conflicts. As an example of how sophisticated the psychoanalytic thinking relating to the problem of hysteria has become, Glover's (1949) formulation is quoted here. According to this author there are ten major factors involved in the production of a hysterical conversion symptom, namely: (1) somatic compliance, (2) frustration, (3) introversion, (4) regression, (5) reactivation of an Oedipus situation which has been held in faulty repression and of which the negative (homosexual) aspects are strongly emphasized, (6) breakdown of repression, (7) displacement, symbolization and/or identification with the incestuous object, (8) breakthrough of innervations, (9) inhibition or exaggeration of somatic function giving rise to crippling or painful symptoms, (10) somatic dramatization of unconscious phantasy formations. However, in this context it should not be forgotten that classic hysterical pictures have been unmasked to be organic conditions, for example cases of porphyria.

CHAPTER 5

PATIENTS AND METHODS

The Patients

All of the cases in the follow-up study came from the Psychiatric Division of the Municipal Hospital in Copenhagen.

The study was to a large extent dependent on the availability of addresses of the patients to be examined. As the National Registration Office was not set up until some time around 1924, it was considered advisable to use the hospital records from 1 January 1924 until 31 December 1926. During this three-year period 150–200 persons with supposedly psychogenic psychoses had been patients in the hospital. In the blueprint of the research programme this number had been deemed adequate for the purpose.

The files of the Psychiatric Division of the Municipal Hospital list a patient under the month of his discharge, which is not ideal as there is a mixture of old and fresh cases that influences the age factor undesirably in studies such as this one. However, this objection carries little weight here because patients in a psychiatric reception division remain there only a short time.

All case histories for the given three-year period were gone through, and all cases that were diagnosed 'psychogenic psychosis' or 'psychogenic mental disturbance' and any other patient whose disorder could possibly be psychogenic, although the recorded diagnosis was not a complete one, were included on the basis of the criteria of psychosis given in Chapter 3. Among them were 12 cases with unspecified diagnoses—11 with only symptomatic diagnoses, and 1 without diagnosis.

All patients who had been hospitalized due to psychotic conditions at one time or another before 1924 were excluded to avoid the incorporation of a selected group of recurrent psychoses. On the other hand, all patients who suffered from neuroses or other non-psychotic nervous conditions before 1925, even if hospitalized on that account, were included if they fulfilled the criteria.

The material extracted from the hospital records was then carded.

43

Representative Value of the Material

A number of factors limit the representative value of the material: diagnostics, socio-economic, and cultural factors.*

Diagnostics

Every psychiatrist is diagnostically biased. Although the material was selected in such a fashion that this factor is reduced as much as possible, the spirit of Wimmer is perceived in the selection of patients. It is particularly striking that many cases of fresh schizophrenias were included in the 'psychogenic' category during the years here under investigation (see for instance the last several cases of paranoid syndromes in Chapter 8). For obvious reasons this is not a relevant factor with regard to the 79 cases verified as psychogenic psychoses. On the contrary, this diagnostic variable should only enhance the representative value of the material because Wimmer's magnanimous attitude towards the idea of psychogenesis can only have strengthened the probability that all psychogenic cases have been included. Or, to rephrase this pertinent point: uncertain and doubtful psychogenic cases were not excluded from the material.

Socio-Economic Factors

Most of the patients in the material had a humble social and intellectual background. Only a few had been to a secondary school or came from an upper-class milieu. The wealthy and the socially prominent usually are admitted to private psychiatric clinics or go to health resorts abroad. Just how significant this social lopsidedness is for the present purpose can only be guessed at. It probably is a factor of minor importance only. Hollingshead and Redlich's (1958) study of the distribution of psychiatric illnesses at different socio-economic levels should be mentioned in this context. These authors found a much higher incidence of schizophrenia in low-class families than in the upper-class families and attributed this partly to the 'loveless infancy', supposed to be more prevalent among the poor as compared with the wealthy. It is also worth noting that 95 per cent of persons in state prisons were from the lower classes, which may be an expression of defective superego development and socialization in the low-class population.† However that may be, Hollingshead and Redlich's results lend little support to any misgivings concerning the representative value of the material from a socio-economic point of view. It should be kept

---

* Psychogenic psychoses in children will be discussed in Chapter 10.
† See the section on prison psychoses in Chapter 11.

in mind, however, that we are dealing with a city population and that the rural population is not represented at all (*cf.* Faris and Dunham, 1939).

With respect to socio-economic categories I have used the classification of the Danish *Statistical Yearbook*. The 170 cases fall into the following—rather vaguely defined—six groups: 8 'executives and the like'; 16 'independent skilled workers'; 51 'employed skilled workers'; 32 'salaried employees and public servants'; 52 'unskilled workers'; 11 'intellectuals'.

Culture and Psychiatric Illness

The cultural background is also a factor germane to the particular problem we are concerned with here. The manic-depressive psychosis may, as Zilboorg (1944) has suggested, be the only major mental disease that has changed comparatively little over the ages. The psychoplastic superstructure of the schizophrenias must certainly have been submitted to remarkable alterations during the last two or three thousand years. As to the psychogenic psychoses, it is extremely difficult to infer anything about their incidence and their clinical appearance in past centuries. The constitutional soil on which they grow within one particular culture may not have changed much since ancient times. On the other hand, the environmental factors are completely different today from what they were for instance in the Middle Ages, when it was perfectly acceptable for people to be hallucinated part of the time as Eliot, amongst others, has pointed out in his essay on Dante (1929). Also, it should not be forgotten that the age of the Reformation may have brought about a drastic change in the psychological climate, with far-reaching consequences for the symptomatology and the frequency of psychoses in general and psychogenic psychoses in particular. Fromm (1941) has made some interesting comments to this problem.

What has been said here obviously also applies to the symptomatological changeability of the psychogenic psychoses and to the problem of their incidence in regard to contemporary cultures. We are, to use a metaphor, less surprised to come across cases of Mediterranean anaemia in the United States than in Denmark, and we must be prepared to find that the psychogenic psychoses are highly dependent on the culture in which they develop. The manic-depressive psychoses and the psychogenic psychoses probably represent opposites in these respects: the former are reliable and alter not where they alteration find; the latter are chameleonic, capricious and shifting. Deliberations of this kind have incited Yap (1962) to become particularly interested in the

45

subject of psychogenic psychoses because from a nosological point of view:

> ... this category appears to offer a rational device for the classification of the ... 'atypical, culture-bound, psychogenic disorders' one sees in different parts of the world.

This problem will be discussed further in Chapter 13.

The present material is representative for a group of first admissions to a public psychiatric hospital of psychoses occurring in a Danish city population around 1925 *and at the time diagnosed, and later verified, as psychogenic reactions.*

The Methods

Although personal interviews are superior to written questionnaires, they are not always possible. Out of discretion some women who had suffered traumatic sexual conflicts and had later married were not contacted as their husbands might possibly be unaware of the psychotic episodes and the nature of their causation. A few of the patients were living abroad at the time of the follow-up, and some simply refused to reply to personal or written attempts at establishing contact: 53 of the patients were dead.

It was possible to locate most of the 117 living patients through the National Register, and the rest, with the exception of 3, were found through the Salvation Army. Despite the claim that it is possible to locate anybody in Denmark we must admit that this was not completely true in this study.

There were altogether 98 patients personally interviewed, of which 53 were verified psychogenic psychoses.

In 69 cases (53 dead plus 16 with whom it was impossible to get a personal interview) it was necessary to obtain information from other sources. In addition, it was in many cases desirable to supplement personal conversations with the patient with information from relatives, the family doctor, etc.

All causes of death were ascertained, most specifically for the purpose of determining all suicides.

Information about patients in mental hospitals at the time of the study was received from the physician in charge in addition to the written hospital records.

As far as the heredity of the patients is concerned, I obtained every information possible. The dearth of information in the case histories in this respect is lamentable. The University Institute of Human Genetics in Copenhagen keeps carded information on all people handled in

PATIENTS AND METHODS

psychiatric reception wards, mental hospitals, and homes for the feeble-minded, but unfortunately information on psychopaths, alcoholics, etc., is scant.

A few other sources of information, of no particular interest to the English-speaking reader, have been included in the tabulation below.

TABLE 1

The Subsequent Life History of All Cases and Sources of Information

	No. of cases
Dead (29 in Mental Hospital)	53
Living, in Mental Hospital	30
Living, out of Mental Hospital	84
Unknown	3
	170
Personal interview with patient:	
in Mental Hospital	29
in his home	25
in my office	44
	98
Supplementary information from other sources:	
Relatives, friends, employers, neighbours, and others	63
Family doctor	16
The University Institute of Human Genetics	4
Police	6
Death certificates	16
The Tribunal of Disablement Pension	12
Foreign Mental Institutions	3
Others (National Health Insurance, embassies, prisons, etc.)	6

The follow-up study was undertaken from 1940 to 1943, so that the period of observation covers some 16 years. This is a sufficient period of time to allow for the development of the principal psychoses, although many of the patients at the time of the follow-up study had not reached the danger zone for the involutional psychoses. A longer time period would raise the percentage of deaths (almost 30 per cent in this material) and further limit the possibility of personal observation of the patients. This point of view agrees with the stand taken by Mayer-Gross, Slater and Roth (1960).

47

Part II

THE CASE MATERIAL

CHAPTER 6

THE EMOTIONAL SYNDROMES

The psychogenic emotional syndromes include psychoses which to a greater or lesser extent are characterized by pathological affective reactions. At times simple affective states are seen in which the emotional content alone dominates the clinical picture. But quite frequently we find psychoses that are more 'extensive' in form (Wernicke, 1900; Jaspers, 1923) where complicated psychopathological reactions of a non-emotional kind also appear (hallucinations, paranoid thought complexes, depersonalization, neurotic and hysterical reactions, etc.). It is not surprising that simple forms are rare as we are dealing with responses to what are usually complex (for example, ambivalent) conflict situations which involve the whole personality in a wide range of possible reactions. As Hoffmann (1926) correctly points out, many such depressions are only comprehensible when one takes into account the total character structure. One frequently sees quite opposite trends in the same character make-up (for example, both syntonic and schizoid). This not only gives a polymorphous imprint to the depression but the intra-characterological tension in many cases increases the readiness for psychogenic reactions.

The reaction may manifest itself in an acute crisis in affect that passes quickly over, or in a more protracted change of mood. Patients with chronic neurotic disturbances or nervous states are commonly seen—to such an extent that it is perhaps the neuroses, even more than the constitutional psychopathies, that provide the rich soil for the growth of the psychogenic psychosis. The existent nervous state acuminates in an acute psychosis brought about by the accentuation of an old conflict— the mechanism is here often of a catathymic nature—or by a sudden psychic trauma.

Depressive Syndromes

(40 cases)

In this context it would prove impossible to discuss the extensive literature dealing with the historical development of the psychoanalytic concepts of depression. Interested readers are referred to the excellent and scholarly study of the subject by Mendelson (1960).

Depressive syndromes may make their appearance in the most

51

diverse psychoses. The follow-up studies have shown that in an appreciable number of the psychoses originally considered psychogenic, the depression has been a secondary pathoplastic mechanism in a non-psychogenic psychosis, usually a schizophrenia. A few cases have proven to be depressive phases of manic-depressive psychoses. In the rest of the cases the supposition of psychogenic psychosis has been supported by the follow-up. The psychogenic depressive forms have been grouped according to Lange's (1926, 1928) division of 'reactive depressions or melancholias' and 'psychogenic depressions'. Lange's 'psychically provoked melancholias' provide a bridge between the endogenous manic-depressive melancholias and the true psychically conditioned depressive forms.

It must be emphasized that the distinction between the individual groups is far from sharp, and in practice also the division is apt to be quite arbitrary. Concerning the controversy about the independence of 'endogenous' and 'reactive' depressions it should be mentioned that Lewis (1943) is of the opinion that there is no real difference between them whilst Roth (1959, 1960) and Kay (1959) have stressed the possibility and desirability of a distinction.

'Reactive Depressions' ('Melancholiform Reactions')

(4 cases)

Reiss' (1910) work on constitutional depressions and the manic-depressive psychoses remains one of the most important in the literature on the clinical and nosological aspects of depression. He defines as 'reactive depressions' those depressions which manifest themselves in constitutionally depressed personalities as a result of a sorrowful or shocking external event. He emphasizes that a number of conditions must be fulfilled for there to be a dependence between the trauma and the reaction. First of all, the experience must have sufficient strength to be regarded as a serious affect trauma for the patient. A working knowledge of the patient's personality structure is here the basis for reliable judgment. Further, the reaction must have a temporal relationship to the trauma and its content must be centred on the conflict or at least be understandable on the basis of the patient's character structure. Finally, the duration of the depression must not be too long, and, particularly, a solution of the conflict should lead to amelioration of the patient's condition.

This definition of the reactive depression not only foreshadows Jaspers' criteria of psychogenesis from 1913 but it is also almost identical with the one found in the American Psychiatric Association's listing of mental disorders (000–$_x$06) from 1952.

The psychic basis for the development of the reactive depression is, according to Reiss, the constitutional depression. There is some uncertainty as to the relationship of these psychopathic depressions to the cyclothymic forms. Schneider (1942) emphatically stated that most forms of constitutional depressions are completely different from endogenous depressions. Kretschmer (1931) and his students came to the same conclusion on the basis of constitutional studies, as did Braun (1928). Lange's (1926, 1928) experience seemed to point in a similar direction even though he stressed the impossibility of setting up sharp divisions in this complicated area until we possess more differentiated hereditary information.

Case 1

An unmarried 33-year-old nurse with several cases of constitutional melancholy in the maternal heredity.

History—The patient came to Copenhagen from Western Jutland for her nurse's training. She always had a melancholy outlook on life. At the age of 27 years she was converted to Catholicism and three years later admitted as a novice to a seminary, but within a few months broke down because of the isolated cloister life and intense religious brooding and she became depressed. After a short time in a general hospital she improved sufficiently to resume her nursing duties. Two years later she broke down again and permitted herself to be hospitalized in the Municipal Hospital where she stayed for three months. She seemed quite labile, alternately optimistic and despairing. Temperamentally she appeared sthenic, somewhat rebellious and inclined to be critical and querulous. There were hints of a previous morphine addiction. She was sent to St. Hans Hospital* where she remained for eight months. Here she showed depression and agonizing religious speculation. Later she became extremely changeable in mood and very quarrelsome. There followed a short period of massive depression. She was discharged in good condition, if not completely stable.

Follow-up—A heavily built, athletic, 50-year-old woman, currently a patient in a psychiatric reception ward. According to the hospital records she had been nervous and depressed, and addicted to morphine which she took to relieve arthritic pain. At first she claimed that her unhappiness was a religious problem, but after some probing revealed that a severe sexual conflict was the cause of the depression. For some years she had had an affair with a married man. The relationship was in many ways a very happy one, but her religious scruples finally forced her to break it off. At first she was relieved, but then felt empty, futureless, and suicide seemed a soothing possibility. She continued her work as an assistant nurse until her present hospitalization, and hoped to resume it on discharge.

Conclusion—There is no doubt that this is a case of constitutional depressive predisposition. As with so many of this constitutional type,

---

* St. Hans Hospital is the mental hospital receiving the patients from the Psychiatric Division of the Municipal Hospital in Copenhagen.

the patient's life is a long history of suffering as every problem, and particularly the moral and religious, is grotesquely out of proportion. The depressive predisposition, the religious convictions and the possibly irreparable sexual-moral conflict force a serious prognosis in this case.

Definitely a psychogenic reaction.

Case 2

A 24-year-old cabinet maker, admitted after having been accused of making advances to little girls in the park.

History—The son of an impulsive father and a normal mother, he had always been serious, laconic, reserved, unsociable, and unemotional, but had never shown amoral tendencies. He had acquired gonorrhoea and syphilis the year before his admission and had received adequate treatment. His mother stated that he had been peculiar for some time, unwilling to look for work, shy, and much addicted to sitting and brooding at home. He thought that possibly some woman had 'made a mess' of him, but showed no definite paranoid thought complexes. During his hospital stay he was quite apathetic and hypochondriacal, with strong depressive features. The sensorium was clear and there were no definite schizophrenic symptoms. He was discharged after a month to his mother with a diagnosis of possible schizophrenia, perhaps psychogenic apathetic depression with ideas of reference.

Five years later he was back in hospital, again because of his advances to little girls. This time he had beckoned a little girl into the bushes, let her urinate, touched her leg and masturbated in her presence ostensibly to be arrested and thus obtain the financial security he could not produce himself. His sexuality was not very strong. During this hospitalization he was calm, somewhat hypochondriacal, but showed no sign of psychosis. He was discharged after 10 days with a diagnosis of *psychopathy*.

Several years later he suffered from a depression because of loss of work and family conflicts and was for the third time admitted to the hospital. He had lived with his two siblings in his mother's home. Everything seemed sad and difficult to him, and he could not pull himself together to look for work. He contemplated suicide without making any actual attempt. The clinical picture during his hospitalization led to a diagnosis of *depression*. After a month he was transferred to St. Hans Hospital where he was diagnosed *psychopathic constitution, depression*. Here he was at first mute and rather unpleasant, but his condition improved after three months and he was discharged in his usual condition. Wassermann reaction negative for years.

Follow-up—In reply to a written communication the patient seemed suspicious and fearful that police interest in him would be aroused.

In an interview he, at 42 years of age, seemed quite as described in the hospital records. He showed no signs of schizophrenic personality changes. He stated that things had gone well for him since his last hospitalization. He had been working constantly, had moved in with a married sister and a brother and got along well there. He was still inclined to be serious in mood, but free of massive depression since the last hospitalization. Investigation of his police records showed several encounters with the

54

law mostly over his advances to little girls, and he once served a 100 days prison sentence on that account, but there were none after 1939 (follow-up in 1942).

Conclusion—This case appears to be a constitutionally depressed person with easily aroused despondency and an inclination to choose a desperate solution in a difficult situation (the pseudo(?)-criminal actions). There are also certain paranoid features in his suspicious reactions to his environment and his tendency to ideas of reference. The case is a typical example of reactive depression.

Definitely a psychogenic reaction.

The classification of the following two cases is less certain.

Case 3

A 36-year-old unmarried housekeeper, admitted after attempting suicide by an overdose of sleeping pills. Her maternal grandmother was impetuous, her father suffered twice from 'convulsions'.

History—The patient was brought up in a working-class home in a large provincial city. She suffered from 'teething convulsions', and was first toilet trained at the age of 6–7 years. She appears to have had normal intellectual capacities. From childhood she was serious and pessimistic, particular after a strong erotic trauma when 21 years old, when her lover, whose child she was expecting, abandoned her. Since that time she had been subject to a serious neurosis marked by asthenic-depressive symptoms with episodic hysterical reactions: 'nervous attacks' with stiffness and tingling sensations in her arms and legs and brief amnesias in situations which were upsetting to her. Just before her admission she had been working as housekeeper for her uncle and his two sons. She had had an affair with one of her cousins who deserted her after some time. She was deeply affected and since then had been severely depressed.

During hospitalization she was extremely depressed, weeping and inhibited. After two months she was decidedly better and was discharged although still in an uncertain mood.

Follow-up—The patient, aged 52 years, was a small women who moved stiffly with a peculiar facial expression and a dull monotonous voice. She suffered from chronic psychic rigidity and a serious psychic invalidism. She stated that the asthenic-depressive syndrome had never left her, although there was some improvement after the menopause three years previously. Her condition had been at its worst in her mid-forties when, as she reluctantly admitted, paranoid symptoms appeared. Records from the mental hospital in Aarhus, where she was a patient for two months, when she was 45, supplemented the patient's statement. The paranoid episode took place while the patient was working in a boarding house in Copenhagen. She believed erroneously that one of the boarders, a young man of 23, was in love with her. She was filled with shame when she realized her error, left her job and went to a brother in Aarhus where she was depressed and anxious, full of delusional forebodings and anticipations of punishment (beheading) for her erotic wishes. She almost never went out as it seemed to her that everyone noticed her. Since then she had lived alone in a room, taking half-day jobs in the house and collecting disablement pension.

She admitted reluctantly that she had been hospitalized several times in the ensuing years 'for her nerves'. The hospital records revealed that she was not considered psychotic during any of these episodes.

Conclusion—This is a constitutionally depressed woman to whose temperament is added features of sensitivity and hysteria—an alloy which Reiss considers quite common. After the severe erotic disappointment at 21 years there developed a strong neurotic state governed mainly by the asthenic-depressive symptoms. At 36 the patient again succumbed to a severe sexual trauma and her condition rose, for several months, to a psychotic level.

This case is a perfect illustration of the blow to a patient's self-image* as the cause of paranoid reactions (see Chapter 13); the bitter awakening after the experience with the young man in the rooming house led to what Kretschmer (1918) calls 'shameful ethical insufficiency' and the patient reacted with ideas of reference (*Beziehungswahn*) of the sensitive type.

Case 4

An 18-year-old apprentice mechanic, admitted to the Municipal Hospital for depression.

History—After his mother's death the previous year he became depressed, felt tired, lost interest in his work, and was disturbed by vague feelings of anxiety. In the last two months before his admission he heard voices, among others his mother's, and saw faces in the night. He was a quiet patient during his hospitalization, moderately depressed. He heard reproaching voices and saw vague shapes in the hall.

Follow-up—As a man of 36 years of age he was asthenic in physical type, friendly without being affable, made an intelligent impression and seemed more cultured than his training would suggest. He was certainly introspective by nature and showed a good understanding of his conflicts. He characterized himself as serious, thoughtful, a bit of a brooder, somewhat unsure of himself, and energetic.

He believed his mother's death to be the cause of his depression. He was very attached to his parents and his home. He denied any other trauma. He remembered very little about his illness.

Two years after his depression he developed pulmonary tuberculosis which was cured after a few years. At 26 he married. Ten years later the

---

* The German *Persönlichkeitsbewusstsein* is not easily translated into English. I have chosen *self-image* as the designation for that complex of—more or less conscious—ideas, notions and feelings any person has about himself. The whole problem of the conceptual relationship between 'mind', 'consciousness', 'self-consciousness', 'self', 'ego-ideal', etc., has been competently discussed by Allport (1949), particularly in his Chapter 6. In modern terminology self-image is used a great deal in the psychology of schizophrenia and consists by definition (Arieti, 1959b) of body-image, self-identity, and self-esteem.

marriage broke up because his wife, who had been unfaithful to him, wanted a divorce. He volunteered that he had a tendency to premature ejaculations. He had always been sexually shy and had had only very episodic experiences outside of his marriage. He suffered somewhat, but without deep depressive reactions to his wife's infidelity and the divorce.

He had been economically quite successful, having his own cigar-box factory, and knew of no hereditary predisposition to psychiatric difficulties.

Conclusion—The patient was a depressive-asthenic psychopath without definite neurotic symptoms, with a single depressive reaction to his mother's death.

Definitely a psychogenic reaction.

'*Psychogenic Depressions*'

(20 cases)

Those cases that are designated by Lange (1926) as psychogenic depressions occur after a psychic trauma in psychopathic and neurotic individuals of all types from hysteric and erethic temperaments to paranoid and schizoid personalities. The affect is centred around the pathogenic experience and is highly susceptible to changes in the situation. These patients—in contradistinction to the melancholics— are inclined to find the cause for their misery in their surroundings, their mood is more likely to be irritable and aggressive than purely sorrowful. Most of all they lack the manic-depressive inhibition.

Wimmer (1916), whose depressive cases belong chiefly to this group, points out the feelings of martyrdom and the pathophilia which often distinguishes these patients. The differences between the two forms of depression is well expressed in Kahn's (1927) short formula: *Der Melancholiker leidet, der reaktiv Depressive tut sich leid* ('the melancholic suffers, the reactive depressive permits himself to suffer').

As is self-evident, 'psychogenic depressions' may be complicated by the pathoplastic effect of a cyclothymic predisposition—a factor which makes it difficult to classify even cases where a satisfactory description is available.

In 5 of the following cases (5–9 inclusive) the depression has developed in clearly psychopathic-neurotic personalities.

Case 5

A 20-year-old male office worker, suffering from an asthenic-depressive syndrome.

History—He had always been 'nervous', was anxious by nature, easily frightened, unsure of himself, inclined to brood, and at times suffered from religious scruples.

Some months before his admission he developed a depressive-asthenic syndrome and was fearful of going out in the street. He had frequent choking sensations during which he fell off his chair without losing consciousness. During his hospitalization he was at first described as unhappy, anxious, hypochondriac, miserable over religious speculations, feared damnation, believed that he was about to die. After six weeks he was transferred to St. Hans Hospital where it was soon discovered that the psychic conflict consisted of strong guilt feelings because of masturbation. For almost all of his two year stay he suffered from extreme depression, self-reproaches, frequent weeping, and hypochondria. He complained of painful feelings of insufficiency and depersonalization and obsessive thoughts. He improved a little at the end of his stay.

Follow-up—At 36 years of age the patient presented himself as an asthenic person; he seemed to be vague, uncertain, peevish and often hiding behind embarrassed forced laughter. After his discharge from the hospital he collected disablement pension for several years because of his nervous state. At 24 he started working again in an office and got along satisfactorily. He was married at 25 and had two healthy children. His asthenic symptoms were far less severe than formerly and only one neurotic symptom (claustrophobia) remained.

Conclusion—Here a depressive-hypochondriac condition developed in an asthenic insecure psychopath because of a serious ethical conflict of a sexual nature with social invalidism lasting more than two years.

Definitely a psychogenic reaction.

Case 6

A 35-year-old office worker, suffering from an agitated depression and preoccupied with metaphysical questions and convinced that he is guilty of all the evil in the world and that his life is a lie.

History—The patient's father was serious and brooding. His mother died at the age of 63 of senile dementia and hypertension. The patient himself was intelligent, studious and went to college. He had always been eccentric, with peculiar ideas and philosophical-religious-political interests. Both parents died a few years before his admission.

During hospitalization he appeared deeply depressed, silly, affected, and bombastic in behaviour, but without definite schizophrenic symptoms. He was preoccupied with religious and sexual problems—he never felt an urge to have anything to do with women and feared that he was not truly masculine.

Follow-up—The patient died at the age of 48 years of a cerebral haemorrhage after suffering from malignant hypertension.

He had married when aged 37 years and it was possible to locate his widow. She stated that the patient had been impotent during their entire married life. Their relationship was that of nurse and patient. He drank and smoked a great deal and was always tired and indisposed, but diligent in his work and advanced well in his office. His home life was peculiar. He spent his evenings preoccupied with his own thoughts, restless and serious, mumbling Amen and Hallelujah, and was never sociable.

The year before his marriage he spent some time in a psychiatric clinic where he appeared depressed, full of self-reproaches, preoccupied with religious problems, once heard voices with religious content. The family doctor considered him a very pleasant and intelligent man. His wife had undoubtedly not been unfaithful to the patient.

Conclusion—A chronic depressive-asthenic state had developed here in an eccentric introverted psychopath, at one point accentuated to the point of psychosis. The structure of the disturbance is a complicated one. To a certain degree the asthenic syndrome may have been accentuated by the hypertension and the arteriosclerosis of the brain, which is possibly also responsible for the total impotence rare in non-organic disease in young men. The sexual disturbance led to a serious and insoluble conflict which fixated the patient's depressive condition. The psychopathic predisposition, the organic brain disease and a profound inner conflict all combined to produce the illness.

Definitely a psychogenic reaction.

Case 7

A 26-year-old telephone operator, suffering from a depression and wishing to die, constitutionally irritable and querulous.

History—A paternal uncle suffered from schizophrenia. The patient had taken her mother's death a few years previously very hard and was most upset when her father, on his remarriage, requested his children to leave the home. She was friendless and lonely.

During hospitalization she was harrowed, depressed, and weeping, later labile with some stereotyped expressions. She spent the next eighteen years more or less constantly in the hospital. Twice she was discharged and later readmitted because of irritable-aggressive outbreaks. At various times she showed either predominantly irritable-aggressive, depressive, or flat schizoid features with wavering diagnoses depending on the most vivid presenting symptoms.

Follow-up—In a conversation with the patient, now 44 years, she appeared unbelievably talkative, complaining of the treatment she received at St. Hans Hospital. She denied psychotic symptoms of any sort. In a conversation with a brother, he voluntarily said that the patient had been normal as a child and developed her characterological peculiarities during adolescence. She was not believed to have ever had sexual relations.

Conclusion—It was impossible to make a definite diagnosis. Psychopathy, schizophrenia and manic-depressive psychosis were all considered. Because of the lack of definite schizophrenic symptoms, one is inclined to consider the patient a psychopath of the 'explosive' type (Schneider, 1923).

Uncertain case.

Case 8

The 20-year-old daughter of divorced parents. Father an egoistic tyrannical executive, mother remarried to a correct bourgeois. The patient herself was childlike and showed strong emotional reactions.

History—The patient became shocked and depressed following the death of her fiancé in an automobile accident. Hallucinations of his voice were possibly hypnagogic and continued during her short hospitalization.

Follow-up—Shortly after discharge the patient met and married on twenty-four hours notice a man who committed suicide a few years later. There was one child. She then went to Canada and after some years of working at various jobs she married a calm and stable mechanic. She seemed to have adjusted well to the marriage and her new milieu.

The patient's sister, when interviewed, was sceptical of the trauma and considered it a product of the patient's imagination. She felt that her sister liked to dramatize herself and enjoyed creating a sensation. The minister of the church to which she belonged as a child was also inclined to believe the story a fantasy product. He remembered her as a tense and highly strung child.

Conclusion—The patient was a self-assertive pseudological hysteric. The traumatic event was in all likelihood fictitious. The follow-up suggests that the case is better placed under disturbances of consciousness than under psychogenic depressions. She probably had episodic twilight states in which she was dominated by her fantasies to such an extent that reality testing was impaired. Conditions of this type have been described by Stemmermann (1907). It is perhaps astounding that the patient was able to make such a solid later adjustment as seems to have been the case, but it must be remembered that an hysteric who can be so exhausting to her family can also evoke their toleration with her childlike impulsiveness and warmth.

Definitely a psychogenic reaction.

Case 9

The 48-year-old wife of an army captain, previously admitted after attempting suicide by an overdose of morphine.

History—The patient, described by her family as temperamental, impulsive, charming, sociable and intelligent, suffered from a mild depression because of a trite marital conflict which led to the suicidal attempt at the age of 42 years. At 46 she had undergone a hysterectomy. At about the same time her son was killed in an accident and the patient reacted by throwing herself into an extravagant life which surpassed the family's financial means. Her husband claimed that she had always been very changeable in mood, charming and capricious at times, irritable and quarrelsome at other times. During hospitalization she was quiet and depressed, somewhat self-reproachful and at first half stuporous.

A year later she was again admitted after several episodes of stuporous states provoked by conflicts in the marriage which was now dissolved. She was admitted in a stuporous state and died some weeks later of bronchial pneumonia.

Follow-up—An interview with the patient's daughter revealed that the main conflict of the patient's life was undoubtedly the marriage. The couple were diametrically opposed in temperament, the husband being pedantic, honest and dull.

Conclusion—We have here the case of an emotional-explosive woman with several psychotic reactions: short-lasting but sometimes severe depressions and episodic stupor states. The trigger is typical of the hysterical woman: imprisoned in a marriage with a thoroughly correct and boring man who provides no possibility of outlet for her wider temperamental range, thus laying the ground for the intense explosions.

Definitely a psychogenic reaction.

The next 15 cases of 'psychogenic depression', often complicated by hysterical admixture, are less marked by psychopathic-neurotic features, and so have, to a greater degree, the character of an acute crisis in affect, strikingly in contrast to the otherwise more or less normal personality.

Case 10

A 26-year-old unmarried seamstress, admitted after an attempted suicide by drowning.

History—The patient had been depressed for some time ostensibly because of a severely traumatic experience. She had had an affair with a man of a higher social class who brutally deserted her when she became pregnant. With great secrecy she went to a small provincial town where the infant was born dead. On her return to Copenhagen she became increasingly depressed, sleepless, saw shapes in the night and was afraid that the police were after her. At this point she attempted suicide.

Gynaecological examination revealed that the patient had not achieved parturition and that it was doubtful that she had been pregnant at all. The patient then admitted that the story had been fabricated to revenge herself on her lover who had actually deserted her. It then came out that she had often pressed him for money and that she had formerly had an affair with a man who had been forced to go to America to escape the ensuing scandal.

During hospitalization the patient was depressed and subject to hypnagogic hallucinations. In addition to the erotic disappointment and the precarious position into which she had placed herself, it further appeared that the lover had forced her, to her great consternation, to perform fellatio and swallow the sperm.

Follow-up—The patient died of tuberculosis at the age of 37 years. She had married and her husband was contacted. He claimed that she had been completely normal for the 10 years of their marriage.

Conclusion—This case presents nothing of great interest. In contrast to Case 8 there is here no pseudological fantasy but a conscious distortion of the facts for a particular purpose.

Definitely a psychogenic reaction.

Case 11

A 28-year-old woman, the widow of a smith. A brother hospitalized four times for atypical manic-depressive states.

History—The patient had always been inclined to anxious-asthenic reactions in difficult situations. Until the age of 20 years she suffered from occasional convulsions with loss of consciousness, foaming at the mouth and tongue-biting. A cerebral concussion at 25 accentuated her symptoms.

At 28 she married a man who suffered from tuberculosis. A few months after the marriage he hanged himself, supposedly because of his lung disease. The patient then became severely depressed and suffered from visual and auditory hallucinations of her dead husband.

Follow-up—The patient appeared a leptosomic but otherwise quite normal middle-class woman. She had had no psychiatrically significant symptoms or episodes since the depression at 28, from which she recovered quite quickly. She had no pre-psychotic neurotic symptoms except for a lack of interest in sex and complete frigidity. She suffered from anxiety and some compulsiveness with the menopause. There had been some valvular heart pathology for the past three years for which she collected disablement pension.

Conclusion—Most probably an asthenic woman who developed a hysterically coloured depression in response to a severe psychic insult.

Definitely a psychogenic reaction.

Case 12

The 34-year-old wife of a book-keeper, admitted for a severe depression.

History—The promiscuous sexual behaviour of the patient's father was reflected in the patient's history. She appeared quite normal in her role of mother and housekeeper, but was constantly unfaithful to her husband, usually with chance acquaintances she met in the street. The family finances had taken a turn for the worse which may have been partly instrumental in causing her depression. Over the next few years she was hospitalized a few times for depressions which both her brother and husband considered to be brought about by her uninhibited sexual behaviour. She had admitted to her husband that the last of the children was not his. He also claimed that the patient showed perverse tendencies, wishing to be beaten and to have intercourse with a young adolescent boy. She appeared to have had no manic periods(?).

Follow-up—Aged 51 years the patient was an attractive leptosomic woman who seemed reserved and had difficulty in discussing the unavoidable subjects of the interview. She claimed that although her husband was fully potent and could produce orgasm in her, she did not feel satisfied with him and found him boring in every respect. She claimed that she had not been unfaithful since her last hospitalization and had had only the usual nervous symptoms during menopause five years previously.

Conclusion—One of the most difficult areas of differential diagnosis is in the case where there is evidence for both endogenous changes and psychogenic reactions. The latter often appear as 'intermittent reactions' (Schneider, 1927), for example, when a painful inner conflict manifests itself at times as neurotic or psychotic symptoms and at other times has no visible manifestations.

Such is the case here. As is apparent from the description, there is some basis for supposing both psychogenic reactions and a distinctly endogenous course with alternating depressive and manic phases.

The classification is uncertain.

Case 13

A 25-year-old woman, married to a postman.

History—The patient became deeply depressed after the death of a child (of diphtheria). She had apparently been quite normal before the child's death.

Follow-up—The patient did not respond to communications but her husband was contacted. He stated that the patient recovered very slowly from the depression. She had always been rather difficult, obstinate and liked to have her own way, but otherwise normal. During the depression she reproached herself with the thought that she should have called the doctor sooner.

Conclusion—The uncertainty of the melancholiform features precludes placing this case among the 'reactive depressions'. As the normal personality is not depressive the case should be included with the 'psychogenic depressions'.

Definitely a psychogenic depression.

Case 14

A 25-year-old woman with a degree in philosophy, working as a translator.

History—The patient had been engaged to a fellow student for two years when he was killed in a bicycle accident. She became depressed, self-reproachful and spoke of suicide without making any attempt. She both felt that she should have urged her fiancé to be more cautious and that he was not really dead.

Follow-up—The patient had later married and for reasons of discretion she was not personally contacted. Her mother, who was seen, volunteered the information that the patient when young had been vulnerable and sensitive, somewhat spoiled at home and well liked in company. After the depression she had been more serious. At 44 years of age she married a schoolteacher and the marriage was happy.

Conclusion—Like the previous one, this case had mild melancholiform features. The depression, however, gives a superficial impression (no inhibition) and was so short in duration that it must certainly be considered psychogenic rather than a psychically precipitated melancholia. The disturbance appears to have led to a slight characterological change.

Definitely a psychogenic reaction.

Case 15

The 32-year-old wife of a college professor, expecting her third child, admitted for a depression supposedly because of the financial ruin of her father and a fear that the family's finances could not support the expected baby.

History—The patient was German by birth, brought up in a comfortable middle-class home. During a visit to Copenhagen she met and after two years married her husband some seven years prior to her hospitalization. She had suffered from depression with insomnia and dizziness for the past year.

Follow-up—The patient had been divorced. She was found to be living with a business man who, supposedly because of a lengthy divorce process, was unable to marry her. The lover was present during the interview and very little information was obtained. The patient stated that she had had no further psychiatric difficulties and she appeared quite normal.

Her former husband was contacted and he gave a fuller picture. The marriage had never been particularly happy. The patient's sister, whom she visited frequently, was married to a multi-millionaire and the contrast between the utter luxury of their life and her own small apartment and the eternally overworked husband was apparently a great strain. In the years following her hospitalization she began to frequent night clubs and restaurants with friends unknown to her husband and did not conceal her infidelity.

Conclusion—The conflict in this case was conditioned by the contrast between the way of life the patient had known in her childhood and during her visits to her sister—and the petty bourgeois life the marriage provided. The contrast was so great that she was unable to adjust to it. The result was first a simple psychogenic depression and later a desperate embracing of those pleasures she found insufficient in the marriage and her milieu.

Definitely a psychogenic reaction.

Case 16

The 18-year-old daughter of a street-walker, father unknown.

History—The patient had been hospitalized twice before, the first time for *epilepsy*, the second time for a *possible hysteria*. Some time before the present admission she had suffered from a depression with religious self-reproaches. She had worked for two evangelical teachers whose intense and strict religion had influenced her deeply.

Follow-up—At 34 years of age she was happily married and no longer suffered from convulsions or other psychiatric symptoms. She considered the depression to have been precipitated by the religious influence at that time—denying any erotic complication. She was pyknic of body type.

Conclusion—Despite the diagnosis of the first hospitalization it seems doubtful that this patient could have been epileptic. She had a very emotional temperament. In the years following puberty she succumbed to a short but well defined depression during a period of religious absorption. We cannot tell if the religious stress found a point of attack in an inner sexual conflict.

Definitely a psychogenic reaction.

Case 17

A 31-year-old former matron in an orphanage arrived with her 4-year-old daughter and applied for admission because she feared that she would harm either the child or herself in her depressed state.

History—There was evidence of mental disturbance in the patient's maternal history and her father was an alcoholic. This was the patient's second admission for a depression which sprang from her difficulties with her lover (the child's father) who treated her most cynically. In this instance the lover had insisted that she should nurse another of his mistresses who was recovering from an abortion. His power over her was so great that she attempted to comply with his wishes but broke down over the strain.

Follow-up—In a personal interview the patient appeared a normal middle-class woman of pyknic body type. She stated that it had taken a long time to recover from her depression but once achieved she suffered no further psychiatric symptoms. She supported herself and her daughter as an office worker and lived a very uneventful life. She claimed that before the depression she had always been optimistic and not at all inclined to over-react to difficult situations. In her erotic life she appeared to have given up.

Conclusion—As a result of a serious conflict there developed a long and severe depression. However, the normal personality was healthy and the patient abreacted the trauma completely and achieved a good adjustment to her life conditions.

Definitely a psychogenic reaction.

Case 18

A 32-year-old unmarried nurse, admitted after having attempted suicide with an overdose of veronal.

History—There was evidence of mental disorder (disturbances of consciousness) in the maternal history. The patient had become depressed because her lover of several years' standing, a married man, had deserted her. Her pre-morbid personality appears to have been normal. She made a good recovery during hospitalization.

Follow-up—The patient did not wish to be interviewed because she feared to have 'the old wound torn open'. One of her colleagues, who was interviewed, stated that the patient had had no further serious difficulties, but had always been touchy with 'hysterical', unbalanced reactions, particularly towards her family. She was well liked in the hospital where she worked.

Conclusion—This case—because of the superficiality and short duration of the depression—stands on the borderline of the nervous conditions.

Definitely a psychogenic reaction.

The last 9 cases (10–18 inclusive) are examples of predominantly *simple* depressions, although so severe that they have here been considered psychotic. At the most one finds—as is so often the case with psychogenic depressions—an admixture of asthenic symptoms or transient hypnagogic pseudo-hallucinations and at times manifestations of mild self-reproaches; only in Case 12 do we find melancholiform features which leads us to suspect an endogenous depression. And in this case there may also have been manic periods. In some other cases there were episodic exaltations.

In the next 6 cases we find *extensive* (*cf.* page 51) depressions with a more varied and complicated symptomatology. The transitions between the two types, as might be expected, are quite gradual.

Case 19

A 25-year-old seamstress, separated from her husband, admitted for a depression culminating in an amnestic fugue of several hours the day before admission.

History—Since her marriage to a truck-driver at 19 years of age she had suffered from bad moods, headaches, and fits of trembling. The husband, who was dishonest and brutal, often beat her and their child, and was unfaithful. She attempted to separate from him shortly before her admission. Her symptoms were accentuated by unpleasant fights with her husband's family who reproached her for wishing to leave him. She saw shapes in the night and suffered from an asthenic-depressive syndrome and an amnestic fugue preceding admission.

Follow-up—The leptosomic patient at 42 years gave an impression of a pleasant, intelligent, healthy woman. After discharge she had gone back to work and achieved responsible business positions. A second marriage had also not been successful, but she divorced the man without the previous upheaval. Aside from the frequent headaches she lived a satisfying quiet life with her daughter.

Conclusion—This case illustrates the manner in which a disturbance of consciousness with a fugue can make an appearance in a condition dominated by asthenic and depressive symptoms.

Definitely a psychogenic reaction.

Case 20

A 33-year-old woman, married to a grocer, suffering from a depression.

History—At 26 years of age she had married, having had a child some years previously with another man. The marriage had not been a happy one and quarrels developed between the patient who was impulsive and hot-tempered and her husband who was a heavy drinker. She displayed a depressive-asthenic picture with milder hysterical features. She returned shortly after discharge as her impulsiveness increased at home. She showed wide mood vacillations with dramatic behaviour. Six months later she was admitted to St. Hans Hospital where a diagnosis of *dementia paralytica* was considered. Here she was restless, labile in mood, increasingly confused with possible auditory hallucinations, soiling and smearing, disconnected in speech, talking a good deal about her purity and the possibility of her husband's death. A lumbar puncture uncovered a possible syphilitic infection and it turned out that she had contracted syphilis at 23 years of age and had subsequently been treated for it. Wassermann reaction negative in blood and spinal fluid.

Follow-up—The patient died of a purulent salpingitis and heart disease at 42 years. The husband was interviewed and gave information reluctantly. He stated that the patient was a capable and energetic woman but hot-tempered and difficult to live with. She had shown no psychiatric difficulties before her depression and did not appear demented afterwards. The family doctor, who had never treated the patient for syphilis, claimed never to have seen signs of general paresis. He thought that the husband's dissipation could well have caused marital conflicts. A psychiatrist who had had contact with the patient when she was 39 years old felt 'that she gave the impression of a patient who had had a psychosis'. She never appeared to him to be classifiable as a case of general paresis. The rapid improvement following hospitalization was another factor against such a diagnosis.

Conclusion—The diagnosis is uncertain. In view of the material the most reasonable diagnosis is, perhaps: depressive-hysterical psychosis in a patient with asymptomatic neurosyphilis.

Uncertain case.

Case 21

The 29-year-old wife of a journeyman baker, admitted because of a post-partum depression.

History—The patient had always been nervous and sensitive. She suffered from nocturnal enuresis until 14 years of age. At 27 she aborted in the second month of pregnancy and two years later gave birth (forceps delivery) with great loss of blood. She was listless and tired afterwards. Some months later she was hospitalized for parametritis and nervous symptoms appeared, including obsessive thoughts of cutting the baby in pieces. She was transferred to the Psychiatric Division of the Municipal Hospital where she was depressed and increasingly suspicious of possible attack (men shooting her) and thought that her husband was unfaithful to her. She became hallucinated with ideas of reference. She showed some inhibition. She was transferred to St. Hans Hospital where she showed signs of 'amentia' (in the Continental sense of that word; *cf.* pages 3–7), although she remained oriented in all spheres. She recovered within two months and was discharged normal, if a little subdued.

Follow-up—At 46 years of age the pyknic patient apparently was a healthy woman. She could contribute no further information about the psychosis. She had later had another child with no difficulties.

Conclusion—The case must be classified with the post-partum psychoses. Although these were frequently discussed in the literature at the beginning of the century interest in them has waned. This is because the original supposition of a specific somatic aetiology was gradually relinquished. From Runge's (1911) research we know that 80 per cent of these cases are equally divided between schizophrenias and manic-depressive phases while amentia appears in 15 per cent of the cases. Of the latter very little is known except concerning the infectious cases. The aetiological factor of *Erschöpfung* (exhaustion), so eagerly adopted in the earlier German literature, is more often a semantic habit than a reality. Ewald (1928) accepts the significance of psychogenic factors. For example, he notes that severe obsessive jealousy sometimes appears during lactation, which can be explained as a psychogenic reaction stemming from the interruption of the couple's sexual life, permitting doubts to be cast on the husband's fidelity. Zilboorg (1928, 1929) has, from a psychoanalytic point of view, discussed the unconscious association between the ideas of childbirth and castration and claims that the precipitated schizophrenias are much more common than the manic-depressive conditions. Benedek (1952) has emphasized the oral nature of the post-partum symbiosis between mother and child.

It appears most natural to view the psychosis in this case as arising psychogenically in a woman of labile temperament. The somatic weakness following birth and lactation constitutes a possible predisposing but hardly a causal factor.

Definitely a psychogenic reaction.

Case 22

The 34-year-old wife of a ship builder, suffering from depression.

History—The patient had been depressed for some time because of marital conflicts (suspected infidelity on the part of the husband) and family difficulties with a brother. She developed convictions of being followed, was anxious and contemplated suicide (her mother's mother had committed suicide at the age of 78 years) without any actual attempt, but was not inhibited. A month later she was admitted with the same symptoms plus obsessive jealousy and a tendency to fabricate.

Follow-up—Interviewed at the age of 50 years this leptosomic middle-class woman seemed quite normal. She stated that her husband had later admitted his infidelity but that the marriage had improved in the course of a few years. The couple had two children and the patient's mental health remained good.

Conclusion—This is a case of an 'extensive' psychogenic depression with passing obsessive thoughts and vague paranoid ideas. The psychogenic nature of the disease cannot be doubted and a process psychosis cannot be considered.

Definitely a psychogenic reaction.

Case 23

The 47-year-old wife of an electrician, admitted for a depression during menopause.

History—The patient had become depressed some months before admission when the child welfare authorities had threatened to remove her unmarried daughter's child from her home. She was depressed and had ideas of reference. She was hospitalized twice again during the next year with the same clinical picture. There were hallucinations of voices using vulgar language to her and an acute sensitivity to the neighbour's criticism. She also suffered from a febrile phlebitis.

Follow-up—Aged 64 years the patient was a thickset pyknic elderly woman, rigid in her responses, but friendly, as was her husband. The patient stated that the child had been dearly loved by her and her husband and that she had had no further psychic difficulties except for a depression following the death of the child after an operation.

Conclusion—The case demonstrates how an injury to the self-image can lead to a paranoid reaction. The role of the menopause in the development of the disorder is probably a predisposing one. It is well known that a psychogenic vulnerability can be significantly increased during the years around menopause.

Definitely a psychogenic reaction.

Case 24

A 34-year-old unmarried seamstress, hospitalized for a depression with hysterical symptoms and anxiety.

History—The patient's father was 'nervous' and possibly suffered from convulsions. The patient was of low intelligence (conceivably because of a forceps delivery, as her ten brothers and sisters were of normal intelligence) and had had convulsive attacks as a child which were diagnosed as conversion reactions. Her nervousness and anxiety, which had always been present, increased after the death of her mother and an illness of her father. There was no evidence of psychosis after a short time.

Follow-up—The patient died of heart disease when 46 years of age. Her brother was interviewed and described the patient as nervous, sensitive to noise, with phobic reactions to going out and being with a large number of people. She never married and supported herself with her sewing.

Conclusion—This is a patient with a mild mental deficiency, possibly associated with birth trauma. In response to the mother's death and the father's illness she became depressed with an obtrusive anxiety. She was inclined to anxious and phobic reactions.

Definitely a psychogenic reaction.

Psychically Precipitated Melancholias

(2 cases)

This group is composed of those cases designated 'psychically precipitated melancholias' by Lange (1926). They are manic-

6 69

depressives in whom a depressive phase is precipitated by events or psychic conflicts accentuated by environmental factors. The events, respectively conflicts, which play an important part in the thought content of the illness, retreat quickly in favour of the melancholic delusions with a sense of guilt and self-reproaches and, as one frequently finds, well developed inhibition. The psychosis takes its own endogenously determined course independent of the persistence or removal of the precipitating agent. In these patients there are at times additional endogenously precipitated phases.

It is hard to say if this type of depression is a frequent one. As is well known both the patient and the relatives are frequently most eager to present an external event as responsible for the outbreak of the depression. The majority of these suppositions are, probably, pure fiction: the depression appears spontaneously but the patient and the people in his environment believe that they can see sufficient psychological motivation for the outbreak of the illness in an external accidental event. War experiences confirm this point of view. In Birnbaum's (1915–19) survey of psychiatric experiences during World War I it is quite clear that there was no significant increase of circular psychoses. Experiences from World War II (Jung, 1961) and concentration camps seem to confirm this view (see Chapter 1). The whole problem of psychic precipitation of manic-depressive phases, however, is a very intricate one, as can be seen in the discussions of the problem in the textbook by Mayer-Gross, Slater and Roth (1960) and in an article by Arieti (1959a). In the present material there are only two cases that can be classified in this group with any certainty.

Case 25

A 44-year-old nurse, the wife of a college professor, admitted after a suicide attempt by drowning.

History—The patient's maternal family showed some history of mental disturbances. An uncle (M.D.) was addicted to morphine. She married at 30 years of age and the first years were happy, but the husband suffered from intense epileptic attacks through which she nursed him (she had been trained as a nurse). When 43 years old she suddenly discovered that her husband had been unfaithful to her, and, combined with the strain of her professional and household duties, she became deeply depressed with hypnagogic hallucinations. During her six months of hospitalization she showed self-reproaches, arithmomania, and free-floating anxiety.

Follow-up—In a personal interview this 62-year-old pyknic-syntonic woman revealed that the depression had coincided with the years of her menopause. She stated that she always had been optimistic before the depression and it had been some years before the asthenic and obsessive-compulsive symptoms which followed the depression had cleared up. She had been completely healthy ever since.

Conclusion—There is, unfortunately, nothing in the records concerning the degree of inhibition. If there had been inhibition, it can hardly have been conspicuous. Nevertheless, there can be no doubt about the melancholic nature of the disease. The depression has a decidedly endogenous character—a depth and duration which precludes reactive or psychogenic depression. The fact that the case is complicated by asthenic and obsessive-compulsive symptoms does not change the diagnostic supposition; Lange (1926) frequently observed just such secondary symptoms in his patients with psychically provoked melancholias.

Psychically precipitated melancholia.

Case 26

A 24-year-old unmarried gardener, admitted after a period of intense depression.

History—The patient was hospitalized for over a year, being at first depressed, taciturn, brooding over religious problems with self-reproaches and some hallucinations. He was a lonely person, had worked at several jobs before settling down as a gardener. He felt that his boss was dissatisfied with his work, which was not the case. Gradually his condition changed to show a more schizophrenic picture with autism, some violence, more hallucinations and echolalia. Towards the end this cleared up and he was discharged as completely cured.

Follow-up—In a personal interview the patient appeared a youngish man of 40 years of typically pyknic build. He appeared neither psychotic nor neurotic. For the past 9 years he had been happily married and had got along well in his work. He felt his depression to be a reaction to his mother's ill health (she died of a heart disease during his hospitalization) plus the hard physical labour and unsatisfactory diet which were conditions of his job at that time. Also, he felt very lonely and was extremely poor. He came from a strictly religious evangelical home and was quite preoccupied with religious problems during his depression.

Conclusion—The diagnosis of schizophrenia is contradicted by the course of the disease. The condition was probably a precipitated melancholic phase. The hard physical work plus the lack of adequate nourishment can be viewed as predisposing factors.

Psychically provoked melancholia.

Other Depressive Syndromes Including Pre-Schizophrenic Episodes (14 cases)

First, two circular depressions will be presented.

Case 27

A 36-year-old married musician, admitted for a depression.

History—The patient was always rather pessimistic and serious, but otherwise normal. When aged 20 years he was depressed for a short time, possibly because of an erotic disappointment. He had been a heavy drinker for some years. At 34 he suffered a minor head injury. The month before his admission he became depressed, supposedly because of economic difficulties. He thought people noticed him on the street. As his depression increased he displayed self-reproaches, anxiety, and fearfulness, and finally, an almost total stupor, although without catatonic features. At the end of a year he was discharged as normal.

Follow-up—The patient committed suicide when 46 years of age by shooting himself in the mouth. An interview was obtained with the patient's son who could provide no explanation for the depression, nor for the suicide. The patient's wife had divorced him because of his inability to support the family and he had lived with his mother until his death. He managed to find occasional jobs playing the flute in cabarets.

Conclusion—Despite the fact that there is an unfortunate lack of information in this case it seems most reasonable to consider the patient a constitutional manic-depressive suffering from endogenous depressions. The records give no indication of reactive or psychogenic depression and it could at best have been a psychically provoked melancholia. We can also suppose that the patient committed suicide during a new depressive phase.

Definitely an endogenous depression.

Case 28

A 39-year-old cleaning woman, unmarried, admitted for a depression.

History—One of the patient's brothers was schizophrenic and two others psychopathic. Her mother suffered from convulsions. The patient's intelligence was somewhat below normal and she was not given to strong reactions. She lived with her parents. Some time before the outbreak of the depression she had taken to going to religious meetings with an eccentric friend who exerted a considerable influence over her and the depression was very religiously coloured. She heard reproaching voices, believed she was going to die, and that her food was made of dead people and rats. Once she went into a foggy state. She showed no schizophrenic symptoms but was in brief periods manic. After two years she died of acute gastroenteritis.

Follow-up—An interview with the patient's sister revealed that the patient had been a sickly child who grew up to be healthy. The patient had been in her menopause at the time of the depression.

Conclusion—It is impossible to determine whether this is a spontaneous or a psychically provoked melancholia. The development of the psychosis during the menopause is not a decisive factor. The significance of the climacterium in the construction of a psychosis can be psychogenic (sexual resignation) and possibly also somatic (endocrine changes); at this point very little is known on this subject. Lange (1928) believes it possible to ascribe a major role to the climacterium in terms of a somatic (metabolic) precipitation of melancholias.

Definitely a (psychically triggered ?) melancholia.

72

The following 8 cases are schizophrenias which were very depressively stamped in the beginning stages.

Depressive initial phases are far from rare in schizophrenias but they are typically short-lived. Both the laity and many psychiatrists are inclined to interpret aetiologically uncertain cases as psychogenic reactions. Many such depressions are therefore assumed to be related to more or less well demonstrated psychic traumata and conflicts until the symptoms of the schizophrenic process appear. Even though the prodromal depressions in schizophrenic psychoses approximate the picture of endogenous or psychogenic depressions, more precise observation of the patients frequently shows a peculiarity of the affect. It is more rigid, less capable of modulation, has no true depth and therefore does not make the same appeal to the environment as the affect in melancholia.

In all such cases one must first decide whether the symptoms and the course of the disease justify the diagnosis of schizophrenia. Psychogenic depressions may at times develop from purely psychic foundations into chronic, lifelong states which sometimes achieve a schizophrenia-suspect appearance. Bresowsky (1933) has observed—with 7 case histories as clinical illustrations—how diagnostically dangerous such psychoses may be. He believes that the transition to 'chronic psychopathic' states is fairly common. There is a particular difficulty in differential diagnosis between psychogenic disorder and schizophrenia when a 'psychopathic-negativistic continuance' (*psychopathisch-negativistischer Dauerzustand*) develops and the patient can isolate himself for weeks through irritability and uncommunicativeness—but where the further course of the disease shows that there could have been no destructive process psychosis.

When the diagnosis of schizophrenia can be verified one must attempt to decide whether the connection between the experience and the outbreak of the disease is accidental or real, that is, whether the schizophrenia has been psychically precipitated, a question which very often cannot be answered.

Case 29

A 22-year-old white-collar worker, admitted for a depression.

History—The patient had always been inclined to speculate over religious problems. After he lost his job because of a general lay-off of workers he became depressed and reproached himself on religious grounds. During the three years of his hospitalization he developed depressive-paranoid symptoms with a religious content. Having committed sin against the Holy Ghost he was convinced he was going to die. He heard

voices. The depression disappeared after a few months and he became
increasingly autistic. He died of tuberculosis while in hospital.

Follow-up—His sister, in an interview, described him as having been,
as a child, conscientious, quiet, and a little withdrawn with a tendency to
brood over religious themes.

Conclusion—The diagnosis of schizophrenia is likely here, even if
one cannot exclude the possibility of a protracted atypical melancholia.
There is no definite information on the degree of inhibition. If it is a
schizophrenia there are several ways to account for the depressive
stamp. The most prevalent theory is that it represents the patient's
constitutional manic-depressive predisposition. It is also possible that
the schizophrenic process itself can produce the melancholiform picture.
Bleuler (1911) considers both possibilities demonstrable. Finally, the
depression could be psychogenic.

Probably a schizophrenia.

Case 30

The 56-year-old widow of a photographer, admitted for a depression
during her climacterium.

History—Both the patient's brother and sister appear to have been
mentally disturbed. The patient's sister was diagnosed as a paranoid
schizophrenic and died in a mental hospital. The patient was normal
until she became depressed after her husbands' death from cancer of the
lungs. She suffered from attacks of anxiety with physical symptoms and
numerous hallucinations, visual, auditory, and olfactory. After going
through a period of near-stupor the patient became agitated and restless,
with loss of sphincter control and screaming attacks, and finally withdrawn and unapproachable. At the end of two years she died of cancer of
the stomach with pernicious anaemia.

Conclusion—It is extremely probable that the psychosis was a
schizophrenia emerging during the unusually late climacterium and
possibly precipitated by the traumatic experience of her husband's
death.

Our knowledge of the role of somatic disease* as aetiological or
precipitating factors in psychoses is too insufficient to formulate an
interdependence between the psychosis and the pernicious anaemia
probably caused by the cancer of the stomach.

Definitely schizophrenia, possibly psychically triggered.

Case 31

A 33-year-old single prison matron, admitted for a depression.

History—The patient's uncle was an alcoholic. She had always been
serious and pessimistic with high moral standards, subject to attacks of

* For a survey of the literature, see Hoskins (1946) and Bellak (1948).

sleep-walking until the age of 18 years. At 20 she had influenza with a high fever and subsequent poor sleeping habits and mild asthenic symptoms. The cause of her depression was given as difficulties in an affair with a man who was involved with a previous mistress whom he could not leave for business reasons. The patient had had an abortion and was fearful that her associates might know of it, felt herself observed in the street, etc. She reproached herself and attempted to find expiation through cutting off most of her hair. She developed hallucinations, ideas of reference, many bizarre unequivocally schizophrenic symptoms, autism, hallucinations, and baroque thought complexes. At the end of a year she died of acute gastro-enteritis.

Follow-up—One of her prison colleagues was interviewed and stated that the patient had been well liked and attempts had been made to cheer her up during her depression. The cause of the depression was believed to have been the discovery that the lover was married.

Conclusion—This is a schizophrenia, possibly psychically precipitated (the threat of the loss of an important object), with the depressive pre-morbid personality appearing in the depression during the beginning stages. The mild paranoid stamp manifested in the beginning of the psychosis is evidently a psychoplastic symptom which makes its appearance because of the special character of the psychic trauma (a blow to the self-image due to the strict moralistic attitude the patient takes towards her conflict).

Definitely schizophrenia (psychically precipitated?).

Case 32

The 37-year-old wife of a fireman, admitted for a depression.

History—The patient's siblings, mother, and maternal grandmother all appear to have been psychically abnormal. One sister was definitely schizophrenic. The patient's pre-morbid personality was described as stable, cold, quiet, serious, and pessimistic. She married at 26 years of age and gradually became eccentric and withdrawn, barely speaking to her husband or son. The depression followed a divorce notice from her husband. The patient was released after a month's hospitalization.

Follow-up—The patient was seen in her home, but remained in the kitchen, while her husband answered questions usually referring to her as 'it'. Because of her depression he had given up his plans for divorce. The patient, who had always been frigid, became increasingly withdrawn and peculiar to the point that she now functioned mechanically like a robot in the household, barely maintaining contact with her husband and son, sleeping in a corner of the room and scarcely ever changing her clothes.

Conclusion—This case must certainly be considered a schizophrenia because of the marked autism.

Definitely a schizophrenia.

Case 33

A 34-year-old unmarried nurse, admitted because of a depression.

History—A brother of the patient developed a hebephrenic schizophrenia and died in a mental hospital. The patient had been stable and well liked until an erotic conflict (her fiancé's family disapproved of her and she eventually broke the engagement) arose. A religiously tinged depression followed, with a great deal of self-reproaches and self-accusations. Ideas of reference appeared with convictions of her sexual 'dirtiness' and 'naughtiness'. She became violent and destructive, hallucinated, and finally increasingly autistic. She died two years later after having developed distinct paranoid ideas of a persecutory nature.

Follow-up—No new material was revealed by the follow-up (her family, her doctor and some of her friends).

Conclusion—There can be no doubt of the schizophrenic outcome of the disorder. There may have existed a complex personality structure with cyclothymic components which are mobilized by the schizophrenic psychosis and form a pathoplastic covering for the basic disease. A psychic triggering is possible.

Definitely a schizophrenia (psychically precipitated?).

Case 34

The 45-year-old climacterial wife of a cigar dealer, admitted for a depression.

History—The patient helped her husband in his cigar business. When it began to fail the patient developed a depression and suggested mutual suicide to her husband. During hospitalization the depression gave way to a paranoid schizophrenia with megalomanic content. At first she thought herself Queen Maud of Norway, and, finally, contracted an imaginary marriage with a doctor who had three names but only one office. She was able to work efficiently in the hospital laundry.

Follow-up—With some difficulty contact was established with the patient in the hospital. She was pleased with her new marriage, although she did not see her husband often but had long conversations with him via air waves. She did not appear demented.

Conclusion—The illness appears to have broken out spontaneously and the rather minor psychological stress, was used pathoplastically.

Definitely a schizophrenia.

It is most likely also that the following case is an example of a paranoid development, but a satisfactory follow-up proved impossible.

Case 35

A 43-year-old woman, married to an iron dealer, admitted for a depression a few years after a premature menopause.

History—The patient lived with her husband and bore him two children several years before their marriage, which appears to have been a harmonious one until the patient discovered that the husband had a mistress. Shortly after this discovery he suddenly left the patient to live in sin with his lady friend. She developed an anxious depression which cleared up after some seven months.

Follow-up—It was impossible to contact the patient. The building superintendent's wife was interviewed and described the patient as a seclusive and somewhat peculiar woman. She once rushed into the informer's kitchen with an accusation of tampering in the apartment while she was out.

Conclusion—The possibility of a paranoid development is most likely
Uncertain case.

Case 36

A 33-year-old unmarried houseworker, admitted after attempting suicide.

History—The patient was born in Iceland. She left her home there shortly before the admission to follow a man to Germany. She had seen him only once and had never spoken to him. In Germany she discovered, to her consternation, that he was married. She was sent to Denmark by the police, and when later put on board a ship for Iceland attempted to jump into the harbour. She was severely depressed, at times stuporous, and appeared hallucinated. Her condition gradually improved and after nine months she was discharged to a sister living in Copenhagen.

Follow-up—It was impossible to obtain reliable information about the patient. Only the above mentioned sister, who appeared psychotic in an interview, stated that the patient, now living in Iceland, was still insane.

Conclusion—Although the information on the case is scanty there may well have been a malignant psychotic process.
Uncertain case.

Cases 37–39 are of particular interest. They are patients—all three women—who develop depressions with a melancholiform stamp in connection with sexual traumata. After a time they recover and, now in good health, are able to work for a period varying from two to five years. They then become psychotic again and, in the course of time, the disturbance is revealed as a true schizophrenia.

These are examples of a type of psychotic development described by Strömgren (1940) with reference to a case of particular interest from a hereditary point of view. The primary benign psychosis is termed a 'pre-schizophrenic episode'. In his work, Strömgren requests careful study of the symptomatological characteristics of such episodes. This is partly because of their theoretical interest and partly because it would be desirable to be able to state the malignant prognosis as quickly as possible for eugenic reasons.

77

There are two fundamental possibilities, both probably clinical realities, concerning the origin of the pre-schizophrenic episodes. The psychosis may be completely independent of the schizophrenic predisposition, for instance a psychogenic psychosis or a manic-depressive phase. Mention should here be made of Urstein's (1909) classic work on manic-depressive conditions which after some years develop into psychoses that in all probability are schizophrenias. In this case it is a question of a 'simple addition' of psychoses with different aetiology. This suggests Hoffmann's (1923) 'alteration of appearance' (*Erscheinungswechsel*), in which the same genotype contains several predispositions which come to the fore at varioust imes in the life history due to differences of genetic maturation.

The other possibility is that of an early atypical manifestation of the schizophrenic genotype with full remission. At some later time there is a new outbreak of the schizophrenic psychosis, this time permitting no doubt about the nature of the process and the poor prognosis. In such a case, again according to Strömgren, the pre-schizophrenic process is a schizophrenic 'equivalent', that is, the manifestation of the specific genic formula, while in the first case (where the episode is genetically independent of the schizophrenic predisposition) there exists a possibility of schizophrenic colouring because of the schizophrenic constitution.

The existence of this particular psychotic development: *episode–interval–schizophrenic psychosis* has long been known, but the complicated question of 'mixed psychoses' and schizophrenias with good initial remission has not been exhaustively discussed.

Popper (1920), in his wartime experience, found that many individuals, when hit by severe stress, will react with a schizophrenia-like illness which afterwards leaves a fully intact personality. Thus, an endogenous reaction form, the schizophrenic reaction syndrome, is defined, which, together with the other reactions of an endogenous type (hysterical, depressive, manic, 'degenerative', etc.), create a counterpart to Bonhoeffer's exogenous reaction types. For a more detailed discussion see Chapter 13 and Langfeldt (1939).

Kahn (1921) clarified Popper's formulations with the concept of a type of specific reaction readiness that belongs to the schizoid-schizophrenic predisposition and that can be precipitated by not only psychogenic but also by endocrinological or other somatic causal factors.

As Strömgren points out, Popper's schizophrenic reaction type can be either an equivalent or an independent psychosis in relation to the schizophrenic genotype.

Case 37

A 30-year-old married female teacher, admitted for a depression.

History—The patient's father, brother, and sister all had cyclothymic temperaments and a paternal uncle had both manic and depressive phases. The patient was intelligent, cyclothymic and inclined to brood. In the eighth year of her marriage she discovered that her husband was unfaithful to her and went into a depression of the melancholic type with hypochondriasis and anxiety. She had 'funny thoughts' and was afraid of becoming insane. She was hospitalized for almost a year and recovered completely. Five years later an attachment she formed with a fellow teacher was dissolved when her friend's interest in the relationship cooled, and she again went into a depression. This time auditory and visual hallucinations were added to the previous symptoms and the picture became increasingly schizophrenic.

Follow-up—In a personal interview 13 years later she presented the picture of a typically demented schizophrenia.

Conclusion—The pre-schizophrenic episode can hardly be considered a schizophrenic equivalent but rather a psychogenic depressive reaction or a (psychically provoked) melancholia with the atypical symptomatology possibly being the result of an affinity to the schizophrenic genotype; assuming the episode to be a melancholic phase, we would here have a case of manic-depressive psychosis followed by the development of a schizophrenia as described by Urstein.

Uncertain case (the episode).

Case 38

A 23-year-old unmarried houseworker, admitted because of eccentric behaviour in the home where she worked.

History—There were several cases of defective mental functioning in the patient's family. She herself had had no difficulties until shortly before her admission when she was seduced, on a vacation trip, by a travelling salesman. She responded with strong self-reproaches and feelings of uncleanliness. There was some depersonalization and some incipient paranoid responses. After a short period during which the patient was supposedly normal, she became severely psychotic again—but this time in the form of a pronounced delirious state which lasted two months, after which she recovered and functioned well for 4 years. She kept a milk shop and later became housekeeper to a widower with two small children. She entered into a sexual relationship with him and undoubtedly had hoped of marriage. When he announced his intention to marry another woman she developed a schizophrenic psychosis. Like the first psychosis, this one was also marked by a strong shift in mood from a manic to a depressed state which gradually gave way to a frank schizophrenia.

Follow-up—The patient, seen in the hospital, was autistic, aggressive, and showed schizophrenic personality defects and flatness of affect.

Conclusion—The first two psychotic episodes apparently showed no

79

schizophrenic features and were probably not schizophrenic equivalents but psychogenic psychoses.

Uncertain case (the episodes).

Case 39

A 16-year-old unmarried houseworker, admitted for a depression.

History—There was an impressive history of mental disturbance in the maternal family, mostly of a manic-depressive type. When aged 8 years the patient suffered a sexual trauma when she was lured into a lavatory by a man who lifted her clothes and poured water over her. The pre-psychotic personality was normal. A severe depression broke out after an unknown man took her for a walk and caressed her. She was very agitated and filled with self-reproaches, at times in a stuporous state, hallucinated with a conviction that various parts of her body did not belong to her. She smeared with her faeces. The depression lifted after several months and for a while she was manic. After eight to nine months she recovered with amnesia for the psychotic period and was mentally healthy (as claimed by both her father and a sister when interviewed in the follow-up). Two years later she suffered an erotic disappointment when a boy friend broke off with her and a schizophrenic picture developed. She was discovered to be tubercular shortly before her hospitalization and died a year later of pulmonary tuberculosis, still in an autistic state.

Conclusion—The patient's first psychosis must be viewed as a severe (psychically precipitated) atypical melancholia with a manic terminal phase. The atypical features are the disturbances of consciousness and the schizophreniform symptoms. It is interesting to note that the innocent erotic trauma probably was intensified by the childhood trauma of a similar nature: her reaction to the flirtation was, therefore, catathymic.

If we consider the pre-schizophrenic episode psychically precipitated there are three possible explanations:

(1) It is to be considered as originating in the manic-depressive predisposition plus the psychically precipitating incident. The schizo-phrenic constitution has only a pathoplastic effect.

(2) The pathogenesis is explained by the schizophrenic predisposition plus the psychically precipitating incident, while the circular constitution colours the episode pathoplastically. In this case we may speak of a schizophrenic equivalent.

(3) Both the circular and the schizophrenic constitutional elements are pathogenetically effective and the activity of both is set in motion by the psychic trauma. At the moment we are able to delineate the theoretical possibilities but are in no position to choose between them.

Uncertain case (the episode).

The following is a case of general paresis with a prodromal depression.

Case 40

A 36-year-old unmarried bakery worker, admitted after attempting suicide by hanging.

History—The patient was of subnormal intelligence but had always been otherwise mentally normal. He became depressed a few weeks before his admission, supposedly because he had stolen a very small amount of money (which he later paid back) and was overcome with pangs of conscience. He gradually became agitated, affected, childish and silly, shouting and gesticulating, but with no indication of intense mood behind his behaviour. He was discharged into his parents' care without change.

Follow-up—A few months after his discharge he attempted suicide again (by drowning). He was hospitalized three times more, and was permanently hospitalized ten years before the follow-up. The diagnosis was *general paresis* with the characteristic changes in the cerebrospinal fluid. He underwent malarial therapy. In a personal interview he gave the impression of having adjusted well to the hospital and was not eager to leave.

Conclusion—This is a general paresis with a depressive prodromal stage and with the peculiarities typical of paralytic depressions: insipidity, affectation, and childlike pitifulness. The inferior mental endowment in this case provides a fertile soil for the development of this particular state.

States of Elation

(8 cases)

As is true of depressions, states of euphoria or elation (the concepts taken in their widest meaning) also appear in almost every type of psychosis; principally, of course, as phases of manic-depressive psychoses, next in organic psychoses and schizophrenias, in epileptic psychoses and imbecility, and, finally, also in psychogenic psychoses.

There are three types of elation belonging within the area of psychogenesis. First, psychically precipitated manic states in manic-depressive psychoses. Second, a 'reactive mania' which arises as a qualitatively adequate but exaggerated reaction to a euphoric experience. Third, a 'reactive exaltation' or, as it is also called, 'desperation exaltation' or 'hysterical mania' (Wimmer, 1916) which is also covered in Schneider's (1919b) 'flight- or anxiety-mania'.

That manic as well as depressive phases may be triggered by external somatic (for example, head injuries and infectious diseases) and psychic influences is generally known and needs no further discussion here (*cf.* pages 69–90).

There is more dispute on the subject of true 'reactive manias'. Bleuler (1937) doubts the existence of such a state, while Bumke (1929) and Bonhoeffer (1911) regard mild exaltation states as rare

81

responses to joyful events. Schneider (1927) also recognizes the existence of such states and maintains that they do not always necessarily presuppose a circular anlage. Lange (1928) considers such reactive manias extremely rare, while Birnbaum (1928b) cautiously confines himself to references to other opinions. Zahle (1940) has reported a case which seems to fulfil all the requirements for a true reactive mania. In a later paper Zahle (1951) has discussed this problem in more detail. All in all, it would appear that a 'reactive mania' exists but is a rare psychopathological phenomenon.

The last of the three forms, 'flight-mania' or the 'reactive exaltation' appears with scarcely more frequency. Here we have a pseudo-manic state, usually with a very infantile colouring, in people who in anxiety-filled or otherwise threatening situations attempt to save themselves by flight into an inadequate affect. One finds this form most frequently in mentally retarded psychopaths of the emotionally instable type, often accompanied by clouding of consciousness which conditions the well known post-paroxysmal amnesia. Flight-mania is observed most frequently in very dramatic situations, catastrophes, etc. Kleist (1918), Lange (1928), and Birnbaum (1928b) speak of such reactions as common war syndromes.

From a psychoanalytic point of view, Lewin (1950) has made an important contribution to the study of the intimate psycho-dynamic mechanisms of elation. One can safely assume that his monograph will remain one of the classics within this area of dynamic psychiatry.

In my material, Case 41 is definitely, and Case 42 most likely flight-mania, while Case 43 is a borderline psychotic excitement state in an hysterical-neurotic woman. This last case can only conditionally be considered flight-mania.

Case 41

A 27-year-old hospital porter, admitted in an aggressive excited state.
History—The patient was somewhat under average intelligence but otherwise quite normal until he was assigned to the hospital autopsy room two days before his admission. He came home in a very agitated state, domineering and destructive, talking about and also behaving like a military border guard. The preceding day he had met his old lieutenant-colonel in the street and he had suggested such a job to the patient. During the few days he spent in the hospital he was preoccupied with his military career, but quickly returned to normal.
Follow-up—The patient showed and claimed no further psychiatric difficulties.

Conclusion—This case is a typical example of 'flight-mania', precipitated by the macabre experience in the autopsy room. It is interesting that the content of the psychotic episode stems from the concomitant experience of a completely different order, namely the meeting with the former military superior and the suggestion of a career in uniform, which probably had a flattering and fascinating effect on him. Structurally the episode must be considered as pathogenetically determined by the experience of the autopsy room, while the encounter with the army officer was the decisive pathoplastic factor.

Definitely a psychogenic reaction.

Case 42

A 22-year-old unmarried musician, admitted during a paranoid hallucinatory attack with pronounced hysteriform features.

History—The patient came home exhausted one night after playing at three dances and the next morning his symptoms broke out. He was dissatisfied and suspicious of his fellow musicians, the piano and the musical notes. He thought himself followed and believed everyone wanted to cheat and deceive him, etc. He had auditory hallucinations and suffered from anxiety. He was quite excited in mood and seemed artificial in facial expression and gestures. Within six weeks he returned to an almost normal state and was discharged.

Follow up—The patient appeared normal although not too intelligent, rather psycho-infantile and somewhat hypomanically cheerful. He claimed to have suffered no further psychic disturbance after the one episode. He remembered his illness well, but could give no information as to its cause.

Conclusion—The lack of information about a psychic trauma makes it naturally difficult to classify the case as an hysterical mania. But the construction of the pre-morbid personality (supposedly a somewhat inferior hypomanic), the nature of the disturbance and its further course all suggest that such a classification is the most likely one. Other diagnostic possibilities aside from a mild atypical endogenous mania are difficult to support.

Probably a psychogenic reaction.

Case 43

A 30-year-old unmarried female organist, admitted in a disturbed state with religious hallucinations.

History—The patient's maternal family showed evidence of mental disorder (addiction, obsessive-compulsive personalities). She herself was admitted on her father's insistence when she showed a religious preoccupation with elation that appeared to him morbid. The patient's family considered her peculiar and, although she denied hallucinations, she gave a decided impression of being hallucinated during her month's hospitalization.

Follow-up—At 45 years the patient appeared active and energetic, typically pyknic in body type. She claimed that difficulties with her family over her religious activities had led to her hospitalization. After her discharge she had broken with the family and lived with a woman and her son who were devotees of the same religious group, and she had no further difficulties.

Conclusion—During a conflict with her father the patient developed a (hallucinatory?) hypomanic state. Only deep psychopathologic exploration could reveal the neurotic structure involved.

Definitely a psychogenic reaction.

The following two cases belong to the manic-depressive type of disorders.

Case 44

A 29-year-old private secretary, admitted in a manic state.

History—The patient's heredity over two generations showed a number of individuals with more or less serious disturbances, most centring around manic-depressive disorders. The patient herself was intelligent and well educated. She had worked for some years as a translator in a large insurance office. In the months prior to her admission her usual nervousness was greatly accentuated and when admitted she was in a state of great restless agitation. She developed a fever after three weeks, whose cause could not be precisely determined and she died a week later. Epidemic encephalitis was considered the most likely diagnosis. An autopsy was not performed.

Follow-up—An exchange of letters with the patient's sister revealed that the patient had been, when normal, lively, active, and outgoing. The patient had fallen in love with a foreigner shortly before she fell ill.

Conclusion—The hereditary picture here suggests a manic phase in a manic-depressive psychosis. The phase was possibly triggered by the erotic conflict situation in which the patient found herself shortly before the outbreak of her illness. The psychosis culminated in a delirious state of such intensity that one might well speak of an acute delirium. Several authors have suggested an affinity between delirium acutum and manic-depressive psychosis.

Probably a manic phase in a manic-depressive psychosis.

Case 45

A 39-year-old married cemetery keeper, admitted in a state of agitation.

History—The patient's mother had suffered a psychotic attack during her menopause with manic symptoms. When it passed she was left with a character change of a paranoid type. The patient, according to his wife's testimony from the follow-up, had always been irritable and aggressive in temperament and sexually demanding but otherwise normal until the outbreak of his psychosis. He was then in a state of intense exaltation with auditory hallucinations and the belief that it was necessary for him to father the new Messiah with a lady of his acquaintance. Before the end of a week in the hospital he ran a temperature and died of pneumonia.

Conclusion—The most likely diagnosis for both the patient and his mother is a manic phase in a manic-depressive psychosis, his spontaneously aroused and his mother's provoked by the menopause. Unfortunately, there is no information on other phases of the life cycles which could support such a supposition.

Uncertain case.

The remaining 3 cases are schizophrenias with a beginning phase characterized by manic symptoms.

The manic prodromata in schizophrenia have, like the corresponding depressive (*cf.* page 73) usually a particular quality arousing suspicion as to the malignant nature of the psychosis.

Case 46

The 31-year-old wife of a coachmaker, admitted after rather sudden behavioural changes.

History—The patient's sister died in a mental hospital (diagnosis of *hysterical confusion, possible manic-depressive psychosis*). The patient had always been irritable and somewhat aggressive in temperament, but otherwise normal until she suddenly became foolish and euphoric, talked a great deal about religion, and suicide which she did not attempt. When admitted she was excited, but after transfer to St. Hans Hospital she developed inhibition and was almost stuporous for some time, after which her state became increasingly autistic and it was obvious that she was schizophrenic. A psychogenic psychosis had at first been suspected, but it was impossible to obtain any information on a possible psychic trauma and the progress of the disease revealed the malignant process. The patient was still hospitalized at the time of the personal *follow-up*.

Definitely schizophrenia.

Case 47

The 42-year-old wife of a factory foreman, Swedish born, admitted in an exalted state with religious content.

History—The patient was, before her illness, a very intelligent, warm and capable pyknic woman whose difficulties appeared to have begun after she read a book on metaphysics. It became increasingly obvious that there was a schizophrenic process involved and, until her death by suicide 16 years later, she was intermittently hospitalized because of auditory hallucinations with religious content.

Conclusion—The psychosis was possibly precipitated by the climacterium. The pyknic body type and the supposedly predominantly syntonic personality appear, as is so often the case (*cf.* Mauz, 1930, and Langfeldt, 1939), to have protected the patient from a massive defect of the personality.

Definitely a schizophrenia.

Case 48

A 27-year-old unmarried housemaid, admitted in a state of extreme agitation.

History—The patient, normally pleasant and stable in personality, became suddenly very restless and uncontrollable following an episode in which the master of the house made her a gift of some elegant underclothing, which irritated the lady for whom she worked. When admitted she was in an exalted mood, talking, smiling, singing hymns. She gradually became increasingly autistic and remained hospitalized for eleven years with a diagnosis of schizophrenia. The hallucinations and paranoid thought processes which she had developed tapered off and finally disappeared. After discharge she resumed her work as a housemaid.

Follow-up—The patient was a stylishly dressed 43-year-old leptosomic woman. In conversation she gave a euphoric but flat affective impression, otherwise she appeared quite normal. According to an employer and a sister she had had no difficulty in getting along in her work. She married a working-man, and the marriage was said to be a happy one.

Conclusion—It is difficult to place an unequivocal diagnosis of schizophrenia. The most likely diagnosis is that of a long-lasting schizophrenic 'push', leaving only a slight damage to the personality.

Episodic psychoses in mental defectives often have a schizophrenia-like appearance. The possibility of an episodic, for example, psychogenic, schizophreniform psychosis in a mentally inferior person cannot be completely disregarded.

Probably a schizophrenia.

CHAPTER 7

THE DISTURBANCES OF CONSCIOUSNESS

Our knowledge of disturbances of consciousness is marked by such incompleteness and uncertainty that a satisfactory systematization is difficult to achieve. No one of the various attempted classifications does full justice to the facts.

As mentioned in Chapter 4, Strömgren's division (1945), slightly modified, is used here. The classification then is the following: dissociations of consciousness; turbid states I, deliria; turbid states II, hallucinoses; stuporous states.

Disturbances of consciousness in general are purposeful reactions. They attempt to protect the individual from the painful consequences of, usually, acute situations that cannot be worked through with the help of more normal psychological mechanisms. These pathological reactions may, therefore, be teleologically evaluated. The problem whether this is true for all psychogenic reactions will be discussed in Chapter 14.

The efficacious pathological mechanisms in the group of disturbances of consciousness all belong to what Kretschmer (1923, 1926) calls *primitive reactions*. These result in either impulsive and often quite dangerous actions or, even more primitive, in a 'hypobulic' fit of motor activity in the form of more or less differentiated hysterical attacks or, finally, in 'hyponoic' turbid or dissociative states.

These phylogenetically preformed types, as is natural enough, appear most frequently in psycho-infantile individuals in distinction to the psychologically better organized and more individually coloured *personality reactions* (expansive, sensitive, and autistic paranoid developments, Kretschmer, 1926). However, they also appear in more mature adults when the stimulating experience is strong enough to break through the barrier of the developed personality.

One must also presuppose a particular constitutional predisposition that permits the psychic trauma to produce a particular type of reaction. We can assume that the strength and suddenness of the trauma also play a role in this connection in that the most overwhelming and the most acute experiences appear to be able to evoke the most primitive reactions. Closest to normal states are the peaceful cloudy conditions, sometimes complicated by amnestic fugues, while the hypobulic and

87

hyponoic states show the greatest degree of primitivization the psyche undergoes in its attempt to free itself of the pathogenic situation.

Dissociations of Consciousness

(29 cases)

Among the 24 cases in this group which were verified as psychogenic by the follow-up there were no less than 16 (7 men, 9 women) with amnestic fugues.

Case 49

A 47-year-old railroad worker, admitted because of a fugue.

History—The patient had been rather downcast since the death of his father six months previously. On the day his fugue began he had consulted a doctor who informed him that he had gonorrhoea. He retained no memory of the forty-eight hours of the fugue. His wife, with whom he had been having difficulties because of her menopause, knew nothing of his extramarital affairs or the venereal disease. He was released after three weeks, mildly depressed.

Follow-up—At 62 years of age the leptosomic patient appeared quite normal and claimed to have had no further psychiatric difficulties. He had got along better with his wife and his depressive symptoms had disappeared.

Conclusion—According to the information given, there appears to have been no constitutional predisposition to psychogenic reactions. The psychogenic readiness was instead conditioned by the death of the patient's father and his marital conflicts. Psychogenic agents can create the necessary temporary predisposition which other psychogenic factors (in this case the awareness of the venereal disease) act upon to form an acute psychotic reaction (*cf.* page 196).

Definitely a psychogenic psychosis.

Case 50

A 50-year-old married dock worker, admitted because of a fugue while under the influence of alcohol.

History—The patient had suffered a head injury a few years previously and had been nervous and inclined to headaches and some 'nervousness'. He had been out of work for some time before the transitory fugue and had suffered a financial setback. When seen for the *follow-up* at the age of 68 years, the leptosomic patient stated that he was subject to such fugues (two of them leading to hospitalization) for some years, but they, along with his post-concussion symptoms, had eventually disappeared.

Conclusion—The structure of this case is interesting because of the complicated interaction of the various determinants. On the basis of all the information obtained a constitutional predisposition may be excluded. The head injury, on the other hand, is definitely a predisposing factor. Brain injuries are well known as predisposing agents for psychogenic reactions. Kretschmer (1919a), in his concept of 'traumatic brain weakness' (*traumatische Hirnschwäche*), describes such exogenous predispositions for psychogenic reactions and demonstrates their significance for the development of psychogenic paranoid reactions. Wimmer (1916) and Birnbaum (1918, 1928b) also emphasizes the predisposing significance of head injuries. The drinking was a precipitating factor.

The automatisms may, therefore, be considered as exogenously (psychogenic-toxic) caused reactions within the framework of the conditional (head injury) predisposition.

Definitely a psychogenic reaction.

Case 51

A 25-year-old mechanic, admitted by the police after having committed arson and theft.

History—Some months before his admission the patient had been in a bicycle accident and had suffered a mild head injury. Afterwards he was unable to speak for a couple of days and subject to dizziness and 'fainting'. At the same time his girl friend turned out to be pregnant (the child died shortly after birth). His criminal behaviour had extended over several years. During hospitalization he was viewed as an hysterical psychopath. A few months later he suffered a short-lasting amnestic fugue and was hospitalized for one day.

Follow-up—It was at first impossible to locate the patient but his former wife was seen. She portrayed him as a charming man, possibly mythomanic, boastful, promising everything, producing nothing. Later a brother was contacted and gave a completely different picture. He saw his brother as perfectly normal, with no further criminal activities after the last arrest, now holding a responsible position in a large firm and happily remarried. For considerations of tact the patient himself was not contacted.

Conclusion—As in the previous case a head injury appears to have been a disposing factor—in this case as an accentuation of a constitutional psychogenic reaction readiness. We have here three determinants: the constitutional and conditional predisposition plus the conflict situation: the criminal activities and the complicated relationship with his girl friend.

Definitely a psychogenic reaction.

Case 52

The 38-year-old wife of a house painter, admitted after a fugue of several hours' duration.

History—Aside from some banal nervousness in the patient's mother's history there was no evidence given of previous difficulty. The patient's fugue was a reaction to a dishonest action on the part of her son which might have involved police action. The day after she had learned about this she had her psychotic reaction. In a few days the patient recovered partial memory.

Follow-up—This was the only psychotic episode in the patient's life. The son's misdemeanour did not turn out to be so serious as had been anticipated and she had been normal ever since.

Conclusion—We have here a simple psychogenic fugue, a flight from a distressing situation. It is scarcely believable that the patient's pre-morbid psyche can have been so normal as the records would have us believe. It is most likely that the favourable circumstances of her life overshadowed the psychogenic predisposition which was only provoked by the painful situation.

As is so often the case, the reaction here followed a short latency period.

Definitely a psychogenic aetiology.

Case 53

The 46-year-old wife of a wholesaler, admitted after a fugue while in her climacterium.

History—One of the patient's daughters was epileptic, another extremely unstable, and her son had alcoholic tendencies. For no ascertainable reason the patient had suddenly got up one morning and disappeared until midnight when her husband found her lying on the floor fully dressed. She was depressive in mood during her hospitalization but better at discharge a week later.

Follow-up—At 62 years of age she seemed quite normal and had suffered no further psychiatric difficulties. She revealed that her husband had frequently been unfaithful at the time of her fugue, but the relationship had become more harmonious thereafter.

Conclusion—The menopause is one of the physiological factors that may create a temporary inclination to psychogenic reactions by strengthening what already exists of a psychogenic predisposition. It is difficult to decide whether the climacterium is the only disposing factor in this case. The information on the patient's children might lead one to suppose a constitutional psychic abnormality, but the lack of material on the patient's and her husband's heredity makes it difficult to come to any definite conclusion.

Definitely a psychogenic reaction.

Case 54

A 17-year-old unmarried sailor.

History—The patient's paternal grandfather committed suicide, one maternal uncle was an alcoholic, and another died in a mental hospital of general paresis. The patient had suffered from enuresis and pavor nocturnus in his childhood, from influenza at the age of 10 years and a head injury at about the same time. He had been in a tragic shipwreck the year before admission and had witnessed the death of the captain and another sailor. He had wandered for some time afterwards in a confused foggy state, working on a farm in Sweden for a while and finally came home. A month before his admission he had stolen some money he was supposed to deliver from one shop to another. After taking a short trip on the money, he gave himself up to the police and was imprisoned. He showed no psychotic symptoms but appeared somewhat subnormal in intelligence. He was admitted again a month later after numerous short fugues in which he seemed to relive the shipwreck situation. The spinal fluid was normal. Wassermann reaction test negative, also in the blood.

Follow-up—Ten years later the patient was permanently hospitalized half a year after setting fire to an almshouse. A few years later it was possible to place a diagnosis of *chronic epidemic encephalitis*. Ten years later he hanged himself while in the hospital.

Conclusion—We can safely assume that the patient's initial disturbance was a psychogenic psychosis. Of course, it is possible that the encephalitis was already at work at that time (the negative spinal fluid findings do not exclude the possibility of encephalitis) and that it provided an exogenous predisposition. The desperate, impulsive fire-setting could also be a sign of the encelphalitis. According to Thiele (1926) the post-encephalitic 'pseudo-psychopathy' shows a great tendency to motor discharge along with a dissolution of subcortical inhibitions following injury to the subcortical ganglia. The patient's impulsive suicide may be viewed as evidence of the same mechanism.

The psychic reactions of the long period following the catastrophe is an example of delayed psychogenic reactions. We see here a 'recurrence of affect', several times, as mild 'reminiscence deliria' (*délire ecmnésique*) complicated by amnestic fugues.

Definitely a psychogenic reaction.

In the following cases the emphasis is on the constitutional psychogenic predisposition while the acquired predisposing factors play only a modest role.

Case 55

A 24-year-old married carpenter, admitted in a stupor and after a fugue.

History—On his admission after being found unconscious on a stairway, his wife stated that he was very hot-tempered, given to intense choking attacks during which he was either almost unconscious or extremely destructive. He had had several amnestic fugues. In a few days the stupor cleared up and he revealed that he had been having difficulties with his wife (they were divorcing) and he had been out of work for some time and depressed over it. Three years later he was hospitalized for a depression following a near-accident while driving his car. It was then reported that

91

he had suffered a syphilitic infection at 20 years of age. At 33 he was depressed again after the death of his daughter in an accident. At 40 he was once more hospitalized with asthenic and dyspeptic symptoms. His Wassermann was positive and he was treated for syphilis. A year later he was seen for the *follow-up* and a clearer picture of his reserved introverted personality and the unhappiness of his marriage (his wife had been unfaithful) was secured. He was leptosomic.

Conclusion—In this patient the disposition for psychogenic reactions is purely constitutional. According to the information given the venereal infection can hardly have been a predisposing factor. The serious psychopathic character-traits, the tendency to acute explosive primitive reactions, combined with the psychogenic factors to explain the patient's reactions.

Definitely a psychogenic reaction.

Case 56

A 35-year-old married mason, admitted after several fugues and suicide attempts.

History—The patient had had influenza two years before his admission. The marriage was breaking up at that time as his psychopathic personality traits made it impossible for his wife to live with him. He was hospitalized a month later for a fugue following an attempt to break into his wife's apartment and was arrested (they were now separated). The next year he was hospitalized for a depression. A few months after his discharge he committed suicide by shooting himself in the chest outside his ex-wife's apartment.

Conclusion—We have here a psychopathic predisposition which breaks out from time to time in psychotic outbursts. It is possible, but not proven, that the influenza strengthened the psychopathic anlage.

Definitely a psychogenic case.

Case 57

A 35-year-old waiter, admitted after an amnestic fugue.

History—The patient's brother had recently died and on the day of his funeral the patient's wife died. He was hospitalized four times in the following four years for fugues and cloudy states, once after a criminal proceeding against him for theft. At one point he showed a Ganser's syndrome and episodic deliria, and he was hallucinated several times. There was some evidence of morphine addiction.

Follow-up—At 53 years of age he was seen in his home and claimed to have been free of psychiatric difficulties since his last admission, but now suffered from liver troubles. His second wife was interviewed alone the next day and described him as extremely difficult to live with, egoistic, irritable, given to making scenes when he did not have his own way, and subject to very aggressive attacks on her. His liver difficulties came from his heavy drinking.

Conclusion—The patient was a psychopath of the irritable-aggressive and explosive type. He reacted to the conflicts in his environment with various psychogenic syndromes: cloudy states, at times complicated by fugues, mild depressions, a Ganser's syndrome, and short deliria. It is not clear whether his alcoholism was well enough entrenched to have been a factor at the time of his first hospitalization.

Definitely psychogenic reactions.

Case 58

A 39-year-old woman, married to a cabinet maker, admitted for reactive depression and fugue.

History—The patient was found wandering around the streets in her night-gown. She was depressed because of separation proceedings brought about by her husband. She was again admitted a few months later after an amnestic fugue, depressed because she had given up her rights to the children (and because of a theft, see the follow-up).

Follow-up—The patient died of a heart disease at the age of 47 years. Her husband, with whom she had been reunited described her as an industrious housewife but attempting to live beyond their economic and social means. She had, at one point, stolen some money and had been put on probation. She had been very suspicious of her husband's fidelity but otherwise little interested in their sex life.

Conclusion—The patient was a labile and very ambitious psychopath who, after a few months' interval, reacted to first a marital conflict and later a criminal affair by wandering in a cloudy state.

Definitely a psychogenic reaction.

Case 59

A 58-year-old wife of a worker, admitted after wandering around in a cloudy state.

History—The patient was unstable, irritable, aggressive, and given to emotional outbursts and fainting fits. She had attempted suicide several times, once just before her admission. She claimed that the cause of her difficulty was her husband's infidelity.

Follow-up—The patient died of a heart attack when aged 75 years. Her husband was interviewed. He had known the patient since childhood and was 10 years younger than she. Her jealousy had been a constant conflict but he claimed to have given her no cause for it.

Conclusion—We have here a series of short psychogenic reactions in an emotional and explosive woman provoked by marital conflicts (not least of which was the age difference).

Definitely a psychogenic reaction.

Case 60

The 37-year-old wife of a bicycle repairer, admitted after an amnestic fugue.

History—The patient, who had always been reserved, asthenic, and 'nervous', had discovered a few days previously that her husband was unfaithful. He promised to mend his ways but came home the morning of the day of her amnestic fugue, having again spent the night with another woman. There was almost complete recovery of memory after twenty-four hours.

Follow-up—After the amnestic fugue the patient's asthenic symptoms worsened and she was never again free from them. In a personal interview at 62 years of age she revealed that she had divorced her husband and married a greengrocer with whom she was able to get along. He drank a little but was not unfaithful.

Conclusion—The patient was probably already neurotic before the fugue began. In any case she was incapable of abreacting the shock of her husband's infidelity in a normal fashion.

Definitely a psychogenic reaction.

More complicated psychic disturbances were found in the following 3 cases, all of them women. The amnesias were more comprehensive, approaching the state of generalized amnesia, in one case there was a mild stupor and in another case a wish-fulfilment in fantasy.

Case 61

A 20-year-old unmarried housemaid, admitted after wandering around the street in a twilight state.

History—There were several cases of psychic abnormality in the patient's family (manic-depressive psychosis, addiction). She had always been 'nervous', unstable, and hot-tempered. The hospitalization followed a period of difficulties with her employer (theft ?) and her family, with whom she had never been able to get along too well. Her slightly stuporous state cleared up very slowly, as did her massive amnesia in all three spheres. In the next ten years she was hospitalized nine times for similar hysterical reactions often with hysterical seizures as an attention-getting device. At 30 years of age she died of chronic epidemic encephalitis (following an operation for torticollis) considered to have set in, at the earliest, two years previously.

Conclusion—In this case the psychogenic predisposition probably had both a constitutional and an acquired (neurotic) origin. The severe psychopathic-neurotic personality structure exploded frequently in small psychogenic reactions, none so serious as the first.

Definitely a psychogenic reaction.

Case 62

An 18-year-old student, daughter of a factory worker, admitted after a fugue with complete amnesia for all events within the last day and for personal identity.

History—The patient's father, divorced from her mother, was paranoid. His father's sister was mentally ill and an uncle committed suicide. The patient had always been mentally healthy until the previous day when her boy friend parted from her. The memory of her own identity was restored when she was identified and her name was spoken to her, but she did not remember what had happened during the fugue.

Follow-up—The patient had married and lived in a provincial town with her husband, a college professor, and three children. For reasons of discretion she was not contacted, but the family physician was seen. In the ten years he had known her, the patient had always been healthy. Her husband had been seriously ill with an organic disease and she had nursed him well.

Definitely a psychogenic reaction.

Case 63

An 18-year-old housemaid, admitted while in the midst of a fugue.

History—The patient was found wandering around the railway station disoriented in all three spheres. She stated that she had come to Copenhagen from her native town on the train with her father, had fallen and hurt her head and could no longer find him. On admission she appeared frightened. Her mother came the next day and informed the authorities that the patient's father had died seven years previously. There appeared to have been no acute psychic trauma preceding the episode. After two weeks in the hospital she again appeared normal and the amnesia had disappeared.

Follow-up—The patient, now married with two children, was seen in her native town. She seemed normal, likeable and co-operative. She felt that her amnestic episode was occasioned partly by the deeply felt loss of her father and partly by her distress for her mother whose second marriage was not a happy one (all the children had left the house because of the stepfather).

Conclusion—The psychogenic factor in this case is the father's death and the mother's unfortunate remarriage. The reaction is a systematized autopsychic amnesia and an attempt at the resurrection of the father in a wish-fulfilment in fantasy. The head injury appears to have had nothing to do with the appearance of the psychosis.

Definitely a psychogenic reaction.

In the last case of amnestic fugue no definite diagnosis was possible.

Case 64

A 17-year-old unmarried housemaid, admitted after having several times wandered about at night in a fugue followed by amnesia.

History—A brother had had a short-lasting depression following marital trouble. He recovered fully. The patient was described by her father as moody, introverted, industrious, but spoiled and unpredictable. As a child she suffered from short attacks of loss of consciousness and, up to the present, sometimes found herself in a twilight state. Her boy friend had parted from her some months previously to the first hospitalization and she had been depressed and bitter ever since. In the course of the next sixteen years she was hospitalized five times: twice following erotic disappointments, twice because of her uncontrolled behaviour at home and inability to get along with her family, and once following an attempted suicide. A diagnosis of dementia praecox was considered because she complained of feeling something strange and peculiar in her body.

Follow-up—When seen at the age of 33 years she was a tall, thin, pale, leptosomic woman who gave the impression of some mental inferiority, childishness, and colourlessness of mood. The only subject to which she warmed was her quarrels with her neighbours. Symptoms and signs of psychosis were absent.

Conclusion—The diagnosis is uncertain. The complete lack of definite schizophrenic and epileptic symptoms would lead one to believe that it was a chronic neurotic condition in an asthenic and mentally retarded psychopath.

It should perhaps be pointed out that in only one of the 16 cases of amnestic fugues was there any doubt about the diagnosis, and in no case was there any reason to presuppose an epileptic clouded state with fugue.

The remaining 13 cases of twilight states were not accompanied by fugues. The first 6 were mild, short-lasting (few hours to 24 hours) reactions.

Case 65

A 19-year-old female student (teachers' college), admitted in a restless cloudy state.

History—The patient's father was a catatonic schizophrenic. She had had her last menstrual period nine months previously and the size of her waist could only admit of one conclusion, but she denied obstinately having had an experience capable of bringing on pregnancy. The night before admission she was cloudy, anxious, restless, and vomiting. A doctor was called who administered morphine to calm her and she was admitted to the hospital where she gave birth to a baby the next day.

Follow-up—In a personal interview seventeen years later the patient reported that she had not suffered since from any psychiatric difficulties The baby had been adopted by her mother and the patient had finished her studies and become a schoolteacher. The rigid lower middle-class attitudes of her home had brought about her reaction to the difficult situation.

Conclusion—The patient's short anxious-agitated cloudy explosion was undoubtedly of psychogenic origin. It is also reasonable to suppose that the pregnancy itself provided a temporary psychogenic predisposition.

Definitely a psychogenic reaction.

Case 66

The 31-year-old wife of a workman, admitted for a post-operative psychosis.

History—Five weeks before her admission the patient had undergone an uneventful appendectomy. She had been afraid of the operation. Three days before her admission she had suddenly become agitated and developed a delirious state, crying out descriptions of what had happened to her during the operative experience. It was impossible for her husband or the neighbours to quiet her, but she recovered on admission.

Follow-up—In a personal interview twenty years later she said that this was the only psychotic outbreak to which she had ever succumbed. In the interview she appeared somewhat suspicious. She denied ever being 'nervous'.

Conclusion—In this patient we have a complete 'reminiscence delirium' some time after an operative experience (*cf.* Wimmer's (1916) differentiation between complete and dissociated 'recurrence of affect') in the form of an anxious clouded state in which the operation scenes are relived.

The literature on post-operative psychoses is not very comprehensive. The most outstanding work is Kleist's little monograph (1916) in which 10 such cases are described. According to Kleist the most common forms of this rare psychosis are clouded or delirious states, anxious restless episodes, or stuporous states. These he classifies as 'heteronymous symptom complexes' ('homonymous' states are the manic, melancholic, paranoid, and irritable-dysphoric syndromes). The psychosis typically breaks out one or two weeks after the operation ('interval psychosis'). All of Kleist's cases were major operations, 4 of the 10 patients died, but the prognosis for the psychic disturbance was good for the remaining 6 cases. Kleist considers the aetiology to be organic, that is, toxic-exhaustive. It is impossible to prove or disprove such a contention. It may be that the causes for the organic mental disturbances are to be found in changes in the body-fluid balance and the electrolytes. In the present case a psychogenic reaction seems by far the most likely.

In this context it should be mentioned that there are anxiety dreams in which a shocking experience (for example in a fox-hole) is being re-experienced in order to abreact the quantities of excitation caused by the experience. The same principle is being used therapeutically under similar circumstances and has been discussed on pages 36–37.

Definitely a psychogenic reaction.

Case 67

The 45-year-old wife of a typographer, admitted with clouding of consciousness.

History—The patient's breakdown was occasioned by her eldest son's marriage—she did not like her daughter-in-law. She was consequently hospitalized four times, each time in connection with some family difficulty to which she responded with asthenic-depressive symptoms and some clouding of consciousness. She recovered quickly each time.

Follow-up—It appeared eighteen years later that the leptosomic patient's plans and attempts to dominate the wives of her children had led to a break with all of them, leaving only her husband and two dogs, on whom to extend her loving concern. She suffered from a serious sexual conflict in that her husband was partially impotent. She attempted to regulate the situation by means of masturbation which aroused feelings of shame and guilt.

Conclusion—This patient is by temperament given to strong reactions which dispose her to short-lived disturbances of consciousness in every difficult emotional situation. As is true of so many patients who have a tendency to psychogenic reactions, her personality is asthenic.

Definitely a psychogenic reaction.

Case 68

The 31-year-old wife of a mason, admitted in a twilight state.

History—When quite young the intelligent patient had married an alcoholic man who was unfaithful and from whom she was divorced. Some years later she married an older man, a widower with 10 children. There were serious economic difficulties in the middle of which the patient suddenly decided that the urgently required solution of their problems was for her to find a new apartment immediately. She got up in a state of confusion attempting to leave the room by way of a second floor window 'because it was the easiest way to the street'.

Follow-up—The leptosomic patient who made a completely normal impression claimed that the attempt to jump out of the window had appeared logical to her in her clouded state and had by no means been an attempt at suicide. It had been the only disturbed episode of her life.

Conclusion—The strained economic situation in which the patient found herself precipitated a desperate action while in a cloudy state.

Definitely a psychogenic reaction.

Case 69

A 49-year-old married saddler, admitted from the ophthalmic ward because of his disoriented state and agitated behaviour. He thought the doctors were going to give him chloroform.

History—The patient had been in an accident in which a piece of metal had been lodged in his eye. He was moved to the psychiatric ward because of his uncontrollable behaviour. In a few days he quietened down and was moved back and the eye was enucleated.

Follow-up—The patient was interviewed when aged 68 years in the little village where he still worked as a saddler He denied any fears of either the accident or the hospital and considered himself unqualifiably normal except for an asthenic fatigue syndrome which had lasted some years after the accident.

Conclusion—The psychotic episode can only be viewed as a psychogenic reaction occasioned by the shock of the accident and the strange hospital environment. See conclusion to Case 66.

Definitely a psychogenic reaction.

Case 70

A 29-year-old unmarried chimney sweep.

History—This patient presented a complicated history of difficulties which led to diagnoses of *mental inferiority, psychopathy, possible epilepsy, hysteria*, and *alcoholism*. His grandfather, uncle and father were all alcoholics. He received a head injury as a child when his father knocked him down a flight of stairs, had epileptic (?) fits after the age of 11 years (but) not as an adult), nocturnal enuresis until 20, a serious case of influenza at 22, and was struck by lightning at 24. Most of his early adult life alternated between prison sentences for theft, etc., and hospitalization because of his twilight states. He was near panic during thunder storms and produced hysterical pseudo-hallucinations. He was eventually placed in a hospital for psychopaths where he was still interned at the time of the *follow-up*, when he was aged 47 years.

Conclusion—The patient was a constitutional psychopath, slightly mentally retarded, whose abnormality was possibly somatically accentuated by the childhood head trauma, his alcoholism and the attack of influenza. We know very little about the after-effects of being struck by lightning, but it is certainly a traumatic experience which may in itself have sensitized the patient to psychogenic reactions. The fear of thunder storms thus would be a typically catathymic reaction. The convulsions and the visual pseudo-hallucinations were part of the patient's hysterical reaction tendencies.

Definitely psychogenic reactions.

The following two cases represent a more protracted course of the disease.

Case 71

A 27-year-old single workman, admitted from prison.

History—As in the previous case, this patient was also a criminal psychopath with a history of alcoholism in the family. He suffered a retrograde systematized amnesia (*amnésie à propos*) for a prison sentence he had just served with delusional ideas (poison in the food, etc.). As he reverted to a life of petty crime every time he was released he was eventually permanently placed in a hospital for psychopaths, where he adjusted well.

In a personal interview when aged 45 years, the patient appeared normal, polite and with a realistic understanding of his lack of ability to adjust to society. He seemed quite satisfied with the protection against antisocial behaviour offered him by the hospital.

Conclusion—We see here the ability of the psychogenic mechanism to repress a well defined painful thought complex. One may well assume that there regularly is a clouding of consciousness in patients with such selective amnesias but the clouding does not appear to have been very pervasive in this case. It is also an example of prison-produced paranoid episodes, instructively described by Bonhoeffer (1907) and Birnbaum (1908).

Definitely a psychogenic reaction.

Cases 72, 73, and 74 are of particular interest so far as the psychopathology is concerned and are, therefore, reported at greater length than most of the case histories.

Case 72

A 22-year-old unmarried female office worker, admitted because of criminal activities.

History—The patient's paternal grandmother died in a mental hospital where she was diagnosed senile dementia and Alzheimer's disease. The patient's mother was 'nervous' in her climacterium, and a sister was also described as 'nervous'.

The patient held a number of office jobs. Her pre-psychotic personality was pleasant, honest, truthful, friendly, and industrious. At the age of 13 years she suffered a head injury and at 16 she had influenza without complications.

She was admitted to the psychiatric reception ward after having been arrested by the police for a series of thefts. In the years before the arrest she apparently underwent a gradual personality change which had begun at about 17 years of age. Without any awareness of growing sexuality she developed intense changes in mood. She was often full of inner agitation, troubled about many of the problems of life. She tried to find relief from her tortured state in religion and philosophy and finally became a theosophist. A sister described her as 'exalted and affected' at that time. At 21 she met and began to date a rather aggressive ladies' man who appears to have aroused sexual feelings in her, of which she was not consciously aware until after she had broken off with him, and began to have erotic dreams. She never had had sexual relations, and did not find a new boy friend. She had never been attracted to women.

After breaking off with the man she became increasingly emotionally unstable, 'impulsive', with marked likes and dislikes and explosions of rage over trivia. She was unable to attend social gatherings and often went wandering about the streets in the evening when she realized that her family had guests. Her behaviour was whimsical and only afterwards was she able to understand the implications of her actions. She herself was quite upset over her abruptly changing moods. Her sister claimed that the patient had felt an urge to be dramatic and that she was careless with money.

At this time she had weeping fits and unmotivated laughing. Her religious preoccupation became more intense, and she began to suffer from hallucinations, partly projected voices with religious content (prophetic), but hardly really paranoid in character, partly 'within her head'. She denied any sexual content. The hallucinations were almost entirely hypnagogic. She had also attacks of feeling herself 'possessed' by an electric current through her body, without marked anxiety or sexual feelings and sensations. She had the experience of 'speaking with tongues', as though someone else spoke with her tongue.

In January, 1925 (she was hospitalized in April, 1925), she developed compulsions, in particular an irresistible urge to count everything she saw. About six months before, she had begun to steal various items of clothing and jewellery from the places where she worked. She neither used nor sold the articles she stole.

During the two weeks she was in the psychiatric ward there was no clouding of the sensorium. She was at first rather sure of herself and 'haughty'. She appeared to be intelligent. She described the thefts as an 'urge' that came over her like a euphoric state which she compared to a sexual titillation. After the thefts she found a white vaginal discharge on her bed linen. The same phenomenon occurred after her fits of rage. There were no abnormal somatic findings.

It was concluded in Wimmer's evaluation of the case that the patient was a somewhat 'neuropathic' individual who had suffered from abnormally unstable moods which reached the proportions of an hysterical psychosis which, since the psychic trauma of the previous year (the sexual arousal), had taken on the character of a pronounced mental illness with hallucinations, vagabondage, and electrical 'possession', compulsions, etc. The thievery was considered an impulsion of pathological origin, a 'sexual equivalent' or 'symbolic theft' which in actuality covered an arousal of sexual drive with signs of physiological orgasm. The patient committed the thefts under an irresistible compulsion and treatment of her mental disorder was advised.

Follow-up—The patient had married and for reasons of discretion was not herself contacted. Her mother was interviewed and reported that one year later the patient had been hospitalized once more for about a year and discharged normal, which she had remained ever since. She had married a widower with four almost grown children. A sister was contacted and stated, in a written communication, that the patient had always been hot-tempered, difficult and preoccupied with herself. It was not until her marriage that her sister felt that she had calmed down. (One is reminded of Chrobak's prescription for hysterical young women: penis, three times daily.)

Conclusion—We have here a self-assertive psychopath who, under the pressure of an inner conflict (the unresolved sexual tension), produced a number of hysterical and compulsive symptoms in a mild state of clouded consciousness and hypnagogic pseudo-hallucinations.

It will be seen that Wimmer, although he does not spell it out directly, here comes very close to the typical psychoanalytic interpretation of kleptomania (the symbolic theft of a phallus or a baby). He was quite fascinated by psychoanalytic attempts to comprehend the inner workings of man but remained, to his death in 1937, ambivalent towards Freud and his doctrines.

Definitely a psychogenic reaction.

Case 73

A 29-year-old married painter, admitted in a 'pain delirium'.

History—Several days before admission the patient developed an intense pain in one half of his face. A tooth was extracted with no alleviation of the pain, and no drug was able to calm it. The patient showed signs of pain delirium, moved into a cloudy state with aggressive behaviour and was admitted to the hospital. The pain was considered (x-ray) to come from a periodontitis and cleared up in a few days without treatment and the patient's psychic symptoms disappeared. He was re-admitted ten years later for alcoholism, contracted bronchial pneumonia and died in the hospital. At the time of the follow-up study, his widow had died and it was impossible to find any other relatives.

Conclusion—The psychopathological mechanism here (assuming the patient's pain to be of organic origin) is, in principle, the same as in typical psychogenic reactions: the intense and unbearable pain necessitated the mobilization of a pathological mechanism: the cloudy state protects to an extent against psychic as well as physical pain.

Since antiquity heavy volumes have been written on the subject of pain, ways of inflicting it and ways of alleviating it, the need for pain in the sado-masochistic perversions, to mention a few aspects of the problem. Only recently has a systematic attempt been made to understand the many communicative meanings of pain. Szasz (1957) has interpreted the function of pain as being analogous to that of anxiety and melancholia. It is possible that the patient in this case history produced a psychogenic pain for a purpose which on the basis of the scant information escapes us.

Definitely a psychogenic reaction.

Case 74

The 24-year-old daughter of an army captain, admitted because of a nervous breakdown.

History—The patient was an intelligent, lively, conscientious, cheerful, strongly reacting person, not inclined to depressive moods. After finishing school she held a number of positions as private teacher, governess, etc.

Shortly before her admission she returned to Denmark from France where she had worked as a teacher in a French family. The last part of her stay she spent in Paris where she had very little to eat because of insufficient money. She came home tired and somewhat undernourished only to find that her mother was on the verge of a nervous breakdown because of the divorce of a sister of the patient. The impressionable patient took this deeply, and at the same time was very upset because she had missed her menstrual periods for some time. There was no question of a pregnancy as she was a virgin, but she was very much afraid of being seriously ill. Two weeks before her admission she moved into a delirium became disoriented and fluctuating in mood. She spoke constantly, exclusively about sexual and religious themes (needed to be loved, her body had long been neglected, etc.) and she no longer knew her surroundings. The disorder cleared up slowly at home and she grew calm, but worse again during a febrile period and began to speak of men who stood in a 'guard of honour' for her under her bed; they came out in the night and touched her.

At admission she gave an apathetic impression, her speech was normal, and she gave reasonable information and did not appear to be hallucinated. She had a double phlebitis of the legs with moderately raised temperature. The spinal fluid was normal, Wassermann negative here and in the blood.

During hospitalization her consciousness seemed unclouded, the most noticeable symptoms being the flatness of mood and the numerous peculiar phrases: 'is herself to the point of rage', 'was born deafmute', and so forth.

She shortly began to menstruate and there was a change in her state. Her mood lightened and she used vulgar language, saying that she now had her menses 'with heave ho!'.

She often had spells of uncontrollable laughter, and spoke, although not quite seriously, of being in an artist's home, and was frequently somewhat abusive. She was not embarrassed to be found sitting on the bed pan in the presence of the doctors. She soiled herself several times. She was discharged unimproved.

Follow-up—The patient had married a schoolteacher in a provincial city and was seen there in her home.

She was a tall leptosomic woman of 42 years, quick in speech and movement, undoubtedly hypomanic. Immediate contact was established despite the fact that no previous notification had been made. She gave an intelligent and cultured impression and seemed quite capable of controlling the hypomania. She was alert, interested and talkative without dramatizing herself; in short, she appeared to be a healthy cheerful woman. The home was middle class, a little messy and untidy.

There were no cases of mental illness in the patient's heredity, but a number of relatives on both sides suffered from characterological deviations. Of her parents the mother was the stronger personality, warm, serious, and worrying, while the father was choleric and pedantic, likeable but ineffectual at home. The patient was the fifth of six siblings. One brother was extremely shy sexually and did not marry until he was 50. One sister was rather fanatic with regard to religion. The rest were normal.

The patient was sexually reserved. She married when aged 31 years an only gradually came to enjoy her sex life.

She had had, all in all, seven periods of 'nervous breakdown'. (1) At 16 a short asthenic period with sleeplessness after working too hard at school. (2) At 19 a similar episode after a quarrel with a brother, severe enough to force her to stay in bed. (3) At 20 she became overstrained after working as a private teacher and the asthenic syndrome developed again with intense headaches but no psychotic features. (4) At 24 the above described psychotic episode. After coming home from Paris she was extremely active and probably manic. She suffered a massive attack of insomnia. The psychosis broke out after eighty hours without sleep. At that time she had been in love with a young man she had seen once several years before, and had decided to try to find him, something she never would have considered in a normal frame of mind.

During the delirious period she saw men without heads and thought she had led a licentious life in Paris.

For the following ten years she was completely well.

(5) At 34 years of age she gave birth to a child, and following this she was tired and overburdened with housework, lonely because her husband, due to his work, was away a good deal of the time. She began to imagine that her husband was enormously in debt and that she was a poor wife and mother. She lost her appetite and in her agony decided to commit suicide. She wrote a farewell letter and went into the garden in her nightgown; it was a winter night. She was found five or six hours later, sent to the hospital and recovered. (6) At 35 she suffered a short period of nervousness because of overwork. (7) At 37 she suffered for a while from a (probably spontaneously developing) state of massive insomnia, overstrained nervousness, intense talkativeness, but without psychotic features.

In a written communication, received some time after the interview, the patient stated that she was inclined to attribute her tendency to nervous breakdowns to a serious attack of sunstroke she suffered when 7 years old. In her nervous periods she was troubled by a pronounced heliophobia and at such times sunshine was really painful to her.

Conclusion—It is difficult to make a diagnosis with any real certainty. There are two possibilities: either a series of psychogenic reactions which could simulate an endogenous periodicity, or it could be a periodic endogenous psychosis.

The patient's personality does not go against the psychogenic supposition: she is impressionable and intense in her reactions, with the type of psychic-nervous lability that is so often the basis for disturbances of consciousness of psychogenic origin. The psychosis at 24 years, then, would have to be considered caused by the psychic strain of the family situation and an inner sexual conflict. The hardship of the time—and not least the undernourishment—probably evoked a temporary heightening of the psychogenic disposition. Finally, the picture of the illness was complicated by the febrile phase.

This psychosis does not completely fulfil the last three criteria required by Jaspers. The content of the psychosis is only to an extent a reflection of the conflicts and might even lead one to suppose a schizophrenia. In its course and termination the psychosis seems less dependent on experiential factors than on its own endogenous vicissitudes. Nor can it be considered one of Jaspers' psychically provoked psychoses, as he understands by this concept psychically precipitated catatonias, manias, and other psychoses, far from the psychogenic circle.

We, naturally, come to the question of whether there are psychogenic psychoses which do not fall within the limits of Jaspers' definition. It would be a group of psychotic conditions in which the psychogenic factor is the causal agent but of no significance for content, course, and termination. This problem has also been discussed in the introductory chapter and will be further debated in Chapter 14.

The question of whether one can here speak of a purely endogenous psychosis—either an atypical manic-depressive phase or, with less definiteness, an endogenous periodic psychosis*—is more a matter of terminology than reality.

In any event this is not a very likely diagnosis. In the first place it is impossible to establish a true periodicity; in the second place the body type is leptosomic, and in the third place only the episode when the patient was 34 years of age was so dominated by affect that it could be considered typically manic-depressive. The hospitalized psychosis was even marked by apathy in the beginning stages. On the other hand, it must be admitted that the prodromal symptoms, particularly the insomnia and the menostasis, are common symptoms of initial phases of manic-depressive disturbances (Lange, 1928).

In this case, as well as generally concerning psychogenic psychoses, the constitutional and biological points of view, on the one hand, and the psychological, on the other, are not alternative. In most cases we must presuppose an interdependence between the endogenous disposition and the external or inner conflict situations. The predisposition may also be quite variable in quantity (for example, due to somatic-periodic fluctuations), and in certain moments of an individual's life may achieve sufficient strength for the spontaneous outbreak of psychosis while in other moments it remains latent until a precipitating agent—for example, a psychological—appears.

Considerations of this kind are often found in Continental psychiatry: one observes the symptomatology—the clinical surface—and the course of the disease and then attempts to pigeon-hole the patient diagnostically. In contrast, American psychiatry is quite nonchalant concerning diagnosis. A European psychiatrist visiting the United States is usually rather shocked by the ease with which his American colleague makes a diagnosis of schizophrenia—until he realizes that in America schizophrenia is definitely not considered an illness with a distinct unfavourable outcome. In pragmatic America a Kleist and his broodings over a neatly constructed diagnostic system would not be highly thought of. The American psychiatrist is much

---

* Kleist argued strongly for many years in favour of such periodic 'autochthonous' psychoses.

more interested in the dynamic processes in the patient and their inter-play with his social and interpersonal situation. This is reflected in the different terminology and jargon of the two traditions.

It may further psychiatric progress more to adopt the dynamic diagnostic approach as it is being tried, for example, at the Menninger Clinic in Topeka—what drives is this patient struggling with, what is his ego-strength, and what defence-mechanisms is he employing?—than to meditate on what diagnostic system he best fits into. And today we do not have a satisfactory psychiatric nosology. Often we do not know what kind of disease we are treating. Our diagnoses are very frequently followed by question marks, or they ought to be. Menninger (1959) does not believe in natural mental disease entities. He strongly favours a unitary concept of mental illness and he talks with scorn about 'diag-nostic name-calling'.

At the present time we are being inundated by an abundance of tranquillizers, anti-depressive drugs, etc., but how and when to use which one is often puzzling. It has been said that psychiatry today is in the same position as the medical profession would have been in two hundred years ago if it had been in possession of our modern anti-biotics. We know now that typhoid fever is caused by a well defined pathogenic agent and the common cold by a virus. Our colleagues two hundred years ago did not know this. And we are ignorant as to the cause of, for example, 'schizophrenia'. Is the answer to be found in early and severe disturbances in the relationship between the infant and a 'schizophrenogenic' mother or must the biochemists solve the riddle?

I have been told that years ago in Vienna, when pathology dominated medical thinking, the doctors would meet for lunch with beaming faces, 'It has been a most satisfactory morning—we have had such interesting autopsies'. Nobody doubts the significance of autopsies and pathology, but the patient is more important than his diagnosis.

The split between German and American psychiatry may have be-come less wide since World War II but it still exists, see for example Eliasberg (1959). Lidz and Lidz (1950) are of the opinion that sociology and cultural anthropology have become the foundation of American psychiatry, thus divorcing it from the parent science of medicine. Romano (1949) writes:

> Psychiatry, like social anthropology, is currently engaged in attempt-ing to bridge the gap between the physical and biological sciences on the one hand and the social sciences on the other. It may well be that psychology and psychiatry will eventually acquire the same relationship to the social sciences that physics and chemistry have to biology.

In the first chapter of the textbook by Mayer-Gross, Slater and Roth (1960) this standpoint is being criticized in no uncertain terms. Time will, as always in such matters, prove to be the judge.

Uncertain case.

Case 75

A 48-year-old wool dealer, admitted from another ward because of mental disturbance.

History—The patient, while on his bicycle, was run over by a train and suffered a fractured pelvis. In the hospital he developed symptoms of agitation, insomnia, and was disoriented (thought he was in another section of Copenhagen and that the year was 1872). The spinal fluid was normal; however, the pressure was not measured! His symptoms cleared up and he was discharged as normal.

Follow-up—The patient died at 59 years of an abdominal tumour. His wife was interviewed and stated that the marriage had been an unhappy one as the patient had been jealous of her three children by a former marriage. They had divorced and, according to what she had heard from mutual friends, the patient had been drinking heavily in the years before his death.

Conclusion—The possibilities of both organic, for example, oedema of the brain, and psychogenic disorder, or a mixture of the two, are both evident in this case.

Uncertain case.

The original psychogenic diagnosis was proved definitely wrong in two cases only. The course of the illnesss demonstrated one case to be a schizophrenia, the other a general paresis.

Case 76

A 32-year-old unmarried Russian-born machine worker, admitted from prison.

History—The patient, who was a quiet person without much need for contact with other people, had been interned in Denmark during World War I after escaping from a German prison camp, and remained afterwards as a labourer and then as a factory worker. He began an affair with a married woman which, after a couple of months, ended in an exchange of blows with the lady's husband. The patient returned later in the day with a knife and hammer and wounded the deceived man. When he was arrested he claimed that the attacker had been the husband (although there were witnesses to the contrary) and claimed that there was a plot against him. He made a suicide attempt in prison and was sent to the psychiatric ward. He was at first taciturn, showed *Vorbeireden* ('talking past the point') and other symptoms belonging to Ganser's syndrome (described in 1898) and signs of clouded consciousness, but became increasingly autistic and his symptoms finally became unequivocably schizophrenic (persecutive ideas). He was still hospitalized at the

107

time of the *follow-up* and presented the picture of an autistic and deteriorated patient.

Conclusion—The patient was most likely in the incipient stages of the schizophrenic psychosis at the time of the attack on his mistress's husband.

Definitely schizophrenia.

Case 77

A 35-year-old unmarried seamstress, admitted after a 24-hour amnesia.

History—The pre-morbid personality was completely normal. On admission the patient was disoriented, quiet, seemed perhaps a little mentally inferior, in no obvious mood. Her mother stated that the patient had become rather peculiar after a date with a boy friend a couple of months previously, but she was never able to find out what had happened on that occasion. The disturbance was considered psychogenic and she was moved to St. Hans Hospital, where it soon became readily apparent that she suffered from *general paresis* with the characteristic changes in the cerebrospinal fluid. The process advanced rapidly and the patient died at when aged 37 years.

Conclusion—This case is a perfect illustration of how dangerous it can be when too much credence is put on relatives' insistences on psychic traumatizations. The flatness of mood in the very beginning should have aroused some doubt about the psychogenic diagnosis.

Certain case of general paresis.

Turbid States I. Deliria

(39 cases)

As will appear, the prognosis for the following group is poorer than for the previous one, from which it can be distinguished above all by the appearance of hallucinations. The prognostic significance of the latter in regard to psychoses considered to be psychogenic will be further discussed in Chapter 12.

We shall first deal with one of those very few cases in which there was no constitutional psychogenic reaction tendency.

Case 78

A 46-year-old German-born cigar-maker, admitted in a delirium.

History—The patient had come to Denmark when aged 24 years and lived here except for the period of World War I, when he served in the German Army. He was a particularly fearless and valiant soldier. His war experiences, and one in particular (in which he lay in a fox-hole with a dead comrade until captured by the French), had an intense effect on him. He was irritable and introverted for some time after the war. The evening before admission he had been drinking mildly with some friends. He came home around midnight and flew into a rage because his wallet was missing.

108

His wife had great difficulty in restraining him from rushing out after the thieves and during the night he had fantasies of war scenes. In the hospital he declared that the fantasies were real hallucinations, experienced as genuine perceptions.

Follow-up—At 62 years of age he gave a completely normal impression and only amplified the points made in the hospital records. This had been the only psychotic episode in his life.

Conclusion—Particularly painful and long-lasting war experiences here led to a mild chronic nervous condition (an emotional-irritable syndrome) in a constitutionally healthy personality. The effects of the alcohol plus the experience of being robbed caused the irruption of a reminiscence delirium whose content was the painful wartime episodes about which he had often had nightmares when war scenes were relived vividly and in detail.

This case represents a fringe group of psychogenic reactions: the constitutional predisposition is minimal and the traumatic intensity of the experiences maximal. The case is psychopathologically interesting in two respects. First, it is an example of an 'overindividual' reaction (*cf.* page 16), in which no catathymic potential is necessary to trigger the psychotic episode (in this case as a delayed reaction). Second, it demonstrates, as in Case 66, the principle of abreaction of a violently traumatic event, partly in anxiety dreams, partly in a reminiscence delirium in which the psychic trauma is being repeated 'verbatim' in order to gradually discharge the enormous amounts of excitation caused by the shocking experience.

Definitely a psychogenic case.

The following 6 cases are mild delirious reactions in somewhat psychopathic-neurotic personalities, 5 of them women.

Case 79

A 19-year-old unmarried nurse, admitted because of a nervous breakdown.

History—There was much evidence of neurosis on the mother's side of the family. A month before admission the patient, always quiet, reserved and quite bright, became restless and agitated, full of self-reproaches, with visual and auditory hallucinations. She had dated a young man with whom she had not had sexual relations as she had 'too much self-respect'. The diagnosis was *délire d'emblé*. She was hospitalized five more times during the course of her life with asthenic-depressive symptoms. She began to rely increasingly on sleeping pills and twice attempted suicide by means of these, the second time, at the age of 35 years, successfully.

Follow-up—The patient's father described her as arrogant, sensitive, introspective, quite different from other children and inclined to make herself the centre in any circle. She was religiously disposed and considered quite bright.

Conclusion—The patient was an obviously neurotic woman with deep sexual inhibitions and very little capacity for contact with other people. The picture is one of a diffuse character neurosis as distinguished from monosymptomatic forms of neurosis, with distinct and isolated symptoms in a relatively undamaged personality. The defective character provided a fertile ground for the acute psychotic and asthenic-depressive episodes.

Definitely psychogenic reactions.

Case 80

A 27-year-old woman, separated from her husband, admitted after attempted suicide.

History—As a child the patient walked in her sleep and was taken out of school because of her nervousness. She was educated at home and worked in an office for some time. When aged 21 years she married a cashier who was later arrested for fraud. The patient broke down over this with depressive-asthenic symptoms, heard bells ringing and saw vague shapes. Her suicide attempt was not very serious.

Follow-up—The patient divorced her husband after her discharge and attempted to support herself and her small son. Because of the difficulty of accomplishing this she married a workman who was apparently devoted to her, but with whom she remained constantly dissatisfied because of his social inferiority. For reasons of discretion she herself was not seen, but information was gathered from the family physician. The family's economic situation grew increasingly more strained and the husband made an attempt at swindling (without police action) and the patient again broke down and attempted suicide. She presented asthenic-depressive symptoms and paranoid tendencies with hallucinations (threatening voices and shapes). She was hospitalized and, after discharge, things appeared to have gone better.

Conclusion—This patient suffered from a chronic neurosis with depressive, asthenic, anxious, and hysterical symptoms. When difficulties became too great this state was intensified in a psychotic outbreak with turbidity and hallucinations.

Definitely a psychogenic reaction.

Case 81

A 30-year-old German-born seamstress, admitted for an asthenic condition with hallucinations.

History—Four years before her admission the patient had given birth to a baby (without benefit of clergy). When the child was 2 years old her lover, a civil engineer, moved to the Far East and she had been lonely. A few months before her admission the child contracted pneumonia and died. She began to have attacks of anxiety, heard voices, thought that there was a fire in the attic, felt spiders in her bed, and was often in a turbid state. After discharge four months later the depressive-asthenic syndrome recurred with such force that she again was hospitalized. It was noticed in the hospital that she was inclined to make herself the centre of the ward with the stories she made up.

Follow-up—The patient had married and later died at the age of 44 years. Her husband, a skilled worker, was interviewed and described her as having two personalities, the one pleasant and the other unbearable with fits of temper and extreme irritability. She was sexually frigid but had otherwise been a good wife, although inclined to make up stories and put herself in a good light. She died of cancer of the uterus.

Conclusion—We have here a woman of the depressive-asthenic reaction type, temperamentally labile in mood (dysphoric episodes), with possibly acquired neurotic symptomatology (the frigidity). The case is included among the disturbances of consciousness because of the mild short-term delirious states with hallucinations.

Definitely a psychogenic reaction.

Case 82

A 55-year-old divorced woman, admitted after a convulsion.

History—From the age of 16 years the patient suffered from 'functional convulsions'. At 30 she had married a restaurant owner who treated her brutally and had innumerable lady friends. The marriage was dissolved when she was 51. At 52 she had been treated at the psychiatric reception division for 'chest convulsions'. On the present occasion the attack left her in an anxiety-filled state. She believed she was going to be cremated and that her bed was a coffin. This was preceded by the death a few days previously of a brother-in-law, who was to be cremated. It was discovered that she had contracted syphilis at 26 and had been treated for it, and that she also suffered from pyelonephritis and diabetes. She was next hospitalized at 61 because of a convulsive attack (definitely hysterical), at 67 because of a suicide attempt following a mild depression, and at 69 again because of convulsions. The spinal fluid was not examined and the Wassermann reaction test was not performed.

Follow-up—The patient died of pneumonia at 71 years of age. A son, who was interviewed, considered much of the patient's difficulties to have been caused by the difficult marriage.

Conclusion—The patient produced a number of convulsive attacks in a very difficult marital situation. At a relatively advanced age (55) she reacted to a death in the family with a short delirious psychosis, hallucinating the dreaded cremation, that caused the disturbance. The convulsions of her later years also appear to have been psychogenic.

We have here one of the very few cases in which the criteria of Jaspers seem to be fulfilled. But so far as these criteria are concerned we must regretfully admit the truth of the old saying, that one swallow does not make a summer.

Definitely a psychogenic case.

111

Case 83

A 32-year-old married woman, admitted in a state of restless confusion.

History—The patient, an orphan, presumably with a pre-morbid normal psyche, was brought up by a farmer and his wife. When aged 24 years she married a man who was an eccentric. He had been without work for three years and their relationship was quite strained when the patient suddenly became agitated, aggressive, anxious, disoriented, and heard voices. She talked exclusively about religious matters. A childhood girl friend of the patient to whom she had been closely attached had recently emigrated to America with her husband, and the patient suffered from feelings of both loss and envy. The patient's husband was slightly mentally retarded and interested in hypnosis and had rather bizarre religious ideas.

Follow-up—The patient, a fat little pyknic woman, was interviewed and showed no signs of schizophrenic personality changes. She had suffered no psychiatric difficulties since her hospitalization except from an asthenic syndrome. The husband had been hospitalized briefly at one point because of his own psychic difficulties.

Conclusion—The psychic conflict was only partially clarified in this case and the lack of marital harmony does not seem a sufficiently strong factor to explain such an intense and lengthy (one month) psychotic reaction. A predisposition to psychogenic reactions may have been present but probably not to a marked degree. There can hardly be any doubt that the psychosis was psychogenic, but 'incomplete' in that the content and course of the psychosis do not seem experience-determined.

Definitely a psychogenic reaction.

Case 84

A 39-year-old butcher, suffering from an attack of severe anxiety with hallucinations.

History—The patient's sister had been hospitalized after a schizophrenic break. The patient himself had always been anxious, scrupulous, and indecisive. After finishing school, he had apprenticed himself to a butcher, married, and was on the point of opening his own butcher shop when he was admitted to the hospital. A few days before his admission he had suffered with an intense attack of anxiety with numerous physical symptoms (vomiting, diarrhoea, pain in the chest) as well as a hallucination of a black man with a lot of money who would break his back. In the hospital he was depressed and extremely anxious, claiming to have had (at home) hallucinations of shapes that would harm him and to have considered suicide. He was a slender, almost asthenic man who did not look at all like a butcher and, in fact, he confessed that he could hardly bear to cut up meat. He recovered within a few weeks.

Follow-up—The patient was interviewed in his home when aged 55 years. For some years after his discharge he had suffered from anxiety symptoms though never so intense as in the described episode. Once he had suddenly become paralysed in both legs while working in his store but this cleared up quickly His wife went out of the room at one point

112

and he observed that ever since he had developed a mild diabetic condition a few years previously he had lost interest in sex. His nervous symptoms declined and in the last two years he had felt better than ever before.

Conclusion—The patient was an asthenic psychopath with neurotic symptoms. In unusual and demanding situations these were intensified to the point of paroxysm of anxiety, one of which, at least, was psychotic.

Definitely a psychogenic reaction.

There is a mixed psychogenic-infectious aetiology in the following two cases.

Case 85

The 39-year-old wife of a master-tailor, admitted from another hospital (where she had been for some weeks) because of her disturbing behaviour.

History—Several members of the patient's family were 'nervous'. The patient had always been anxious, excitable, and 'nervous'. She began to hear her sister's voice out in the hall and also developed the idea that the sister was being abducted by bad men. She saw this scene clearly in her hallucinations. She claimed that her difficulties began the year before when she caught her husband kissing the maid. She was very unhappy about him and felt he did not love her enough. She felt that she needed a great deal of love.

A week after admission she developed a middle-ear infection with a spontaneous perforation and a high fever. During this time a delirious psychosis broke out with great anxiety and ideas of persecution (was going to be murdered, etc.). After ten days she recovered with total amnesia for the psychotic episode.

Follow-up—The patient flatly refused to give any information when she was contacted as she was afraid it would bring on another ear infection. Her husband stated that the patient had never before or since suffered an episode such as the one described, but was always inclined to suffer from 'weak nerves'.

Conclusion—This case is an example of a psychogenically introduced delirious psychosis (possibly pre-climacterial) with hallucinations. The turbid state reached its peak during an acute febrile infection, another pathogenic feature added to the psychogenic factor.*

It looks as though there is a dissociation between the psychic trauma and the content of the psychotic state, characteristic of 'incomplete' psychogenic disturbances of consciousness, but there is insufficient information on which to base definitive conclusions.

Psychogenic-infectious aetiology.

* It is a fact that many psychoneurotic, and probably also psychotic, disorders make their debut in connection with organic, for example infectious, diseases. The explanation is probably a weakening of ego-strength caused by the unusual stress on the organism.

113

Case 86

The 40-year-old wife of a master glazier, admitted because of an agitated-hallucinated depression.

History—Predisposition was denied. For most of her adult life the patient was inclined to mild nervous-asthenic symptoms. When aged 40 years her mother died. Her reaction took the form of an accentuation of her asthenic symptoms and a globus hystericus. She developed a sore throat with high fever three weeks before she was admitted to the medical ward because of the severe asthenic symptoms. She was transferred to the psychiatric ward where she was depressed and hallucinated (voices slandering her and her husband) with classic hysterical symptoms (opisthotonos, etc.). A week later her husband removed her to a private clinic.

Follow-up—The patient died of pneumonia at 57. Her husband was contacted by phone and he supplied a further piece of information. While the patient was in the medical ward an elderly woman in the next bed had died and this had revived memories of her mother's death. The patient had had no other disturbed episode at any time in their married life.

Conclusion—As in the previous case we see here the co-operation of infectious and psychogenic factors, the febrile disease intensifying the constitutional tendency to psychogenic reactions.

The mild short turbid state appears to have been caused by the trauma of the fellow-patient's death, an example of the catathymic recurrence of affect in an analogous situation.

Psychogenic-infectious aetiology.

Psychogenic disturbances of consciousness are usually short-lasting psychotic reactions of only a few hours or days. In the next cases the reactions are more protracted.

Case 87

A 36-year-old office worker, separated from her husband, admitted from the medical ward of another hospital because of a psychotic break.

History—A few years before admission the patient had separated from her husband who was an alcoholic. In order to support herself and her small daughter she had found a job in an office and at the same time accepted financial help from a friend of her father's. This man insisted that, in return, she became his mistress. This she did, but it disturbed her a great deal, particularly after she had fallen in love with a young man with whom she also began an affair. The stress of the situation caused a turbid state with hallucinations (there were men lying in the beds next to hers, yelling at her, the nurses tortured her, etc.), agitation, anxiety, and depression. There was a marked feeling of sexual guilt. She recovered after two months and was discharged cured.

Follow-up—Both patient and daughter, now aged 20 years, refused to discuss the psychotic episode. Their present family physician was located and he described the patient as a woman with common asthenic complaints. Her greatest difficulty, during the time he had known her, had been a depressive reaction to her daughter's desire to marry an older man.

Conclusion—We have here an asthenic patient who breaks out in a delirious state over a serious sexual-ethical conflict. The content of the psychosis is largely comprehensible on the basis of the trauma, but the course is rather protracted. There are strong superego reactions.

Definitely a psychogenic reaction.

Case 88

A 30-year-old unmarried white-collar worker, admitted because of his uncontrollable behaviour while in consultation with a psychiatrist in private practice.

History—The mother was a 'nervous' and difficult person. About a month before admission the patient, who had always appeared psychically normal, suffered a severe attack of febrile stomatitis. Several weeks after recovering he broke off with the young woman he had been courting because she had previously been engaged. He then began to suffer from fits of weeping and 'mental confusion', for which he consulted the above-mentioned psychiatrist. On the last of these visits his behaviour very suddenly became intensely disturbed. He jumped on a sofa, had *arc de cercle*, then was lying stiffly à la *lit de parade*. He also embraced the doctor because of the magical strength emanating from the doctor's body. He was described as having behaved like a person in the Middle Ages, possessed by the Devil. He was admitted to the psychiatric ward. There his symptoms were markedly hysterical but there were in addition schizophrenia-like features (voices and sensations of electric currents in his body). Four months later he was released although he still gave a somewhat autistic impression.

Follow-up—At 46 years of age he appeared completely normal. He had subsequently married the young woman in whom he had been interested at the time of the psychotic outbreak and both he himself and other members of his family who were contacted considered him completely healthy.

Conclusion—The range of schizophrenic symptoms is so great that the presence of a few of them cannot be considered diagnostically conclusive. As there was no residual defect in the personality and because of the hysteriform character of the outbreak and the presence of an erotic conflict we may view this case as 'definitely psychogenic'.

An American psychiatrist may have diagnosed the patient as a case of 'cured schizophrenia'.

The psychogenic aetiology of the next 11 cases is debatable and it has not been possible to make definite diagnoses.

Case 89

A 39-year-old unmarried tailor, admitted from another hospital because of his uncontrollable behaviour.

History—The patient had stopped growing when aged 8 years. Like several of his siblings, he had also clubfoot. He had an attack of 'influenza' and shortly thereafter was admitted to a general hospital because of a complete social déroute coupled with heavy drinking. Within a few days he showed great mental agitation and was transferred to the psychiatric ward of the Municipal Hospital. There he was anxious, destructive, and agitated with very lively visual hallucinations and nightly uncanny delirious states in which he was conviced he was to be submitted to torture and to be exhibited naked to a party of men and women. In a few days the attack subsided and he was discharged normal.

Follow-up—At 53 years of age he was again admitted to the psychiatric division in an alcoholic condition and at 57 he became a more or less permanent inmate of a hospital for chronically disabled persons.

Conclusion—Although there is no evidence of an acute psychic trauma, the patient's awareness of his physical abnormality plus the attack of 'influenza' and his heavy drinking may have brought about a short-lasting psychogenic psychosis.

Probably a psychogenic reaction.

Case 90

A 19-year-old milliner, admitted because of a state of mental confusion and agitation.

History—The patient's father, a business man, was an alcoholic, and her parents divorced when she was a small child. Two of her brothers were mentally retarded. She was of normal intelligence, reserved, and unable to play easily with other children. She preferred the company of adults and behaved with a sobriety and reasonableness beyond her years. At the age of 5 years she had an accident. While dressing herself one day in front of a mirror she suddenly had the peculiar sensation that she could see her own future in which she would commit much sin and be lost. She felt weak and clutched at a marble-topped table to steady herself but instead pulled it down on herself. She injured her back in such a way that there remained a permanent kyphoscoliosis. This physical defect, she felt, saved her from the life of sin that would otherwise have been hers. On finishing school she had taken up the study of millinery and at the same time her interest in religion grew to such proportions that it took up almost all the emotional and intellectual interests of her life. At 19 the religiously tinged turbid exaltation-depression state broke out and she was hospitalized for two years. At that time she also was platonically attached to a young man.

In extensive interviews in the *follow-up* she described this period as a dreamy state with hallucinations that she was living in heaven with a female angel friend who counselled and protected her. She felt happy and exalted. After a few months she descended to the infernal regions and her hallucinations took on a coarse sexual character with ideas of being raped

116

with intense genital sensations, accompanied by a loss of bowel control and coprophagia. She recovered, but at the age of 28 years was again hospitalized a few short times because of asthenic-depressive symptoms. She became pregnant at about this time and subsequently married the father of the child, but the marriage was not a happy one because of religious differences and the couple eventually separated. At the time of the follow-up when she was in her late thirties, she showed no sign of psychosis but busied herself with a small circle of religious friends. In the follow-up she was rather inviting sexually. It is probable that there was some amnesia and that her detailed account for the long psychotic period partly was a product of secondary elaboration of her hysterical dream states.

Conclusion—In this case the choice was between a delirious exaltation phase in a manic-depressive psychosis and a protracted psychogenic reaction. There is no evidence of other circular phases or manic-depressive heredity and the probability of psychogenesis appears a likelier one. However, we have here the difficulty of the protracted course of the psychosis. Nevertheless, we must not forget that the internal conflict (sexual and religious in nature) may be a constant source of nourishment for the psychosis as the intensity of the conflict remains unabated, and particularly where the psychosis itself offers wish-fulfilment in fantasy. This is a typical example of how intimately religious interests and sexual drives can be entwined with each other.

Probably a psychogenic reaction.

Case 91

The 43-year-old wife of a house painter, admitted in a hysterical confused state.

History—Two of the patient's cousins (brother and sister) and her son were schizophrenic. Her brother described her as warm and friendly intelligent and well balanced. At 24 years of age she married happily and all went well. During the first years of marriage the patient ran a sweet shop. She began to develop asthenic symptoms which became more severe at the start of her menopause and was hospitalized for a week on this account when she was aged 42 years, and again admitted when she was 43 to the psychiatric ward in a depression which passed into a turbid state with a good deal of anxiety and, eventually, hallucinations (threatening voices). She was discharged six months later, somewhat better. Three years later she was admitted, shortly after the death of her husband, in a typical hysterical state, but her family yielded to her complains about the hospital and removed her after a month. She then lived with various relatives in a constantly deteriorating state until her death a year later from debility complicated by pneumonia.

Follow-up—Both the family physician and the patient's brother were seen. It is most likely that the patient was psychotic at the end of her life (hallucinations and paranoid ideas, which could not be described in any detail), but it was impossible to tell whether the symptoms were truly schizophrenic.

9   117

Conclusion—The schizophrenic heredity and the picture of defect in the last years make it necessary to consider the possibility of a schizophrenic process. But the most likely possibility is that of a psychogenic psychosis—a hysteriform reaction can easily be fixated in a chronic disease.

Probably a psychogenic disorder.

Case 92

The 53-year-old wife of an inspector, admitted from the medical division (where she was under observation for a suspected heart disease) because of an agitated delirious state with hallucinations.

History—The patient had always been irritable and easily offended. Her difficulties began before her hospitalization when she considered terminating her unhappy marriage. Her friends advised strongly against her taking such a step. She became confused but the mildly turbid state cleared up before hospitalization for the heart disorder. On the medical ward she developed a phlebitis with high fever lasting for a short while and the delirious psychosis broke out (*cf.* Case 85). The content of the psychosis was centred around her husband's 'immorality' (the patient thought to be in a house of prostitution and witnessing everything going on there) and it turned out that he had in reality been exceedingly unfaithful to the patient. In two months the turbid symptoms disappeared and she was discharged normal.

Follow-up—In a personal interview the patient, aged 68 years, said that her husband died two years after her psychotic episode and that the nervous symptoms from which she had suffered since hospitalization cleared up following that event. Her family physician described her as a strongly reacting hysteric, 'a Xanthippe', and also stated that she calmed down after her husband's death. Her cardiac disease was diagnosed as dilatation of the heart.

Conclusion—The diagnosis is difficult. Because of the cardiac history one must consider the possibility of an exogenous reaction: a delirious psychosis resulting from a cerebral embolism with the raised temperature playing a role in the initial phase. If this diagnostic supposition is correct, the conflict had only a pathoplastic effect.

On the other hand, there is also a possibility of psychogenic psychosis in such a strongly disposed patient under the pressure of so severe an erotic humiliation as there was in this case.

Uncertain case.

Case 93

A 25-year-old unmarried watchmaker, brought to the hospital confused and hallucinated, feeling himself 'possessed by devils'.

History—The patient's paternal grandmother suffered from delusions of persecution and died in a mental hospital. He himself did well in school and took up watchmaking on graduation. In his early twenties he fell under the influence of a lay preacher and became increasingly pre-occupied with religious speculation. At about this time he contracted syphilis, for which he was treated and cured. His father died when he was 23 years old and this affected him deeply. Two years later a brother was tried and convicted of arson with intent to defraud an insurance com-pany. Two other brothers were healthy. When the patient's mother went to bid his brother good-bye before he went to prison the patient insisted on going along. But the meeting resulted in a mental collapse for the patient and he was then admitted to the hospital. At first he was disoriented, anxious, depressed (with inhibition of the stream of thoughts and of psychomotor activity) and hallucinated (threatening voices). In a few days the picture changed to an intense restless delirium with an inexplicable fever. When this passed after three weeks he showed symptoms of a schizophrenic type, incoherent associations, facial grimaces, fear of poison in the food, etc. By the end of seven months he had improved sufficiently to be discharged.

Follow-up—Aged 42 years he ran a little watchmaker's shop of his own. He gave an impression of heaviness, perseverance and great attention to trivial details and an inclination to marked hypochondria. As there was very little evidence of schizophrenic defect the possibility of an ixothymic state seemed good. He led a rather restricted life but appeared to be quite satisfied with it. Although he had never married he had had several affairs during the course of his life and had two children.

Conclusion—The diagnosis is uncertain. It may have been a schizo-phrenic 'push' or, with equal likelihood, it may have been an unusually protracted and 'dissociated' (or 'incomplete') psychogenic psychosis. Finally, the ixothymic stamp suggests a possibly psychically provoked epileptic equivalent, a delirious state.

Uncertain case.

Case 94

A 29-year-old engineering student, admitted because of a psychotic break.

History—Rigid personalities were common in the patient's family and there had been two suicides in his grandparent's generation. The parents were cousins. He was described as an arrogant, lonely, eccentric, and unsociable person, but precocious and very intelligent. His scholastic record was good and he passed the first part of his engineering examina-tions with no difficulty. Inexplicably he failed the second part, became depressed and three months later broke down completely. He was restless, agitated, anxious, hallucinated (a dream-like state) and unable to eat or sleep. He was calmer, but hardly normal, when he was released to his parents three weeks later. He remained at home for a year but became gradually so threatening towards his family that he was committed to a state hospital where a diagnosis of *dementia praecox* (*simple type*) was made.

Follow-up—Unfortunately, the patient had been released shortly before a visit to the above-mentioned state hospital to see him. The

119

superintendent of the hospital informed me that the diagnosis of schizophrenia could not be considered safely established. According to a brother the patient had gone to Germany in the hope of getting work there in an engineering firm. The World War II made it impossible to establish personal contact with the patient.

Conclusion—It is impossible to place any definite diagnosis in this case chiefly because there are insufficient data to determine what was the patient's pre-psychotic ability to make contact, and to what extent this ability was depreciated by the illness. His failure in the second part of his examinations could as well have been an initial symptom as the psychic trauma that precipitated the illness.

Uncertain case.

Case 95

A 32-year-old salesgirl, admitted after a paranoically motivated accident.

History—The mother and two sisters were erethic. The patient was an unstable, impulsive woman with hysterical tendencies and slightly below normal intelligence. After finishing school she worked as a maid. Her sexual life was abundant although the attachments were superficial, and she produced two children (different fathers). She contracted syphilis when 26 years of age and was treated for it. At 32 she was living under difficult economic conditions with a considerable work load. She developed an obsession that her landlady and the landlady's son wanted to murder her; one evening she thought she could smell blood and chloroform and could hear a noise outside her door. In her anxiety she jumped out of the second floor window and was brought to the hospital with a fractured foot but no head injuries. During the two months she was kept in the psychiatric reception division her conviction of persecution appeared to weaken at times. At one point she claimed that the cause for the outbreak of the psychosis was that she had once permitted herself to be persuaded to commit fellatio which disgusted her. She was transferred to St. Hans Hospital where the extreme mood changes she had previously shown continued and the delusions of persecution reappeared. She was discharged at the end of two months. At 34 she began to indulge in acts of larceny. After an erotic disappointment at 35 she attempted suicide by drowning. She was quickly rescued and hospitalized for a month. She was brought in again by the police when she was 39 because of numerous acts of shoplifting. This time she spent almost a year in the hospital, with a diagnosis of *psychopathy* and hypnagogic hallucinations.

Follow-up—Aged 49 years she lived in a room in a poor section of the city without heat or electric light, partly supporting herself with work as a cleaning woman and partly receiving public assistance. After an initial vulgar and irritable outburst she turned out to be friendly and communicative and claimed to be free of psychological difficulties.

Conclusion—Although there is a possibility here of a schizophrenic 'push', the circumstances do not appear to bear out such a view. A manic-depressive psychosis with a psychogenic-hysterical super-structure also cannot be excluded with certainty. But the probability of a psychogenic psychosis (although 'incomplete') is the greatest, particularly when we consider that the life conditions of this hysterical-explosive psychopath were undeniably very difficult.

Uncertain case.

Case 96

A 24-year-old unmarried female furrier, admitted because of an acute hallucinatory breakdown.

History—The patient's uncle died in a mental hospital with a diagnosis of 'alcoholic paranoia'. The patient's sister also died on a psychiatric ward after having been admitted for an acute delirium following a severe erotic disappointment. Autopsy showed a lobar pneumonia. The patient herself had been healthy and normal as a child. After graduation she got a job in a furrier's shop. There she met and fell in love with a man who was, unfortunately, married. The psychosis began in connection with this trauma and made its debut with insomnia and anxiety. When she began to hear voices day and night she was hospitalized. The voices were exclusively masculine, partly erotically affectionate and partly threatening and critical. She was depressed with turbidity and inhibition and had occasional sensations of influences on her body (sexual intercourse). After six months she was released still mildly hallucinated.

Follow-up—It was difficult to establish contact with the patient, but eventually her father was seen and some time later she herself was inter-viewed. Both had essentially the same story. The patient had never before or since the psychotic break been anything but completely normal. She had continued to work and live at home, a quiet, uneventful life.

Conclusion—There are two reasons for questioning the psychogenic nature of this case. One is the (normal ?) pre-morbid personality and the other is the duration of the psychosis. Naturally, psychogenic distur-bances of consciousness may last for many months, but as this study itself shows, they are typically short-lasting. One *could* consider a schizophrenic 'push' as one of the diagnostic possibilities.

The family heredity also lacks decisive clues. The paternal uncle's alcoholic paranoid psychosis could be a sign of a schizophrenic anlage; many investigators, for example, Neve (1914), Wolfensberger (1923), and Pohlisch (1927), are inclined to view alcoholic hallucinatory and delusional states as schizophrenias precipitated by the alcoholic brain damage. It is more likely, however, that some paranoid personalities with their repressed homosexual tendencies resort to alcoholism for escape from intra-psychic tensions (Thompson, 1959).

The sister's psychosis, like the patient's, leads one to presume that some members of the family were particularly vulnerable to psychic

121

traumatization, without permitting speculations as to the nature of that vulnerability.

As in Case 88, and many other cases in this material, a good many of our American colleagues would have made a diagnosis of 'schizophrenia—cured'.

Uncertain case.

Case 97

The 42-year-old wife of a gardener, admitted from a general hospital because of a prolonged turbid state with hallucinations.

History—The patient and her mother both showed evidence of 'hysterical', irritable temperaments. In connection with her husband's leaving her the patient became depressed and produced a delirious-hallucinatory syndrome and was hospitalized. After three months she regained normal consciousness with complete amnesia for the psychotic period. Four years previously she had developed symptoms and signs of epidemic encephalitis, especially a marked need for sleep.

Follow-up—Aged 58 years the patient was an extremely obese woman with poor hearing, appeared emotionally impoverished and showed severe tremor of the upper limbs (Parkinsonian type). After a thorough examination by a neurologist it was concluded that the patient probably was suffering from chronic cerebellar encephalitis.

Conclusion—The diagnosis of the psychotic episode is difficult. It may have been a psychogenic reaction. On the other hand, delirious states in the course of chronic encephalitis are, according to Wimmer (1929) and Mayer-Gross, Slater and Roth (1960), so frequent that this possibility certainly cannot be ruled out.

Uncertain case.

Case 98

The 47-year-old wife of an unskilled labourer, admitted from another hospital because of her delirious psychotic behaviour.

History—The patient was a capable, industrious woman inclined to be irritable and irascible. She was a housemaid until marriage at 28 years of age. In her late forties she began to suffer from an asthenic-depressive syndrome. She was hospitalized for sciatic pain. After a few days the psychosis broke out. The patient was depressed, anxious, agitated, spoke incessantly without making sense, and was hallucinated. She heard voices threatening her with beatings and thought that her home was full of corpses. She was not oriented. After a month she was discharged in a somewhat better state.

Follow-up—The patient hanged herself four days after discharge. According to her husband, she had been in a poor state after leaving the hospital and took advantage of the first occasion on which she was left alone in the apartment to hang herself.

Conclusion—There is insufficient information to determine whether the patient suffered from a psychogenic psychosis or a non-psychogenic psychosis with hysteriform pathoplastic features. She was supposedly in her menopause when she fell ill.

Uncertain case.

Case 99

A 27-year-old unmarried seamstress, admitted because of a delirious psychotic outbreak.

History—The patient was born and brought up in Iceland. When 24 years of age she came to Copenhagen, supporting herself as a seamstress. She had an affair with a married man which troubled her, and at some point, perhaps before she came to Denmark, had syphilis. She fell in love with a fellow-worker who had no idea of her feelings for him. At this point she became disturbed with incoherent speech, religious preoccupations and hallucinations. On admission to the hospital she was almost stuporous, then became anxious and agitated. It was impossible to obtain contact with her, and she had visual and auditory hallucinations. After four months there was a remission and she was discharged after seven months, seemingly cured.

Follow-up—Despite the fact that every possible effort was made, it was impossible to trace the patient.

Conclusion—One can only speculate about the diagnosis in this case. As there were several schizophreniform symptoms, one's suspicions may well lie in this direction.

Uncertain case.

In the last 17 cases of delirious states the supposition of psychogenesis is, to varying degrees, weakened by the course of the disease: 11 cases proved to be schizophrenias, 3 epilepsy or ixophrenia, respectively, and the remaining 3 in all probability manic-depressive psychoses. The non-schizophrenic cases will be discussed first.

Case 100

A 29-year-old unmarried housekeeper, admitted from the maternity ward in a delirious state.

History—One sister of the patient was schizophrenic, one brother mentally retarded, one brother possibly epileptic. As a child the patient was wilful, self-centred and spiteful. The delirium in the later stages of her pregnancy was apparently precipitated by an epileptic convulsion and was followed by a two-week explosive anxious hallucinated aftermath in which she thought that she had already given birth and had cut the baby to pieces. The patient was discharged because of her imminent parturition and returned to the maternity ward.

Follow-up—A brother of the patient was located (he showed strong ixo-thymic features) and reported that the patient from 32 to 43 years of age had been institutionalized because of epilepsy. For the past four years since leaving the hospital she had most of the time lived with various relatives. The patient was seen where she worked as a housekeeper for an elderly man, but she evaded discussion of her mental illness and the interview was not revealing. She appeared bright.

Conclusion—It is most likely that the patient had a spontaneous epileptic attack before her first hospitalization with a severe delirious state. The turbid condition was pathoplastically coloured by her precarious situation.

Classified as an epileptic turbid state.

Case 101

A 27-year-old sailor, admitted from prison because of his peculiar behaviour.

History—The patient's mother reported that he was quite normal until the age of 27 years except that, particularly after a syphilitic infection at the age of 19, he had always been finical and meticulous. He did not do well in school but managed to graduate, after which he held various jobs until he became a seaman. He suffered a severe head injury at 20. He was serving a prison sentence for theft when the psychosis broke out in a delirious state with a convulsion, anxiety, delusions and clouded consciousness. During the 15 months of hospitalization he was hallucinated most of the time and complained of 'influences'. Between 30 and 35 years of age he was hospitalized for short periods because of psychopathic antisocial reactions with hypochondriasis. The spinal fluid was normal and Wassermann negative here and in the blood.

Follow-up—The patient at 45 years of age was athletic in body type and undoubtedly ixothymic. He had got along doing odd jobs and receiving public assistance. He was married for a short time, but now divorced.

Conclusion—The personality of this patient during the years in which he was in constant contact with the psychiatric division as in the years afterwards seems, both according to the description in the records and the impression made in the follow-up interview, to have been ixothymic. This supposition is supported by the head injury he suffered at the age of 20 years, and by his athletic body type. The turbid state for which he was hospitalized at 27 must be regarded as an ixophrenic reaction, probably exogenously (psychogenically) precipitated, certainly mixed with psychogenic-hysterical symptoms, but in its essence not a pure psychogenic psychosis. The latter diagnosis can probably also be precluded by the long course of the psychosis and because of the lack of interdependence between the content and the legal trauma.

Probably a psychically provoked ixophrenic reaction.

Case 102

A 25-year-old unmarried seaman, admitted by the police in a turbid state.

History—Several members of the patient's maternal family were alcoholics. His father was treated three times for alcoholic dementia.

As a child, the patient suffered a head injury and he seems to have displayed psychopathic tendencies. After graduation from school he became a seaman and enlisted in the French Foreign Legion when 21 years old. While in Morocco he had malaria and suffered another serious head injury after which he returned to Denmark. He held a number of odd jobs for several years and eventually turned to begging and larceny, for which he was picked up by the police and subsequently admitted to the hospital in an apparently not psychically precipitated (although the initial diagnosis was *psychogenic psychosis*) delirious state; he was not intoxicated. The next eight years he spent in and out of mental hospitals in various states of mental confusion, anxiety, dysphoric episodes, and delirium with convulsions (once probably hysterical), and destructive periods. He attempted suicide several times and was finally successful. The body type was athletic.

Conclusion—We can safely assume that we are here dealing with a post-concussional syndrome in a psychopathic individual.

Post-traumatic (ixophrenic) syndrome (head injury).

Case 103

A 24-year-old single woman, a factory worker, admitted to the hospital in an acute delirious state.

History—The pre-morbid personality was without striking features except that the patient appeared mildly mentally retarded.

A few days before admission she became acutely disturbed, fell into a dreamy state, was anxious and cried excessively. Her boy friend had broken off with her shortly before. In the hospital she was not oriented, heard voices and saw shapes, talked about being raped and submitted to torture. She became very agitated and lost bowel control. At times she was smiling ecstatically. After ten months she had recovered completely with an almost complete amnesia for the psychotic period.

When aged 33 years she was again hospitalized, this time for a depression with ideas of being poisoned and infected with syphilis (Wassermann negative). The depression followed by a year the consecutive death of both parents. There were self-reproaches and auditory and visual hallucinations. After two months she recovered without defect.

Aged 39 years she was once more hospitalized without preceding psychic traumatization for a mild depression with transient delusional ideas.

Follow-up—In a personal interview the patient, 41 years of age, appeared typically pyknic, mildly intellectually retarded but with absolutely no evidence of personality deterioration. She had remained single and was well adjusted to her socially moderate circumstances.

Conclusion—The course suggests strongly that this patient suffered from somewhat atypical manic-depressive episodes. The first two may have been psychologically precipitated, the last one probably not.

The atypical features can be explained by the mental retardation as a disposing factor for the turbid hallucinatory reactions and fleeting paranoid ideas.

Definitely a manic-depressive psychosis.

Case 104

A 30-year-old nurse, admitted in a confused state with strong agitation following a month of depression.

History—A brother was 'nervous'. The patient had always been quiet, warm, industrious and with a good intelligence. A few months previous to admission she became agitated and very hyperactive and her work suffered. The condition then changed into a depressed state. She was tired and apathetic on admission and gave as the cause of her distress the fact that she had been requested to take up new duties. She wished to refuse but felt unable to do so. She claimed to have had periods of moodiness accompanied by difficulties with her work since early youth. During hospitalization she suffered from vivid hypnagogic hallucinations but after five weeks was discharged normal.

Follow-up—The patient was again treated at the age of 37 years, diagnosed this time as manic-depressive. She died of pulmonary tuberculosis at the age of 41 years.

Conclusion—There can hardly be any doubt that the first psychotic episode was a manic phase changing into a depressed state in a manic-depressive psychosis, taking the character of a mild delirious exaltation.

Definitely a manic-depressive psychosis.

Case 105

A 24-year-old unmarried female office worker, admitted in a delirious state.

History—The patient was described as always having been 'nervous'. Preceding the psychotic outbreak she had met a young man, a fanatical fascist who not only attempted to convince her that she ought to join his cause but also tried to make love to her (with success ?). At that time she was engaged to a school-teacher. She became depressed and developed ideas of persecution and thought that her fiancé was to be murdered by the fascists. In the hospital she was intensely delirious with great anxiety, heard voices that talked to her about sex and religion and she saw enormous insects, injecting poison into her. She recuperated without deterioration of personality after a psychotic period of several months.

Follow-up—The patient had later married and for reasons of discretion her parents were contacted. They, however, informed the patient's husband, the above-mentioned school-teacher, with whom I had a long conversation. His account for the years after her first psychotic break made it abundantly clear that she was a manic-depressive, who had several minor depressive episodes and three major depressions, each one lasting several months and all of them in the summer. Clinically all the severe periods were dominated by depression, anxiety and auditory hallucinations. There was no evidence of psychic precipitation except for the first one and definitely no deterioration of her personality. There were no manic periods.

Conclusion—The first episode may have been precipitated by the erotic conflict. The diagnosis must be: depressions of the manic-depressive type.

Definitely a manic-depressive psychosis.

The schizophrenic psychoses within this group consist of 5 men and 6 women.

Case 106

A 23-year-old unmarried magazine salesman, admitted from prison.

History—The paternal grandfather apparently suffered from schizophrenia but was not hospitalized. A brother of the father committed suicide aged 50 years after having been 'peculiar' for some years. The mother was an antisocial psychopath. The patient, who had been given a six months prison term for larceny, broke out in fits of rage a few months after imprisonment, with incoherent speech and attempts to tear his genitals off. In the beginning there were hysterical traits in the picture. During the four years of his hospitalization his condition deteriorated steadily, with increasing hallucinations, paranoid (megalomanic) ideas, and autism. He died of pulmonary tuberculosis while in the hospital. Wassermann reaction was negative.

Follow-up—The patient's father was contacted years later. He appeared normal. The pre-morbid personality of the patient was said to have been without psychological deviations.

Conclusion—We have here a case of schizophrenia, perhaps psychically triggered by the imprisonment (*cf.* Chapter 11).

The original diagnosis was simply *psychogenic psychosis*, which reminds one of the cynical saying in Vienna when psychoanalysis was still a young science: 'If you get a real good hysterical case in analysis, you can be pretty sure that it will turn out to be a schizophrenia'. The patients in Breuer and Freud's *Studies on Hysteria* (1895) were probably hysterics although the possibility of inicipient schizophrenias cannot be ruled out.

Psychically precipitated (?) schizophrenia.

Case 107

A 42-year-old married salesman, admitted from prison when he began to suffer from hallucinations.

History—The patient had been imprisoned for larceny. Upon admission he was in a turbid state and hallucinated. He then progressed to increasingly paranoid ideas, that he was the Kaiser Wilhelm, that his food was poisoned, etc., and his speech showed an increasingly schizophrenic stamp with neologisms. After twelve years of hospitalization he died of pneumonia.

Follow-up—It was impossible to contact any of his relatives, but the authorities gave the information that before the admission he had been sentenced four times for larceny.

Conclusion—The same as in the previous case. This patient, also, was first diagnosed as having a *psychogenic psychosis*.

Psychically provoked (?) schizophrenia.

Case 108

A 24-year-old unmarried dairyman, admitted for hallucinations and anxiety attacks while in a somewhat clouded state.

History—The patient was born of an Estonian father and a Danish mother. He spent most of his life in Estonia, but came to Denmark for training in dairy work. He had apparently experienced some rather dramatic episodes with the communists in Estonia. Aside from the hallucinations, he also thought he was being followed, was extremely frightened of thunder, and in addition he developed catatonic symptoms, but after ten months he was released as cured.

Follow-up—After release the patient had returned to Estonia, where he was again hospitalized and died at the age of 42 years of bronchial pneumonia in a state of typical schizophrenia with deterioration of the personality (information from the state hospital in Estonia).

Conclusion—The first psychotic phase was a spontaneous schizophrenic break, which left a modest defect.

Definitely a schizophrenia.

Case 109

A 42-year-old married tailor, admitted because of hallucinations and agitated behaviour.

History—No information about psychiatric predisposition. The patient was a Polish Jew who had lived for many years in Denmark. Before his admission he had been exceptionally busy, which his wife considered the cause of his breakdown. During hospitalization he was restless and constantly hallucinated (shapes, voices) and thought that Wimmer was going to decapitate his wife. After a month, without any improvement, his wife insisted on removing him from the hospital. At 49 years of age he was admitted again. The patient's wife had died and he had remarried. The second wife was a difficult shrewish woman who apparently did anything she could to tease and aggravate him. This time the patient showed no psychotic features and he was discharged after a few weeks. A year later he was brought in by the police as a menace to himself and the community. He remained in the hospital in a steadily deteriorating state.

Follow-up—The patient was seen for the follow-up, but it was impossible to establish contact.

Conclusion—Because of the nature of the symptoms, schizophrenia should have been suspected from the beginning.

Definitely schizophrenia.

Case 110

A 26-year-old single mechanic, admitted because of peculiar behaviour, mostly dictated by paranoid ideas.

History—No information about psychiatric predisposition. The premorbid personality was supposed to have been normal. Several months before admission he broke off an engagement with a young girl 'because she was too pleasure-seeking'. He became absorbed in religious matters, gave up his job because God ordered him to do so, had revelations and wandered the streets in a religious ecstasy. During the short hospitalization he was restless, heard voices, was difficult to establish contact with and probably not oriented. He also displayed dramatic hysterical features and mannerisms. He died two weeks after admission without any definite somatic or psychiatric diagnosis having been established.

Follow-up—It proved impossible to locate any relatives of the patient.

Conclusion—A diagnosis of schizophrenia in this case is, in spite of the hysterical features, more likely than that of a psychogenic psychosis.

Uncertain case (probably schizophrenia).

Case 111

A 23-year-old single housemaid, admitted because of an acute cloudy state with hallucinations.

History—Information was obtained regarding massive psychiatric predisposition on the maternal side, but no details were available. The patient herself was psycho-infantile, slightly mentally retarded and reliable. A few days before admission she became acutely disturbed, declared to be deeply in love with the son of the house and that his biological father was not identical with her mistress's husband. She developed hysterical disturbances of her gait and hallucinations (heard voices and saw both God and the Devil). She herself felt that her symptoms were precipitated by the death of her father and two brothers a short time before the onset of the illness.

Follow-up—After discharge she again served as a maid for a couple of years, but then had to be rehospitalized and within a couple of years she developed a typical schizophrenic clinical picture with autism, negativism and deterioration of the personality. At the time of the personal follow-up she was in that condition.

Conclusion—The initial diagnosis of psychogenic psychoses is understandable, particularly because of the patient's modest intelligence.

Definitely schizophrenia.

Case 112

A 26-year-old woman, married to a hairdresser and admitted in a depressed state with persecutory ideas.

History—No information concerning psychiatric predisposition. Premorbid psyche normal. Three years before admission she married an alcoholic and brutal man who often committed adultery. She became gradually more and more depressed and shortly before admission she developed ideas that a male neighbour intended to kill her. She also had auditory and visual hallucinations (saw and heard her husband being tortured). In a few months she became definitely schizophrenic, autistic with strongly coloured anxious episodes and often soiled herself.

Follow-up—A conversation with a mentally normal sister added nothing of significance to the history. An attempt to establish contact with the patient in the hospital failed completely due to her autism.

Conclusion—It was in the initial stage diagnostically reasonable to assume that the patient was suffering from a psychogenic psychosis. However, the malignant psychopathology soon came to dominate the clinical picture.

Certain case of schizophrenia.

Case 113

A 24-year-old single housemaid, admitted because of depression and persecutive paranoid ideas.

History—The father was 'peculiar', a half-sister in a mental institution (no further information available). Pre-morbid personality: intellectually retarded, 'silly', dishonest. A few months prior to admission she had an extramarital parturition. She had a severe conflict about whether to have the baby adopted. She moved into an agitated depression with paranoid ideas, thought the baby to be dead and that her sisters would kill her. She also heard threatening voices and saw ugly faces. Before long she became increasingly autistic and apathetic with many paranoid ideas (poison in the food, etc.). She died at 42 years of age from a cerebral tumour.

Follow-up—A sister was contacted but could add nothing to what was already known.

Conclusion—Benign psychogenic episodes in mentally retarded persons can in the initial stages be very difficult to distinguish from beginning schizophrenias and it is only fair, diagnostically, in a case like this one to give the patient the benefit of the doubt.

Definitely schizophrenia.

Case 114

A 41-year-old Finnish-born woman, admitted in a hallucinatory confused state.

History—A daughter was severely retarded intellectually. No other information was available concerning predisposition or pre-morbid personality. During a short period before admission the patient was 'nervous', agitated and accused her husband, an unskilled worker, of having infected her with syphilis. In the beginning of the hospital stay she was disoriented and hallucinated (voices with religious content). She was restless and difficult to establish contact with. Wassermann test was negative. Over the years she developed a classic schizophrenic syndrome with autism, hallucinations, and bizarre hypochondriacal ideas. She spent a good part of her day conversing with Jesus in Finnish.

Follow-up—Her autism prevented a conversation with her. Her husband had died a few years before the follow-up and obviously no information could be acquired from the above-mentioned institutionalized daughter.

Conclusion—Schizophrenia should have been suspected from the very beginning. The only possible psychic trauma (which probably was one of the initial symptoms) was the patient's suspicions about her husband's adultery and the possibility of syphilitic infection.

Certain case of schizophrenia.

Case 115

A 27-year-old unmarried housemaid, admitted in a state of disorientation, depression and anxiety.

History—A sister described her at the follow-up as having been habitually depressive, scrupulous, reserved, and conscientious. A few years before admission she was raped by the farmer for whom she worked and she gave birth to a child. During the last few months before admission she was courted in an aggressive way by the businessman in whose home she worked as a maid. In the hospital she was at first absorbed by bizarre depressive ideas, refused to eat 'because she already had gobbled herself up'. She thought to be dead and she was soiling herself. A typical clinical picture of schizophrenic personality deterioration developed within a year and she died four years after the outbreak of the psychosis of an acute enteritis.

Conclusion—The psychogenic diagnosis was probably made on the basis of her assumed catathymic hypersensitivity to aggressive sexual approaches. It has to be admitted, however, that already the initial stage of her psychosis had a schizophrenic tinge.

Definitely schizophrenia.

Case 116

A 41-year-old woman, divorced from a businessman, admitted in a state of anxious depression with confusion and hallucinations.

History—An uncle committed suicide. The patient who was brought up in the country, was bright and always scholastically the first in her class. After having finished school she moved to Copenhagen, where she worked as a chorus girl and as a prostitute. Between the age of 27 and 38 years she was unhappily married to psychopathic businessman who often committed adultery and infected her with gonorrhoea. On admission she was depressed, had contemplated suicide and was in a turbid state, heard herself accused of being a prostitute, had genital sensations and thought she was living in the Middle Ages. There was definitely something hysterical and exaggerated in her productions but, on the whole, it had to be admitted that she was genuinely and severely psychotic. After two months she cleared up and seemed to be in her habitual state. Ten years later both parents died and she developed a paranoid psychosis and was committed to a state hospital where she revealed sexual delusions. She often masturbated in public because she felt hypnotized to do so. She also experienced genital sensations.

Follow-up—Her personality never deteriorated grossly, but her paranoid ideas stayed with her. A diagnosis of a paranoid schizophrenia was made. Her body type was definitely pyknic.

Conclusion—The first psychotic period may have been a 'pre-schizophrenic episode' (*cf.* pages 77–78). The final outcome must be characterized as a schizophrenia of the paranoid type.

Uncertain case (the first episode).

131

Turbid States II. Hallucinoses

(11 cases)

Psychogenic hallucinoses are defined, in this book, as psychoses which are entirely, or almost entirely, dominated by hallucinations, always assuming that the turbid state that, in these cases, invariably accompanies hallucinated states is not so marked as to warrant the designation 'delirious'. In the older psychiatric literature problems concerning the nature of hallucinations and the phenomenological distinction between genuine hallucinations and pseudo-hallucinations were the subjects of lively discussions. Bumke (1929) for instance stated that the two types of hallucinations are capable of sharp conceptual distinction. Jaspers (1923) formulated the difference between these two types of hallucinations, emphasizing that, since pseudo-hallucinations are not experienced as being projected into the external real world, they lack the objectivity (*Leibhaftigkeit*) which characterizes true hallucinations. And Birnbaum (1928b) made a distinction between 'affect hallucinations' and 'complex hallucinations', depending on whether a more general and fortuitous or a more personal and special content finds expression in the hallucinations.

In the era of experimental psychiatry the phenomenological approach naturally appears less exciting than the work with pharmacologically induced psychoses. It is research within the field of hallucinogenic drugs—particularly mescaline and LSD—that now may offer a solution to the riddle of the genesis of hallucinations.

It must be emphasized, however, that at the present time the problem of hallucination is being approached also by psychoanalysis. In a very stimulating paper Katan (1960) has formulated some proposals concerning the metapsychological differences between hysterical and schizophrenic hallucinations. His tentative conclusion is that the hysterical hallucination may be regarded as an ego-defence of the same order as a conversion symptom whilst the schizophrenic hallucination is of the order of the delusion and is, therefore, the result of a psychotic attempt at restitution.

Of the three approaches to the problem of hallucinations, the phenomenological, the experimental, and the metapsychological, the last two seem to me the more promising, the phenomenological approach having spent itself in description.

Hallucinations occurring during the course of psychogenic reactions are sometimes pseudo-forms, sometimes genuine. They can, further, be designated as experiences arising out of the emotionally charged state and must be interpreted as an expression of the tendency of the undischarged emotional build-up to be converted into something more or less akin to perceptions. They are, in their functional nature, closer related to the hallucinations of sleep than to those occurring in organic lesions of the brain. The dream is almost invariably projected on to the 'dream screen' (Lewin, 1946, 1948, 1953) and, thus, has *Leibhaftigkeit*, and with very few exceptions we believe in its content, however fantastic. In the dream, as well as in the hallucinations of psychogenic psychoses, unconscious (repressed) and emotionally highly charged fantasies break through into consciousness in more or less distorted form. The manifest, that is, conscious elements, in these productions originate from the id as well as from the superego and the ego. The dream 'formally' is a psychogenic psychosis in people who are asleep.

It may be characteristic of the capacity of the two sexes for hallucinatory experiences that all 11 patients with hallucinoses were women.

Case 117

A 36-year-old woman, married to a skilled worker and admitted because of hallucinations and transitory paranoid ideas.

History—There were several 'hysterical' personalities in her family. A sister had 'seizures'. The patient herself had always been erethic and suspicious. Shortly before admission she had some banal quarrels with a female neighbour. She could see and hear this woman threatening her and her family with a gun. Apparently there were genuine hallucinations in the daytime as well as hypnagogic hallucinations. She was mildly depressed and anxious but otherwise showed no psychopathology. After two months in hospital she was discharged as cured.

Follow-up—The patient was suspicious about the letter asking her for a follow-up interview but consented to come. She presented herself as a pyknic woman, obviously not very bright but otherwise she gave the impression of normal mental health. Just before admission for the psychotic episode she apparently was in a mild clouded state for about twenty-four hours with partial amnesia, but the hallucinations prevailed in the clinical picture. She passed her menopause without psychic deviations.

Conclusion—We have here a mildly mentally retarded and suspicious woman who under the impact of a trite psychic trauma reacts with vivid hallucinations and fleeting paranoid ideas (*wahnhafte Ideen*).

Certain psychogenic reaction.

Case 118

A 35-year-old Swedish-born woman, married to a policeman, admitted for hysterical seizures and visual hallucinations.

History—The maternal grandfather became paranoid late in life. The pyknic-syntonic, sthenic, and very self-assertive patient had always been lively and gregarious, erethic, with a tendency to exaggerated reactions and very jealous. She had often threatened suicide. When she discovered that for years her husband had had a girl friend she exploded in typical hysterical fashion and became visually hallucinated. She saw black devils under the bed and hanging on the walls; they took the shape of the husband and made fun of her. She also saw Christ, who definitely disapproved of her husband's escapades. During the short stay in the hospital the psychotic symptoms vanished and she displayed a quite charming hysterical personality.

Follow-up—Sixteen years later she presented herself as a completely normal woman who claimed that after the brief psychotic episode her husband had become a model of bourgeois virtues and that the childless marriage ever since had been a happy one.

Conclusion—The husband's adultery must have been a severe blow to this self-assertive and strongly reacting woman, whose self-esteem also was hurt by the fact that she could not bear children.

Certain psychogenic reaction.

Case 119

A 35-year-old woman, married to an unskilled worker, admitted because of hallucinations and a mild depression.

History—There was no information about psychiatric predisposition. The patient had always been 'nervous'. The last few years before admission the husband spent most of his salary on liquor and the financial situation at home was a very difficult one. While drunk he was often abusive. Shortly before hospitalization the patient became depressed and began to hallucinate, partly in a fully conscious state during the day-time, partly as hypnagogic hallucinations. One day an ambulance came driving into the living-room, blowing its horn, on many occasions she saw a man on fire hanging on the wall. She also felt her hair to be cut. She had improved greatly when discharged. The husband reformed gradually and the patient never had any more psychotic episodes. Her menopause at 45 years was without psychiatric complications.

Follow-up—She appeared to be a quiet woman from the working class without any symptoms or signs of a psychiatric nature.

Conclusion—It would require some psychoanalytic interpretation to comprehend the content of the psychosis from the nature of the psychic trauma. Suffice it to say that Jaspers' criteria only partly are fulfilled in this case.

Definitely a psychogenic psychotic episode.

Case 120

A 33-year-old woman (widow for five years) in the retail trade, admitted in a depressed and hallucinated state.

History—The patient was brought up in a petit bourgeois and very puritanical milieu in which sex was synonymous with deadly sin. After the death of her husband she had a couple of love affairs with strong feelings of guilt and shame, but otherwise she led a blameless and probably dull life. The day prior to admission she saw the dead husband driving a car in the street, opened the window and shouted to him. While in the hospital she was depressed and fearful of having contracted a venereal disease. She was also vaguely paranoid, people were talking behind her back about a secret she had and that may prove fateful to her. In an imaginary telephone conversation she had been told that she was a mixture of a man and a woman. After four months she was discharged cured.

Follow-up—In a personal interview she made a healthy and homely impression. She was of pyknic body-build. She led a very quiet life and had acquiesced in it.

Conclusion—No comments seem to be called for.

A case of certain psychogenic reaction.

Case 121

A 23-year-old woman, married to a dyer, admitted because of intense irritability and hallucinations.

History—The mother was always unstable and erethic. The patient herself was a psycho-infantile and moody person and difficult to live with. A few weeks before admission she began to see shapes and to hear voices; the hallucinations were very vivid. The persons she saw and heard were always dead relatives or acquaintances and they regularly were nasty to her. In the hospital she admitted to having had such experiences for some years periodically. She was discharged without definite improvement after a month and was twice more hospitalized for the same symptoms within the next few years and then divorced.

Follow-up—In a long conversation eighteen years after the first hospitalization the patient presented the picture of an extremely infantile individual who spent a good deal of her time, day and night, in a semi-dreamy state in which she was the heroine in fictitious narratives as we know them from the most trite magazine stories. Schizophrenic symptoms or signs were not observed. For years she had received disablement pension.

Conclusion—This woman never matured. She continued from childhood to live in a world dominated by fantasies as we know them from small children. She was probably not unhappy.

Certain case of psychogenic psychosis.

A reliable diagnosis could not be made in the following 3 cases.

Case 122

A 53-year-old woman, married to a retired blacksmith, twenty years her senior, and admitted because of visual hallucinations.

History—At the follow-up a stepson and a stepdaughter gave the

135

following information. The pre-morbid personality was not extraordinary except for the fact that the patient was somewhat superstitious and convinced that to an extent she was able to predict the future. While in her menopause she became interested in spiritualism and began to have visions. They were genuine hallucinations experienced in a non-clouded state of consciousness. She saw very vividly the faces of people and dogs and one day she met the Russian czar in a tramcar. She was convinced that the visions were the doings of evil spirits and that they had the intent to tell her about something frightful that was going to happen. She was discharged one month after admission and remained for the rest of her life in her home. She died of pneumonia ten years after the onset of her illness and her condition remained almost unchanged. There developed no deterioration of the personality and her relationship with her relatives remained normal. However, she isolated herself somewhat from other people, being so absorbed in her pathological productions. No other psychotic symptoms were added to the described clinical picture and her daily behaviour was normal.

Follow-up—See the above information.

Conclusion—We can do little but state that this was a case of a chronic visual hallucinosis with the paranoid conviction of the genuineness of the visions. So far as the aetiology is concerned we might as well admit ignorance. Birnbaum (1920) has described several cases of this variety of psychosis.

Uncertain diagnosis.

Case 123

A 41-year-old single housemaid, admitted because of acoustic hallucinations.

History—The patient, who was beyond any doubt intellectually retarded although otherwise normal, was in the beginning of her menopause when, without any preceding psychic traumata, she began to hear voices, who told her that she was doomed to perdition because of her sexual desires (she never had had any sexual relations, but had often experienced sexual longings). Satan himself frequently communicated with her on this subject and also told her that some night a man would enter her room and rape her. Aside from the sexual content the voices entertained her about religious matters. She was mildly depressed but she presented no other psychiatric signs or symptoms. In the following twelve years she was twice more hospitalized for exactly the same symptoms. No deterioration of the personality was to be observed and no other symptoms were added. Once she heard God tell her that she was Jesus Christ. She was, on the whole, able to ignore the voices and to adjust reasonably well socially.

Follow-up—In a personal interview she confirmed the above information, but could add nothing else pertinent to the case. Five years after the outbreak of the illness she worked for a doctor who supplied information to the effect that she had appeared psychologically normal except for her modest intelligence.

Conclusion—As in the previous case we have here a patient with a chronic (this time acoustic) hallucinosis. It is obvious that id-impulses of a sexual nature as well as superego reactions against them are at work in this patient with a weak ego. The pathogenic factor is an intra-psychic conflict, not a 'psychic trauma'.

Uncertain case.

Case 124

A 33-year-old woman, married to a merchant marine officer, admitted because of acoustic hallucinations.

History—No information concerning predisposition or pre-morbid personality was available. The onset of the psychosis was acute. One evening she suddenly heard her father-in-law tell her that she should visit him and she would then get the man she loved. From the case history (which is very incomplete) it seems likely that she had had a lover at a time when her husband was away from home. During hospitalization she was extremely reserved, would only admit for some weeks to have heard voices talking to her about erotic subjects. There was some depression and spells of crying. She was discharged after a few weeks without any obvious improvement.

Follow-up—The patient did not answer to a written inquiry. When directly contacted in her home in a far from fashionable section of Copenhagen the attempt was without success: she simply slammed the door when she realized the purpose of the visit. She looked untidy and dirty. It proved possible discreetly to obtain some information from a few neighbours and the landlord. It was revealed that she was divorced a few years after her hospitalization and at the time of the follow-up probably made a living as a prostitute. She flatly refused to establish any form of relationship with the people in her apartment building. A correspondence with the former husband added nothing of value to a psychiatric understanding of the patient and two letters to her mother were never answered.

Conclusion—A diagnosis is very difficult to establish in this case. The patient may have been a schizophrenic who never deteriorated to a degree which made an adjustment, however poor, to society impossible. It is, on the other hand, quite possible that she was a psychopath who finally ended up as a street-walker in very poor circumstances.

Uncertain case.

The last 3 cases in this group of hallucinoses have proved beyond a doubt to be schizophrenias.

Case 125

A 40-year-old woman, married to a tramcar conductor, admitted because of acoustic and visual hallucinations.

History—A brother suffered from paranoid schizophrenia and committed suicide. The pre-morbid personality of the patient, who was a pyknic-syntonic woman, was unremarkable. She became acutely psychotic

137

with voices telling her about a certain minister, she knew from her church, and to whom she was to be married. She frequently saw this clergyman at night, heard his deep masculine voice and experienced pleasant coital sensations. During the first hospitalization she was quite happy and completely satisfied with the way things had developed. After three months she was discharged without improvement and shortly thereafter her husband died. The following few years she managed to make a living as a seamstress, but then again had to be admitted because her hallucinations, which had stayed with her, became too obtrusive. The hallucinations, genuine in nature, consisted of the shapes of men standing in her room and addressing her in the most obscene language. She was also told that she would be butchered. She never became severely demented, neither intellectually nor with regard to personality.* Her syntonic make-up probably acted as a protection in this respect. However, the schizophrenic symptomatology was beyond doubt (hypnotism, paranoid ideas, total lack of insight, etc.).

Follow-up—In a personal interview at a state hospital eighteen years after the first psychotic break quite good contact was established with her. Nothing of particular interest was added to what has already been accounted for.

Conclusion—This is a case of slowly progressing paranoid schizophrenia, in the first few years dominated by acoustic hallucinations.

Certain schizophrenia.

Case 126

A 52-year-old charwoman, widow of a worker who died when she was 45 years of age. She was admitted because of an acute hallucinosis.

History—No information concerning familial predisposition. The patient had always been obstinate, erethic and selfish with a very lively fantasy life. Two days before admission she began to hear a male voice telling her to go to certain places which she did. She also saw the man talking to her. Upon admission she was quiet but not completely oriented. There was partial amnesia for her fugues. She insisted that it was a man in the Salvation Army who talked to her and wanted to marry her. Wassermann test was negative. Without improvement she was discharged after a few weeks but had to be readmitted a year later because her symptoms had worsened. She was soon removed to St. Hans Hospital where she remained until her death ten years later of a gastro-enteritis. Her paranoid syndrome developed more and more, men were threatening her sexually, but fortunately the Salvation Army was in constant readiness for instant action to protect her. She became more and more autistic and ill-tempered.

Follow-up—No relations could be located.

---

* The term 'dementia' was used differently by Kraepelin and Bleuler. Very patient psychoanalytically oriented psychotherapy in the United States of 'demented' persons seems to support Bleuler's view that even in severe schizophrenia all basic functions are preserved potentially. The schizophrenic patient has regressed but is not 'demented'.

Conclusion—We have here (as in Cases 123 and 149) a person in whom strong conflicting forces are at work. Sexual id-impulses (the threatening men) attempt to persuade her that much delight is in waiting for her if she obeys their command. On the other hand this patient's superego—and, consequently, the ego—cannot approve of the vanity of worldly pleasures. Finally, the ego must show consideration for the reality principle, that is, for the possible reactions to what might in her milieu be considered improper behaviour. The poor ego is in a tough spot, assailed on all fronts. In principle there are three possibilities. The ego might side with its puritanical superego and renounce the sexual Devil and all his works. The outcome would be a virtuous, dull and Victoria life which *ad libitum* can be considered 'neurotic' or 'normal'. The second possibility is the one chosen by this patient. The id overwhelms the weak ego and inundates it with its impulses and its fantasies in which certainly also elements from the superego are distinctively active. The result is psychosis. The third course this human drama may take is that the ego, with due respect to the demands made by the reality principle, permits the satisfaction of the biological needs. This is what most of us would call the healthy solution.

Definitely schizophrenia.

Case 127

A 29-year-old single chaser, admitted because of acoustic hallucinations, depression, and anxiety.

History—The mother was 'hysterical'. There was some artistic talent in her family. The patient's father committed suicide. The very bright patient had, since her childhood, been prone to exaggerated hysterical reactions. While living in a boarding-house she fell in love with a young man who turned out to be a homosexual. This was a severe shock to her and she became ill with the above described symptoms. She had obsessive 'naughty' thoughts and heard voices reproaching her for them. She could not forget the young man who was the object of her erotic feelings, and often had sexual dreams concerning him. On a few occasions she heard his voice clearly. During hospitalization she isolated herself. At first she was quite pleasant but became increasingly irritable and completely without initiative; she gave more and more the appearance of living in a dreamy world, probably absorbed in her hallucinations. After thirteen years she was discharged unchanged.

Follow-up—In a personal interview a few years later she lived in a single and dingy room in a poor section of Copenhagen. She herself was untidy. It was not easy to establish contact with her but when the attempt finally was successful she made a rather desperate and pathetic strive to prove that her chances in life were still very good aside from a minor nervous breakdown years ago. During the sad conversation she made an unambiguous autistic and demented impression. She had without any doubt deteriorated personally as well as socially. She was unable to support herself and received financial help from the government. It proved impossible to locate any persons who could supply additional information.

Conclusion—This is a case of schizophrenia, possibly precipitated by an erotic traumatization.

Certain case of ambulatory schizophrenia.

Stuporous Syndromes

(9 cases)

The stupor syndrome* will be met with particularly in the schizophrenias, endogenous depressions, anaclitic depressions, epidemic encephalitis, and psychogenic psychoses. Like other dramatic psychiatric symptoms it has been attributed to demoniacal possession.

Psychogenic mechanisms are probably frequently at work in the schizophrenic stupors. Evidence for this opinion is the fact that a schizophrenic stupor sometimes comes to a sudden end when the patient is exposed to an intense, often catathymic, appeal.

We know next to nothing about the nature of stupor in 'functional' as well as in 'organic' psychic diseases.

Case 128

A 27-year-old single female cook, admitted in a state of stupor after a not too serious suicidal attempt.

History—A sister to the mother had for many years been in a state hospital for a paranoid schizophrenia. The mother was 'nervous' with hysterical convulsions. The patient had always been emotional and moody. After having finished municipal school she worked as a housemaid and a cook. The day before admission the young man she had been dating broke with her, and in her desperation she took some bromide. For several days she was completely stuporous. When she came out of this state she was mildly depressed, but seemed, after a few weeks, to be in her habitual frame of mind.

Follow-up—After several attempts the patient was located. Since her discharge she had worked as a cook in a number of different hotels. She presented herself as a pyknic, friendly, and perfectly normal woman. She was a simple and plain person, whereas the above-mentioned boy friend was a dissipated individual. For a few years after her hospitalization she was married to an unstable and adulterous man, whom she divorced. Since then she had led a quiet, uneventful life, satisfied with her work and spending most of her free time reading.

Conclusion—Considering our very limited insight into the mechanisms of stupors we can only conclude that her reaction after the psychic trauma came in as a handy short-lasting defence against the painful situation. We do not know why this patient chose this particular mechanism

* Stupor is here understood as a condition characterized by mutism and akinetic symptoms without an organic basis.

rather than, for example, an amnestic fugue or some other psycho-pathological manoeuvre.

Certain psychogenic reaction.

Case 129

A 37-year-old woman, divorced from a taxi-driver, admitted in a state of stupor, depression, anxiety, and hallucinations.

History—Her former husband was an alcoholic. The only child, a son, was a psychopath and intellectually retarded. After having finished municipal school she became a factory girl. She had always been emotional with asthenic, depressive, and erethic reactions. Her intelligence was average. She was committed by the police after having been stuporous at home for a few days. After one week she cleared up and admitted to having been very upset and depressed for some time because of her son's troubles with the law. She had heard voices (genuine hallucinations), not described in any detail in the case history. There was some amnesia for the psychotic episode. There was nothing peculiar about her when discharged after three weeks. A year later she married a simple and stable man and for several years they were reasonably happy. When he asked for a divorce because he could not, in the long run, tolerate having the patient's psychopathic son living at home, which she insisted on, she developed a syndrome almost identical with the one already described and lasting for about two weeks. Wassermann was negative. She was again discharged in her habitual state.

Follow-up—In a personal interview the patient turned out to be a pyknic, lower middle-class and talkative woman. She was divorced shortly after the last hospitalization and had since suffered from asthenic-depressive symptoms which incapacitated her sufficiently to motivate her being allotted disablement pension. She seemed quite satisfied with her life.

Conclusion—This case is similar to the preceding one. In both, psychic traumatizations are reacted to in the way of stuporous protective mechanisms, in the present patient the condition was complicated by a mild turbid state and with a second attack seven years after the first one, again as a reaction to a traumatic situation.

Certain psychogenic psychosis.

Case 130

A 69-year-old married agent for a wine company, admitted in a stupor.

History—Psychiatric predisposition was denied. There was a tendency to longevity in the patient's family. He never suffered any serious illnesses during his life until he became psychotic, but he had for some years been in financial difficulty and had sought relief in an appreciable consumption of alcohol, although he could hardly be classified as an alcoholic. The relationship between him and his wife also had been strained for a long time. He was perfectly natural until, on the morning of the admission, he could not be awakened. He was not drunk and there were absolutely no clinical signs of cerebral damage. The systolic blood pressure was 160.

On admission he was in a typical stupor which lasted for twenty-four hours. He then appeared perfectly normal, aside from some worrying about his pecuniary situation. He died aged 75 years of pyelonephritis without having had any further psychiatric (or neurological) difficulties.

Follow-up—In a personal interview with the widow and two doctors, who had known him, nothing of pertinent psychiatric interest was added.

Conclusion—We must conclude that this man, in a brief psychotic episode, escaped his worries, having assuaged them for a number of years with a glass in his hand.

Definitely a psychogenic reaction.

Case 131

A 31-year-old woman, married to a taxi-driver, admitted in a semi-stuporous state.

History—Psychiatric predisposition was denied. Habitually the patient was vivacious and charming. The last few months before admission she was overworked, but denied psychic traumata. She became depressed, cried frequently, and appeared more and more apathetic. An angina with high fever complicated the condition. On admission she was as described above. A thorough somatic, including neurological, examination was negative. The spinal fluid (also Wassermann's reaction) was normal. After a week she cleared up, with some amnesia for the preceding period. Within the next two years she was hospitalized twice more with similar symptoms, in addition to which she demonstrated typical hysterical features (diploplegia of not organic origin, hysterical-dramatic behaviour).

Follow-up—In a personal interview the patient revealed herself as a flourishing syntonic person who did not in any way make a psycho-pathological impression. She asserted, in a convincing manner, to have been psychically healthy over the fourteen years that had elapsed since her last contact with psychiatrists.

Conclusion—This patient possessed hysterical proclivities and suffered during three short-lasting periods from a mild disturbance of consciousness with some depression, fatigue, and semi-stupor. It proved impossible to demonstrate any well defined psychic traumata.

Probably a case of psychogenic origin.

Of the remaining 5 cases 2 were definitely schizophrenias while in 3 cases no certain diagnosis could be made.

Case 132

A 20-year-old single housemaid, admitted in a state of depressive stupor.

History—No psychiatric predisposition. Average intellectual capacities. Even-tempered, optimistic, and obstinate. After having finished municipal school she supported herself doing domestic work. She was well thought of. A year before admission she had an unhappy love affair and reacted with a mild depression. A few months before hospitalization this situation repeated itself with another man and this time her depressive reaction was very intense and she was committed in a stuporous state which lasted a few days. She then became acutely and extremely agitated, was soiling, and refused to eat. She developed a high temperature and died a few days later. The autopsy showed bronchitis and oedema of the lungs.

Follow-up—All efforts to establish contact with members of her family and some of her former mistresses were unsuccessful.

Conclusion—Under the circumstances a diagnosis is not possible. It may have been a case of what formerly was called 'delirium acutum', sometimes considered to be a variant of catatonia, sometimes of manic-depressive psychosis.

Uncertain case.

Case 133

A 32-year-old single housemaid, admitted in a stupor.

History—Psychiatric predisposition: no information. Pre-morbid personality: no information. Shortly before admission the patient had an unhappy love affair and since then had been depressed. A few days before it became necessary to send her to the hospital she became 'peculiar' and very reserved. While in the psychiatric ward she was at first stuporous, then began to verbalize and admitted to having heard voices, charging her with being a prostitute. After two weeks she was almost back to normal but had no insight into the pathological nature of her previous condition, although there was no amnesia.

Follow-up—Although every available method of locating the patient, her relatives, and the family she had worked for were tried, the result was negative.

Conclusion—A diagnosis is not possible although schizophrenia appears to be a rather likely possibility, particularly since the psycho-pathological phenomena apparently were experienced in a state of clear consciousness.

Uncertain case.

Case 134

A 28-year-old unmarried architect, admitted in a state of stupor and depression. He was found by the police in a condition of amnestic fugue in a park in Copenhagen.

History—The mother died of uraemia aged 48 years. Of the patient's four siblings, three were without doubt schizphrenics. The patient, asthenic of body physique, was an upright, emotional, and very bright person; he also preferred his own company and never had intimate friends. A year before admission he fell unhappily in love with a young female artist. After having spent a year in Paris 'to forget' he developed the above described symptoms. During the initial phase in the hospital he was stuporous, cataleptic, and soiling. After a few months there was an almost complete but short-lasting remission, after which he again moved into a state of stupor. He died shortly after of a broncho-pneumonia. The autopsy showed nothing of particular psychiatric interest.

Follow-up—In a telephone conversation with the fourth sibling, a brother, who gave no impression of psychopathology, no additional information was obtained.

Conclusion—The predisposition, only partly known at the time of his first hospitalization, and the symptomatology point strongly in the direction of a schizophrenic process.

Probable schizophrenia.

Case 135

A 29-year-old unmarried waitress, admitted three times for psychiatric symptoms of widely differing nature.

History—Nothing is known about predisposition. The patient, who came from a very humble social milieu, went to municipal school and then held several jobs as a kitchen maid. She was always irascible and inclined to mild depressive reactions.

At 29 years of age she was twice hospitalized briefly for affect-explosions precipitated by quarrels with her boy friend and suicidal attempts of a not serious nature. A few months later she was again admitted in a severe stuporous condition. During the following weeks her status oscillated between anxious hyperactivity and stupor. There were short-lasting partial remissions. After a while she admitted to acoustic and visual hallucinations of a frightening nature and felt convinced that there was a group of people conspiring against her. She became more and more silly and autistic in her behaviour. Also, she performed automutilations which only severely psychotic persons would be capable of. She died quite suddenly of what was diagnosed as acute gastro-enteritis nine years after her first hospitalization.

Follow-up—It proved impossible to trace any members of her family or acquaintances of hers.

Conclusion—The comments to Case 106 are relevant also in this case. Definitely a schizophrenia.

Case 136

A 26-year-old single gardener, admitted in a state of depressive stupor.

History—A brother was constitutionally gloomy. As a child the patient had a phobia for darkness and suffered from nightmares. After a two-day lasting fugue with amnesia he was committed by the police in a strongly agitated condition with crying spells and stereotyped phrases like: 'My soul is sick—I am suffering from the vice of lust'. There was no information about any psychic trauma. During the first part of the hospitalization he was anxious and at times very restless. Cataleptic phenomena were observed. After two weeks he cleared up completely for a few days. He then rather quickly moved into a stuporous state, and in a few months had developed a psychosis that proved to be chronic. The schizophrenic nature of his condition was beyond any doubt; its main stamp was that of catatonia. He died six years later of pulmonary tuberculosis.

Conclusion—This is a case of schizophrenia, initiated with a fugue but soon developing into a stuporous-catatonic psychosis.

Definitely schizophrenia.

144

CHAPTER 8

THE PARANOID SYNDROMES

The Continental and the American Psychiatric Tradition

In the first chapter the lack of understanding generally between European-Continental and Anglo-American psychiatry was emphasized. Approaching the problem of paranoia* and paranoid conditions it is wise to bear in mind that this gap has gradually widened and deepened. A glance at the list of references of modern German and American monographs, textbooks, or handbooks on the subject will prove this to be true. Adolf Meyer is a case in point. One of the dominant figures in American psychiatry his psychobiological system is a dim concept only to most Continental psychiatrists. They, on the other hand, are strongly influenced by the thinking and the writings of the eminent French and, particularly, the German students of *die Paranoiafrage*. In American bibliographies these scholars are, with notable exceptions, referred to mainly by European emigrants. However, it must be maintained that the provincial isolationism of America in this respect is not nearly as marked as that of Europe's. The viewpoints of Bleuler and Freud, not to mention many Europeans of less awe-inspiring stature, were warmly accepted by American colleagues. This spiritual hospitality has so far not been convincingly reciprocated. Recently Pflanz (1959), in an evaluation of the psychiatric situation in central Europe after World War II, has emphasized this.

Conservative but vigilant England ought to accept the difficult but commendable challenge of mediator between the two traditions. Psychiatric England could become the bridgehead from which the wealth of fresh and bold ideas, reappraisals, conceptualizations, and experimentations from the vital American psychiatric scene could invade the Continent.

The difference between the two traditions—in itself worthy of special study—reflects basic differences in thinking and principles of research. Examples are innumerable. Here one may serve for many.

* The term 'paranoia' was used by Hippocrates (Zilboorg, 1941) and possibly even earlier. To the ancients it was roughly the equivalent of 'insanity' today.

Kretschmer and the Two Traditions

In Europe every psychiatrist is at least roughly familiar with Kretschmer's ideas concerning certain types of paranoid development. In America he is mainly known as a constitutionalist—a European Sheldon. Kretschmer, on the other hand, in lofty unawareness of the existence of non-Germanic psychiatry, ignores many important contributions to the problem he has devoted so much of his talent to. Even in his third edition, from 1950, of his monograph on sensitive paranoid developments, not a single reference to an English or an American study can be found, and his bibliography is almost entirely limited to what it already comprised in 1918 when the book was first published. It is particularly regrettable that Kretschmer hardly takes any notice of the psychoanalytic contributions to the enigma of paranoid developments. He cites Freud's classic monograph on the Schreber-case* from 1911 in which the problem of paranoia was transformed from one of description and classification to one of genetic development. The many dynamic formulations and provocative ideas later suggested by Freud (for example, 1914, 1915, 1919, 1922, 1923) and other analysts like Klein- (1932), Knight (1940), Cameron (1943), Bak (1939, 1946), Glover (1949) are ignored. The very important paper by Waelder (1951) must also be mentioned here.

It is remarkable that some psychiatrists still believe the analytic conception of paranoia primarily to be concerned with repressed homosexual strivings—an important point in the Schreber paper. Some analysts have for years thought that the struggle with aggressive impulses in such cases is even more important than sexual conflicts. Above all, psychoanalytic attempts to comprehend the dynamic processes responsible for the emergence of paranoid structures are now as much focused on the problem of the choice of the *defence* (Freud, projection: Waelder, denial), by the paranoid ego, as with the nature of the *instinctual drive* it has to cope with. A psychology disregarding unconscious dynamics is incapable of meeting the challenge of the paranoid solution to personality conflicts.

The clinical material in this book does not lend itself to detailed and subtle psychopathological interpretations, and the approach chosen here must therefore be clinical rather than dynamic, academic rather than analytic.

Kretschmer and His Critics

Paranoid syndromes are probably always dependent on a predisposition. Many psychiatrists conceive of this factor as being of a constitu-

* Schreber's autobiography (1903) has now been translated (1955).

tional nature, while many analysts are inclined to attribute a considerable predisposing significance to experiences in infancy and early childhood. Wimmer was a typical representative of the first-mentioned point of view. In his thesis from 1902 he coined the term 'evolutionary paranoia' to describe a series of chronic paranoid forms whose appearance was due to the mere development or hypertrophy of diathetic traits, the paranoigenic temperament.

Also, Kretschmer accepts the principle that the paranoid development is essentially contingent on such a paranoigenic-constitutional predisposition (*die wahnbereite Persönlichkeit*). He has, however, also suggested a theory, already touched upon by Wimmer in the above-mentioned work, according to which there is no such thing as a general predisposition to paranoid reactions but, on the contrary, specific traits predispose to specific forms of reaction. Kretschmer carries this theory to its far-reaching nosological conclusion: there is no paranoia, there are only paranoics. The paranoid disorders comprise a number of widely different types (including Kretschmer's sensitive and expansive variants) each presupposing some particular diathesis which does not commence its morbid development until the individual concerned is affected by a particular episode or life situation, a key event, as Kretschmer puts it. Each single case must be comprehended from its own peculiar characterological and situative premises. This is, thus, a case of reaction specificity: the specific predisposition for the particular form of reaction can only be triggered off by an experience of a specific nature.

Kretschmer's contribution to the paranoid debate has, as Lange (1927) pointed out in an article in Aschaffenburg's manual, reduced the paranoid question to a predominantly psychological problem in which the characterological structure and the fate of the individual are the critical factors. The paranoid problem has thus become one of the principal issues of psychogenesis.

The opinion outlined here can hardly pass without serious questions. Lange, in the article cited above, challenged Kretschmer's implicit psychological view. His argument rested, substantially, on a few case histories of paranoid patients published by Schneider (1920) and Kehrer (1922), which show appreciable divergencies from Kretschmer's models.

The character and social background of the patients discussed by Schneider are virtually identical with two of Kretschmer's fundamental observations (Helene Renner, Anna Feldweg), but the third component of the triad of factors conditioning the disease is lacking: the event. For this reason, Schneider does not consider it possible to regard the

147

psychosis as a reaction, with the result that the paranoid ideas of the patient must be considered 'primary delusions'. On the basis of this observation, Schneider then suggested that 'the event' (that is, the humiliating ethical insufficiency in Kretschmer's patients) is not a determinant of disease at all but, on the contrary, one of its first symptoms, a primary paranoid production.

Kretschmer has met Schneider's arguments in his introduction to the second (1927) and the third (1950) edition of *Der sensitive Beziehungswahn*. He emphasized that a process schizophrenic course may very well be introduced by a sensitive paranoid initial stage and, in so doing, *resemble* a sensitive *Beziehungswahn*. But he also stressed the fact that his sensitive patients—most of them individuals with sexual conflicts: elderly spinsters, on the one hand, and young men with conflicts over masturbation on the other—did not deteriorate in a schizophrenic way and that they remained accessible to psychotherapy.

Kretschmer has, moreover, previously (1919b) accounted for the interplay between endogenic and exogenic (for instance psychogenic) factors in the construction of a clinical picture. In this paper, he expounded, practically simultaneously with Birnbaum (1923), the principles of modern multidimensional psychiatric diagnostics, and he laid stress on the fact that the diagnostic ideal, far from seeking a distinction between endogenically and psychogenically conditioned clinical pictures, is, on the contrary, to analyse each single case with the object of determining the part played in its construction by every factor. In this connection, reference may be made to Bleuler's (1941) lucid and consistent structural analyses of some complicated courses of disease.

Of considerable interest, too, is Kehrer's detailed study (1922) containing a number of penetrating analyses of paranoid psychoses in women between puberty and menopause. He succeeded in demonstrating the development of a typical *Beziehungswahn* with sexual-ethical content in certain women whose character lacked all Kretschmer's essential traits of the sensitively constructed personality. Even though Kretschmer's formulations are not necessarily refuted by the demonstration of these clinical pictures, another of the dogmas of *Der sensitive Beziehungswahn* is seriously shaken: that the sensitive reaction is contingent upon a specific predisposition. Kretschmer's patients must now be regarded as special cases and his sensitive character as a type of personality affording particularly favourable conditions for the development of a sensitive paranoid reaction.

Furthermore, it must not be forgotten that Bleuler (1943) has joined these critics. In a series of cases of possible sensitive *Beziehungswahn*, he doubted the presence of a psycho-reactive disorder. He thought it probable that these may sometimes be cases of schizophrenia with a late age of onset, running a benign course and with a marked psychoplastic apparel.

Recently, Mayer-Gross, Slater and Roth (1960) have criticized Kretschmer's theory. These authors appreciate his intuition and delicate comprehension of the psychological drama taking place in a paranoid personality, but they fail to see that he has ever showed why the patients' ideas acquire the convincing force of delusions, and they maintain that he has overlooked the nature of the delusion as a functionally primary disturbance.

To summarize: Schneider demonstrated that Kretschmer's key event, the 'psychic trauma', is not always necessary for the development of a sensitive delusional psychosis, and Kehrer that this type of paranoid condition can emerge without the presence of a sensitive personality. Kretschmer, in the third edition of his book, criticized Wernicke's notion concerning the concept of supervalent ideas and the circumscribed autopsychoses, stating that these conceptualizations merely reflect observations and not the actual existence of disease entities: Wernicke picked a clinical observation without getting hold of its roots. This very criticism can be turned against Kretschmer himself; the roots of his *sensitiver Beziehungswahn* are missing and they are to be found in the unconscious. His sensitive model is a noble specimen of refined academic-psychiatric observation and formulation, but in spirit it is pre-analytic.

As has already been mentioned in Chapter 4 the paranoid syndromes have been divided into two groups, those with and those without hallucinations, since this classification has been presumed to be prognostically the most valuable.

Syndromes Without Hallucinations

(12 cases)

The follow-up demonstrated 3 certain cases and 2 probable cases of psychogenic origin.

Case 137

A 29-year-old unmarried sailor, admitted because of paranoid ideas of a not too bizarre type.

History—There was no information concerning predisposition. The patient was of average intelligence, had read a good deal and had always been interested in the social sciences. He left school when he was aged 14 years. A few years prior to admission he developed paranoid ideas. He thought that the American Air Force owed him some money and became interested in a scandal concerning a well known Danish financier whose transactions were then making headlines in the European press. The patient was convinced that there was more to the matter than had been revealed in court and he was very indignant because the proper authorities would not listen to him. He felt it to be his duty to 'clean up the mess'. A full-blown paranoid syndrome of an expansive type was the outcome during his two years of hospitalization. Manic or schizophrenic features were not observed.

Follow-up—Eighteen years later the patient, after having first angrily refused a conversation, finally consented to an interview. He had not changed in the least, was still convinced that he knew more than anybody else about the scandal and that his hospitalization had been arranged by authorities who feared his knowledge. He used big words but had never annoyed or molested anybody. At the time of the follow-up he was living in a childless marriage, he was working as a seaman and was capable of making a modest living. Apart from the paranoid complex the personality was absolutely intact.

Conclusion—This is a case of an expansive-persecutory paranoid development without symptoms of a destructive process. I have chosen to call this a psychogenic psychosis although other diagnostic possibilities obviously are present. A clinical conference concerning this patient with a Kahlbaum,* a Kraepelin and a Kretschmer present would, undoubtedly, have been very stimulating to the hearers.

Definitely a psychogenic psychosis.

Case 138

A 53-year-old separated tailor, admitted after having committed a murder motivated by a supercharged idea.

History—The mother and a sister were said to be 'peculiar'. The premorbid personality was without striking features and the intelligence seems to have been average. After about sixteen years of marriage the patient developed jealous ideas, thinking, not without cause, that his wife was unfaithful to him. He began to interpret all her doings as proofs of her adultery and soon he was convinced that she intended to kill him by poisoning his food. His paranoid tendencies culminated when he was in the process of being divorced. He was convinced that his wife committed adultery with her lawyer and he killed this man with a gun. He was sentenced to eight years imprisonment during which time he showed no evidence of psychosis at all. He died of a heart condition a few months after his discharge from the penitentiary. He had contracted syphilis before he married. Wassermann's reaction and the spinal fluid were normal at the time he was hospitalized and again shortly before his death. Hallucinations were never noticed.

Follow-up—For reasons of discretion no relatives were contacted.

* Kahlbaum (1822–99) was instrumental in coining the term 'paranoia' as it was used in German psychiatry half a century ago, that is, as the designation for a chronic systematized delusional state without hallucinations or other schizophrenic factors.

Conclusion—The comments to the psychosis of the previous patient are valid also in this case. One should keep in mind Freud's (1922) distinction between three types of jealousy: one based on reality, another on projection (of the person's own repressed wishes to be adulterous), and a third, which by Freud is considered genuinely paranoid and based on the patient's unconscious homosexual drives. A discussion of this particular patient's paranoid reaction in the light of psychoanalytic insight would prove frustrating because any intimate knowledge about his inner workings are not available.

Definitely a psychogenic psychosis.

Case 139

A 45-year-old unmarried female dental mechanic, admitted because of persecutory ideas of a non-schizophrenic nature.

History—Predisposition was denied. The patient had always been an industrious, conscientious, somewhat conceited, hermit-like and suspicious person. She was proud and somewhat self-opinionated, very shy sexually and had a strong sense of right and wrong. The information concerning this characterological make-up was mostly obtained from a sister. A couple of years prior to her admission she developed an erotic interest in a man who did not reciprocate her feelings. This, supposedly, was the starting point for her self-referring ideas. She was at the time close to her menopause. She could not leave the house or travel without feeling herself under observation by plainclothes men. Her puritanical upbringing and attitude made her feel very ashamed of the fact that not only had she permitted herself to nourish the erotic affection for the above-mentioned gentleman, but she had also on several occasions written him about it. After a few months of hospitalization she was given the benefit of the prognostic doubt and discharged, but had to be readmitted four to five months later with exactly the same syndrome. She was soon removed to St. Hans Hospital where she made an excellent adjustment and was still a patient at the time of the follow-up seventeen years later. The sthenic elements in her personality and her good intelligence made her the natural central figure in the weaving room. The hospital gave both her and her superego wonderful protection against the temptations of real life.

Follow-up—In a long personal interview she reacted in an almost violently emotional way when the catathymic events of the past were touched upon. Otherwise she made a completely normal impression with an absolutely intact personality. The paranoid ideas seemed to have vanished without a trace.

Conclusion—It is interesting in psychiatry to see how it is usually possible diagnostically to approach a particular patient from different angles. This patient, of course, had a paranoid episode with a benign course, at least as long as she was isolated from real life. She could, in the post-psychotic period, naturally be called a neurotic patient, a woman who used phobic mechanisms (avoiding being confronted with life) as a defence against a threatening recurrence of the paranoid psychosis.

She was hardly a typical Kretschmer case: it would seem that the sthenic elements in her personality dominated over the asthenic, whereas, according to Kretschmer, the opposite is typical of the person who develops a *Beziehungswahn*. It would rather seem that Strömgren's theory concerning paranoid developments fits this case. This patient, indeed, possessed a personality structure which caused her dereliction (in the menopause to reveal her sexual interest in a man) to violate her self-image.

Definitely a psychogenic reaction.

Case 140

A 28-year-old male typographer, hospitalized because of paranoid convictions.

History—Predisposition was denied. The pre-morbid personality was without striking features. After leaving elementary school the patient was trained as a compositor. He worked for several years in a big printing office in Copenhagen and slowly developed persecutive ideas concerning his employer, thinking that this man in every possible way tried to annoy him. The crowning insult was the fact that the patient (who had many casual love affairs) after having slept with a girl contracted syphilis as well as gonorrhoea. This had, obviously, been 'arranged' in some way by his chief and he quit his job. Apart from quitting there was no acting out of the pathological ideas. He received adequate treatment for his venereal diseases. At the time of hospitalization Wassermann was negative (blood).

Follow-up—In a very long interview eighteen years after his discharge from the psychiatric ward, the patient, aged 46 years, told this story. The employer was an unusually good looking and handsome man and, although he did not have a beard, he always reminded the patient of Christ. Due to the socio-economic circumstances the relationship between the two men remained a correct and impersonal one. After a while, the patient began to feel that he, too, bore a resemblance to Christ. After a while he felt that the boss, who had been friendly towards him, began to annoy him in many small ways, the culmination being the 'arrangement' which resulted in his contracting venereal diseases. After his discharge from the hospital he got new jobs and was well thought of in them. For a number of years he was, however, quite dominated by ideas concerning the nasty ways in which the admired (and hated) boss had plotted against him; it was in particular the Christ-fantasy that would not leave him alone. Was he himself Christ, or was he not ? One evening, while roaming the streets, he suddenly and vividly saw a figure of Christ in the clouds. It was an awesome experience, a transfiguration of Jesus, but it left him greatly relieved: Christ was in heaven and he himself was a typographer. A few years later the object of his ambivalence died and so slowly did the whole paranoid complex. He married and was at the time of the follow-up leading an uneventful middle-class life. There were never any new pathological productions. He made a completely natural impression, did not reveal psychotic or post-psychotic signs and was not in any way reserved or shy. He seemed to be an intelligent fellow. He was predominantly asthenic.

152

Conclusion—This patient was obviously not suffering from a schizophrenia in the European sense of the word. An atypical manic-depressive phase (one of our favourites when we are in diagnostic trouble) and an epileptic 'equivalent' also are less than likely. It would rather seem to be a case of a psychogenic paranoid reaction, although positive proof is lacking. It is, naturally, tempting to try to fit this psychosis into the theory advanced by Freud (1911) and Ferenczi (1911) concerning the nature of paranoid developments, namely that they are based on strong but repressed homosexual strivings. We know that the explanation cannot be as simple as suggested by Freud in his classic Schreber-case. Among other things, the same person may exhibit both manifest homosexual tendencies and paranoid traits, a fact which in itself partly invalidates what one might call Freud's 'naïve' 1911 theory. That this particular patient harboured ambivalent feelings, including a tender affection and a boundless admiration, for his employer cannot be doubted.

Probable psychogenic reaction.

Case 141

A 22-year-old cabin boy, admitted because of 'peculiar ideas'.

History—A sister (pyknic) hospitalized once for a depression after disappointment in love. Apparently, she was inclined to mild periodic depressions. The patient had, in his pre-morbid years, no conspicuous personality features. While working as a cabin boy he suddenly exhibited paranoid ideas: the whole crew was suffering from syphilis; you could see it just by looking at their eyes. Maybe he, himself, had the disease. In the psychiatric ward he made a rather normal impression, although at times he could act 'silly'. He hinted at having masturbated a great deal. Once he refused the food (fear of poison ?) and was a bit active and talkative. Otherwise, he did not demonstrate any signs pointing at anxiety, hallucinations or other psychopathological phenomena. However, he kept insisting that all the members of the crew had contracted syphilis, and was discharged in this condition.

Follow-up—He was located many years later, living modestly in a Danish village where he worked as an unskilled labourer. He was married and had children. In the interview, most of which took place in the presence of his wife, he appeared to be completely normal and gave all the information that was asked for. The paranoid episode, the only time in his life when he had deviated in any way from the psychic 'norm', began spontaneously and he was unable to add any information of pertinent interest. He was small of build, slim and asthenic.

Conclusion—This is probably a case of a psychogenic accentuation of a neurotic conflict. Guilt-feelings over masturbation most likely had been at work, but we can only guess about the content of the accompanying fantasies (homosexual ? The milieu in which he was at the time of the

153

outbreak of the paranoid misinterpretation might be in favour of such a theory). The psychic disease of his sister and his silly-euphoric state of mind at the time of hospitalization force us, however, to consider the possibility of manic-depressive phase with paranoid (psychoplastic) traits
    Probably a psychogenic reaction.

In the following 4 cases the diagnosis has been uncertain.

Case 142

A 23-year-old married taxi-driver, admitted after having been extremely changing in mood for a couple of months and having revealed paranoid ideas.

History—Average intelligence. The pre-morbid personality was not conspicuous except that he was somewhat stubborn and easily offended. A few years after leaving his elementary school he became a taxi-driver. For a long period before hospitalization he was, for reasons beyond his control, out of work and had a lot of financial worries. His mood changes became extreme; one day he was excited, laughing and very talkative, the next he was sulky and isolated himself. During this period he began to talk about some people plotting against him. He could see stool-pigeons everywhere, all watching him. The paranoid tendencies did not crystallize into any well defined system. There may have been a few days with clouded consciousness and lack of orientation. There were no hallucinations. During hospitalization the consciousness was clear; the delusions had stayed with him and he took the other patients to be informers on him. There was some anxiety and restlessness. He was discharged without much improvement.

Follow-up—In an interview with the patient he made a completely normal psychic impression. His delusions had disappeared spontaneously shortly after his discharge and he had ever since been psychically normal. He was still working as a taxi-driver and was well thought of.

Conclusion—It is really impossible to come to a valid diagnostic conclusion in a case like this. We know too little about the patient's possible inner and outer conflicts to be in a position to postulate a psychotic psychogenic episode in the course of a neurosis. All we can say is that the episode did not initiate a malignant psychosis.
    Uncertain case.

Case 143

A 33-year-old separated typographer, admitted after having for some time been depressed and very suspicious of everybody.

History—Two sisters were 'nervous'. The patient himself described in the follow-up his pre-morbid personality as having been without any striking characteristics. He was considered capable in his profession. At 30 years of age his wife left him, why, has never been revealed. Shortly before he was committed by the police to the psychiatric ward he had had some financial worries and an unhappy love affair. He attempted suicide by

154

drowning and was sent to the hospital. Here he demonstrated a fully clear consciousness, depression with self-reproaches and a strong feeling that everything going on around him was 'mysterious' and that 'the police were out to get him'; maybe he was to be decapitated. On a few occasions he spoke of telepathy. All his verbal productions had a certain 'woolly' vagueness. After twenty months of hospitalization he was discharged in a pretty good condition but still at times revealing his delusional proclivities.

Follow-up—After eighteen years it proved hard to locate the patient but at last the search was successful. He turned out to have become a fat pyknic person, he was living completely alone in a small cottage in the country. He met the visitor with suspicion, but after a while the ice was broken and in the interview, which lasted several hours, he was more than willing to give an account of what had happened to him. He obviously was still a mentally sick person, quite dominated by delusions which had the same vagueness as described above. Over the many years that had passed since he first fell ill he had been aware of 'somebody' who in 'some way' wanted to annoy him if not worse. The 'somebody' might be male friends of the woman with whom he had had an affair shortly before he had attempted suicide. His paranoid misinterpretations of everything going on around him made it impossible for him to hold a job for more than a few weeks and ultimately he was given disablement pension and had ever since lived in solitude in his little house. There was no amnesia for the period of hospitalization. His mood during the conversation was mostly stamped by the indignation he felt concerning the injustice done to him. To mention but one example: he could not even urinate in the open without being observed by neighbours and others who wanted to see if he was a man or a woman. Otherwise he was friendly enough.

Conclusion—There is a strong likelihood that this is a case of paranoid schizophrenia, the patient being protected against gross deterioration, by his pyknic-syntonic equipment. Also, he became psychotic relatively late in life. We may well have here a case in which the 'delusional perceptions' (*Wahnwahrnehmungen*), described by Jaspers (1913) were operative in the initial phase of the psychosis. Upon the soil of those primary and psychologically inaccessible experiences a confused jungle of secondary delusional misinterpretations grew up. A very thorough study of this man's personality and his environment might, of course, have yielded results interesting to the psychologically minded, but it is probable that at least the clinical surface was mostly the effect of psychoplastic mechanisms.

Uncertain case.

Case 144

A 35-year-old unmarried housemaid, committed by the police because of hypochondriacal symptoms and a suicidal attempt.

History—The primitive and intellectually mildly retarded patient had, after leaving school, been employed in domestic service. For ten years

155

prior to her illness she had been working for the same family, and was well thought of (confirmed by this family at the time of the follow-up). For some years before she was hospitalized she had been increasingly possessed by the idea of having contracted gonorrhoea. She had an illegitimate child, 10 years old, when she had her breakdown and had at some time received treatment for gonorrhoea. The supervalent hypochondriacal idea (*überwertige Idee*) became so powerful that at last she made a clumsy and probably not seriously meant suicidal attempt (poison) and was admitted. After several months she was transferred to a state hospital where she was still an inmate at the time of the follow-up. In the beginning she was depressed and also at times erethic and indignant because the doctors would not treat her imaginary venereal disease. As time went by, she revealed expansive ideas of a very naïve nature: the real father of her child was a famous film-star, her daughter was in the process of making a career as a ballerina, and the like.

Follow-up—In a personal interview, the patient turned out to be a heavy, middle-aged woman who in a good-natured way complained about the hospital to which she obviously had made an excellent adjustment and in which she had for years been a trusted and capable worker. The old pathological ideas were still with her, but had faded almost to the vanishing point. Some of the doctors gave information to the effect that the patient at times displayed disturbances of thinking which might be of a schizophrenic nature.

Conclusion—This may have been a case of a sub-chronic psychogenic psychosis in an intellectually retarded woman, or it may have been a mild case of paranoid schizophrenia. The unsatisfied female desires were clearly represented in the symptomatology.

Uncertain case.

Case 145

A 53-year-old undertaker's widow, admitted after having displayed paranoid features of an erotic nature for some time.

History—The patient was an intelligent, conscientious and very sthenic woman, stubborn and self-opinionated. The husband, who died a couple of years prior to her admission, was an epileptic; the marriage had been difficult, sex relations had only existed in its initial phase. She was a good mother to her three children. A few years before she was admitted she began to develop ideas about the family physician being in love with her and wanting to marry her. Everything going on around her, small notices in the papers, the telephone ringing, etc., etc., was interpreted in accordance with this *idée fixe*. Otherwise, she was completely natural and her behaviour was entirely proper. She was hospitalized for almost two years and it proved, of course, impossible to shake her conviction concerning Dr. X. She may at times have been hallucinated, hearing peculiar noises, indicating that she just had to be patient, then some day her knight in shining armour would come and marry her. She was discharged in this condition.

Follow-up—The patient flatly refused to open the door to anybody but her two sons. The information obtained is from a conversation with one of

156

them. The patient kept her paranoid complex intact and elaborated a bit on it over the years. Dr. X had a radio installed in his home in order always to be able to hear her voice, and a nasty gang of people, the 'owls', was attempting to destroy the relationship between her and the doctor. Her modest home, where she lived alone, was kept spick and span and she was usually in good spirits.

Conclusion—This may be a case of a paranoid schizophrenia with a late onset and a relatively good prognosis or it may be a psychogenic development. Who can tell?

Uncertain case.

The last 3 cases in this group were definitely schizophrenias.

Case 146

A 52-year-old divorced woman, admitted after having had persecutory ideas for a few years.

History—A brother committed suicide. The patient, who came from a distinguished family in Copenhagen, was, twelve years before the admission, divorced from her husband who was an author; there were five children in the marriage. Pre-morbidly the patient was average, except for some tendency to become suspicious. In her menopause, she, while living in the United States, became convinced that she was to be a victim of the Ku-Klux-Klan and that everybody, including her own children, conspired against her. There was no information about psychic traumata. During the short hospitalization she did not change. After a few years she had to be readmitted, the illness had progressed, she was now hallucinated, heard threatening voices, was fearful of poison in the food and she became strikingly vulgar in her language; in short, she developed a clear-cut paranoid schizophrenia. She died at 62 years of age of cancer.

Conclusion—This is a case of a slowly progressing paranoid schizophrenia, beginning rather late in life.

Certain schizophrenia.

Case 147

A 20-year-old single housemaid, admitted after having displayed an anxious paranoid syndrome for some time.

History—The patient, who had a humble social background, was a mental defective. In her last job she developed incoherent paranoid ideas: the master of the house had several wives, intended to kill her, etc.

During hospitalization (a few months) her mood changed between anxious worrying about her fate and silly excitement.

Follow-up—The Salvation Army succeeded in locating the patient. About a year after her discharge the patient had to be admitted again and she was soon transferred to a state hospital where she was still a patient at the time of the follow-up. She had, over the years, produced a typical schizophrenia with hallucinations, defect of the personality, aggressive outbursts and autism.

157

Conclusion—The reader is reminded of the classic concept of *Propfschizophrenie*, according to which there exists a genetic relationship between schizophrenia and mental defect. This view has not been supported by modern psychiatric geneticists.

Certain schizophrenia.

Case 148

A 26-year-old unmarried unskilled labourer, committed after an attempt seriously to disfigure a doctor.

History—The father was an alcoholic. The pre-morbid personality was characterized by an average intelligence, reticence, irritability and sexual shyness. A few years prior to admission he was operated on for phimosis. Following this minor operation he felt an increasing weakening of his sexual powers, was impotent with a few girls and his erections abated in number. Slowly he got the idea that the surgeon had deliberately maltreated him and that his sperm now 'went into his stomach'. He made an attempt to blind the surgeon by throwing a bottle of hydrochloric acid in his face. He was at first considered by Wimmer a neurotic individual with a psychogenic supervalent idea, but after a few years in St. Hans Hospital it became obvious that he was suffering from a paranoid schizophrenia with catatonic features. When he was first hospitalized the spinal fluid was normal and Wassermann's reaction was negative, both here and in the blood.

Follow-up—The patient was inaccessible in his autistic state and completely dominated by his hallucinations.

Conclusion—The schizophrenic process may have been precipitated by the operation on his genitals or this event may only have been used pathoplastically by an already existing malignant disease.

Certain (psychically precipitated?) schizophrenia.

Syndromes With Hallucinations

(22 cases)

It must be considered highly characteristic of this group that in only 3 cases had the course of the disease confirmed the supposition concerning a psychogenic aetiology, while in 14 cases a certain, and in 1 case a probable, diagnosis of schizophrenia could be established. In 4 cases it proved impossible to make a certain diagnosis.

The 3 certain cases of psychogenic psychosis will be dealt with first.

Case 149

A 50-year-old spinster, working as a furrier and admitted in a hallucinatory state with delusional ideas.

History—Like most members of her family this intelligent patient was a deeply religious and puritanical person. She had always been industrious, obedient, upright, proud and speculative. She was sexually very shy, was once attracted to a young man, but probably never had any erotic experiences. Without known psychic traumatization she began, a few days before admission, to have religious scruples, was afraid of 'evil powers' and felt doomed to perdition. In the hospital she heard voices, mostly hypnagogic, telling her how sinful she was and that she was going to die soon. She had the corporal experience of being sexually possessed by the Devil accompanied by intense genital sensations. She confessed to having masturbated a great deal with strong feelings of guilt. During the daytime she was mostly completely oriented and clear, but was constantly preoccupied with her very painful conflicts and there was considerable anxiety. The spinal fluid was normal and Wassermann was negative here and in the blood. A diagnosis of *délire d'emblée** (*psychogenic?*) was made by Wimmer. The patient was transferred to St. Hans Hospital where she was still an inmate at the time of the follow-up. In the beginning the condition was an extremely distressing and painful one without hope of any kind. She once heard a nocturnal voice tell her that the pane in the temple of Solomon would be broken. After several months she calmed down and very gradually the psychotic picture faded. After a few years she seemed to be in her pre-morbid state and never again had psychotic episodes or periods. Her menopause began a couple of years after the psychotic break-down.

Follow-up—The patient, aged 66 years, was a syntonic, friendly and humorous old lady with whom immediate contact was established. There was absolutely no sign of personality defect. She conversed freely about anything except sex and religion. The only remnants of the old psychosis were occasional nightmares with a threatening religious content. There was no amnesia for the psychotic period.

Conclusion—As, for example, in Cases 123 and 126, we are here dealing with violent conflicting forces within the personality. It is entirely possible that a biologically caused flare-up of the sexual drive shortly before the menopause in this frustrated female was the last straw that upset the hitherto existing delicate equilibrium between id-impulses and the sadistically moralistic superego resulting in the temporary break-down of ego-control and reality testing, that is, psychosis. We are again (*cf.* Chapter 3) reminded of Freud's complementary series and the quantitative aspect of psychopathology, so strongly emphasized by psychoanalytic psychiatry.

Certain case of psychogenic psychosis.

Case 150

A 43-year-old married office clerk, admitted after he had reacted to a severe psychic trauma with depression and persecutive ideas.

History—Predisposition was denied. The patient was pre-morbidly normal with intelligence above average. When he was hospitalized he had been working for the same firm for twenty years and was well thought of.

* It should be recalled that the French *délire* designates a condition stamped by paranoid ideas and does not mean a disturbance of consciousness.

He was dismissed very suddenly in consequence of a few anonymous letters to the effect that the patient and his wife were keeping a brothel in their apartment. He became depressed, contemplated killing his wife and himself and after a few weeks he became paranoid, had ideas that some people were plotting against him, maybe even his wife was involved in this base attempt to destroy him socially. In this state he was admitted. He soon showed signs of being hallucinated, could, for example, hear his employer sneak around the ward; he was also visually hallucinated (clear consciousness) but unfortunately the content of these hallucinations was not described. He was depressed, terribly worried and somewhat hypochondriacal, but not in a bizarre schizophrenic way. After a year he was discharged improved without the criminal case having been cleared up. The spinal fluid was completely normal and Wassermann negative here and in the blood. The wife made a pleasant and well-bred impression on the staff.

Follow-up—In lieu of a detailed interview about the painful events described above the patient submitted a written statement of his life history from which it was possible to rule out a malignant course to the psychosis. He claimed to have enjoyed complete mental health since the psychotic break-down. He and his wife had made a modest living running a typewriting bureau. There was some resentment expressed in his letter directed against the people who may have been responsible for his breakdown but the letter was certainly written by a sane person. An inquiry to the proper authorities concerning his case only resulted in the vaguest and most unsatisfactory response.

Conclusion—One feels tempted to give the patient (and his wife) the benefit of the doubt so far as the accusations are concerned. But, of course, it is impossible to make a decision. From a psychiatric point of view the significant fact is that a man in a situation that would be traumatic to most people reacted with an understandable depression, but also with more dubious psychopathology (hallucinations and delusions) which, however, turned out to be of a benign and transient nature. This case may lend clinical support to Strömgren's theory that paranoid reactions are the result of insults to the self-image.

Certain psychogenic reaction.

Case 151

A 35-year-old unmarried seamstress, admitted after having suffered from hallucinations and vague paranoid ideas for a long time.

History—There was no information about psychic deviations prior to the patient's illness. Aged 25 years she gave birth to a child while living with her friend, an unskilled worker. A few years later she broke with him and had a brief relationship with another man. When this came to an end she decided to avoid men and ever since then she had lived alone with her daughter making a modest living as a sack sewer. She gradually began to suffer from an asthenic-depressive syndrome with insomnia and hallucinations: saw the child's father and other persons known to her. They never did or said anything. There was considerable free-floating anxiety, tremor of the hands, palpitations and similar symptoms of an anxiety neurosis. She soon began to interpret her hallucinatory experiences in a paranoid way; she was quite convinced that she was being hypnotized by the former boy friend and his family. To her it seemed a striking coincidence that the hallucinations—in the daytime—often occurred immediately after somebody had been at her door on some errand. In this condition she was discharged.

Follow-up—Aged 51 years the patient presented herself as a small, thin, and asthenic lady. Psychically she made a completely normal impression. She said that the above-mentioned symptoms had stayed with her until her menopause, a few years before the follow-up. Once she had an ecstatic-religious experience: heard God talk to her and felt much calmer for a couple of days. During the first few years she learned to some extent to ignore the visual experiences, that is, she gave up the paranoid temptation to 'understand' them and simply accepted them for what they were: the productions of a somewhat sick mind and from then on lived quite peacefully with them because she had to. For a while she suffered from a phobia, was afraid she might jump out of the window.

Conclusion—This is the case of a polymorphous-neurotic woman who for some years suffered from psychopathology of a psychotic nature. The course of her illness demonstrates beyond doubt that for a while the ego was so impressed by the morbid experiences (visions, a voice) that it capitulated and accepted the primary pathological productions as being real and in a secondary elaboration (analogous to the secondary elaboration of the original manifest dream) attempted to account for the experience by paranoid misinterpretation, that is, the patient was psychotic. Later on the ego became wiser and more resolute and sided with the reality principle ('This is morbid, not real'), that is, the patient was again only neurotic. The case seems to favour the point of view expressed in Chapter 3: ego-strength is the incisive factor which decides whether a person becomes neurotic or psychotic and it is perfectly possible to vacillate from one condition to the other.

Definitely a psychogenic reaction.

Case 152

A 32-year-old woman, married to a greengrocer, admitted because of paranoid ideas of a religious nature.

History—At the follow-up a son stated that the patient's pre-morbid personality was without remarkable features. The last few months before the admission she became interested in religious matters and joined an extremist sect. Several days prior to the hospitalization she began to talk about being Christ himself, felt possessed by evil spirits and often appeared very anxious. During her stay in the hospital she was agitated, erethic, and talked incessantly about religious topics along the lines indicated above. The spinal fluid was normal and Wassermann negative here and in the blood. She was discharged improved and readmitted six times during the following fifteen years for symptoms similar to the described syndrome. On a few occasions she seemed clearly manic. In between she was quite natural. She died of a sepsis at 47 years of age.

Follow-up—In an interview with the son with whom the patient had lived during the last five years of her life (she was divorced then) it was revealed that during that period she seemed fairly normal to anybody who did not know her well. However, the son was of the opinion that she was still mentally ill. Apparently, she was somewhat autistic and also there were certain articles of food, particularly milk and butter, she would not touch (phobic fear or paranoid conviction ?). The religious interest had disappeared completely at the time of her death.

Conclusion—A definite diagnosis is not possible. Three possibilities, psychogenic reactions, manic-depressive psychosis, and schizophrenia suggest themselves, although the last two appear more likely than the first one.

Uncertain case.

Case 153

A 57-year-old widow, admitted because of tactile hallucinations and paranoid ideas.

History—There was no information concerning pre-morbid psychic deviation. The patient was sent to the hospital after having expressed unfounded fears of a lodger. She was convinced that this man blew 'ice-cold dust' on her, especially at night, with a bicycle pump. She was completely lucid and oriented and did not appear demented. She was discharged after a week without any change in her mental condition and died two years later of nephritis and a cardiac condition. It was not possible at the time of the follow-up to locate any relatives.

Conclusion—It is impossible to know why a diagnosis of 'psychogenic paranoid episode' was made.

Uncertain case.

Case 154

A 39-year-old woman, married to a skilled worker and admitted because of fears of poisoning.

History—The patient had always been inclined to short-lasting depressive reactions and she was somewhat erethic. She was admitted to the psychiatric ward because of attacks of panic following sexual intercourse, with ideas that her husband poisoned her in the act (misinterpretation of menopause-symptoms ?). He was described by her as being brutal, alcoholic, and adulterous. She was transferred to a state hospital where she was still a patient at the time of the follow-up. Wassermann was negative in the spinal fluid and in the blood.

Follow-up—Aged 58 years she was a very fat pyknic person, listless but not autistic. During her many years in hospital her condition had remained about the same as described, and although she had not seen her husband for years she still felt convinced that somehow their sexual intimacy had harmed her. Occasionally she heard voices.

Conclusion—A chronic mildly paranoid condition of psychogenic origin in a somewhat mentally retarded individual cannot be excluded, neither can a benign schizophrenia.

Uncertain case.

Case 155

A 30-year-old single truckdriver, admitted after having been depressed and paranoid for some time.

History—A paternal uncle died of general paresis. The patient had always been taciturn and self-contained. He rather suddenly revealed peculiar ideas: his pals annoyed and teased him in some not defined way, maybe they put 'something' in his beer to make him feel sick, there was 'something funny' about his boss, possibly of an illegal nature, and maybe he (the patient) was to marry the daughter of the boss. All this was accompanied by an anxious-asthenic syndrome. In the hospital he gave the impression of being a little mentally retarded, there was no clouding of consciousness and no signs of hallucinations. His ideas were as described and he seemed most of all to be in a 'delusional mood' (*Wahnstimmung*) without any systematized delusions. He was discharged unchanged after a few weeks.

Follow-up—The patient had been hospitalized for a few months a couple of years after the first admission. At the second hospital he was considered to be a paranoid schizophrenic with acoustic hallucinations (a voice told him to bury his clothes, which he did, and similar absurdities). Schizophrenic disturbances of the thought processes, for example, 'thought-withdrawal', were also described. In a personal interview in his poor home where he lived alone, eighteen years after he became ill, he was found a very difficult person to talk with. He was a primitive person, did not seem very bright and was extremely circumlocutory; he was also most suspicious. He did not reveal any signs or symptoms indicating an existing and active psychosis. He was working as an unskilled labourer.

Conclusion—From the patient's 'viscous' beating about the bush one might easily get the impression of an ixoid personality and infer that the psychotic period consisted of a series of atypical periodic epileptic equivalents. Some psychiatrists (for example, Kleist, 1926) think that such atypical epileptic psychoses are frequent, others (Mayer-Gross, Slater and Roth, 1960) are convinced that they are rare. One fact remains: much good ink has been wasted in discussing the problem. A paranoid schizophrenia also is a possibility as is a psychogenic psychosis.

Uncertain case.

Of the remaining 15 patients, 1 is considered a probable and 14 certain schizophrenic cases. All of these patients disclosed their mental pathology in a state of clear consciousness.

Case 156

A 55-year-old woman, married to an architect and admitted because of erotic paranoid ideas.

History—A half-sister was probably schizophrenic. The patient was an intelligent, industrious, and optimistic person with aesthetic talents; she was also erethic and histrionic. The marriage was an unhappy one; the husband was a spineless character who quickly spent the rather large capital left him by his parents. Almost a year before the admission the patient began to talk about her erotic interest in the movie-star Valentino. To begin with, her tender feelings were displaced to a daughter but she soon admitted that she herself firmly expected to marry the famous cinema idol and that he had moved to Copenhagen to make preparations for the wedding. In the hospital she was completely oriented, revealed genital sensations and admitted that she was going to give birth to her idol's child. After a while she disclosed persecutory ideas, the landlord was poisoning her with nicotine, snapshots were taken of her in the streets, etc. She did not improve during hospitalization.

Follow-up—The patient, over 70 years of age, refused to be interviewed and a son gave the asked for information. She was still very much alive, physically and psychically, and her paranoid convictions had remained unchanged over the years. She still expected to marry her dreamlover (although he had been dead for many years) and easily rationalized the delay by pointing out the time it would require to arrange for such an event. (One is reminded of Miss Havisham in *Great Expectations*.) She also still felt annoyed by many people. The police had to keep a separate file for her innumerable letters of complaint. For a while she talked about having voices in her knees, but other bizarre symptoms were never observed.

Conclusion—This is a case of Clérambault's syndrome, a *psychose passionelle*.

Probable schizophrenia.

The last 14 cases are certain schizophrenias: 5 of them *may* have been precipitated by environmental stress. Many authors have emphasized the trigger-effect of psychological circumstances. Mayer-Gross, Slater and Roth (1960) warn against overestimating such factors. The problem of psychic precipitation of schizophrenia will be touched upon in Chapter 11.

Case 157

A 23-year-old single unskilled worker, admitted for a paranoid prison psychosis.

History—The pre-morbid personality was unstable with a proclivity for working up stories. While in prison, serving a three-year term for theft (following several shorter imprisonments, also for theft), the patient developed a paranoid psychosis which at first was thought to be a psychogenic reaction in a psychopathic personality, but after about a year the schizophrenic nature of his illness could not be doubted. General paresis was ruled out on the basis of a thorough examination.

Follow-up—In St. Hans Hospital, the 41-year-old patient presented himself as a pyknic person and as friendly as one could expect an old schizophrenic and demented individual to be.

Conclusion—We have here a slowly progressing paranoid schizophrenia, possibly precipitated by the imprisonment.

Certain schizophrenia (psychically precipitated?).

Case 158

A 29-year-old woman, married to a labourer and admitted in a hallucinated and paranoid state following a 'psychic trauma'.

History—The mother and a sister were religious fanatics. Pre-morbidly the patient was intelligent, taciturn, industrious, perfectionistic, and sexually cold. A few months before the admission she was greatly shocked by a sudden and violent fire in her apartment. She was shaky for weeks afterwards and soon began to talk about seeing fires everywhere and about spiritualism, hypnosis, and voices in her head. She was hospitalized a few times over the next couple of years and it became obvious that she was suffering from a schizophrenia of predominantly paranoid type with very bizarre distortions of the body-image.

Follow-up—When visited in St. Hans Hospital the patient was a typically autistic schizophrenic with whom no contact could be established. An interview with her husband provided some of the above information.

Conclusion—This case lends support to the warning expressed in the introductory chapter, namely that an environmental factor which 'objectively' may seem to be an undeniable 'psychic trauma', nevertheless, cannot be taken at its face value. It is, of course, possible that the fire in this case touched a sore and catathymic spot and thereby triggered the schizophrenic potential.

Certain (psychically provoked?) schizophrenia.

Case 159

A 47-year-old single woman without occupation, admitted in a paranoid state.

History—The patient was mentally retarded and lived at home until her psychosis developed. Shortly before she was hospitalized her father was killed in an accident. She was admitted with visual and acoustic hallucinations and delusions about insects crawling into her nose, etc. A diagnosis of *psychogenic psychosis* was made. After a few months she was transferred to St. Hans Hospital and there developed the classic clinical picture of a paranoid schizophrenia in an intellectually retarded person. After nine years she died of an infection in a state of deep deterioration. No relatives of the patient could be located.

Conclusion—The same as in the preceding case.

Certain (psychically provoked?) schizophrenia.

Case 160

A 35-year-old widow of a wealthy businessman, admitted because of persecutory ideas.

History—A brother died of general paresis. The patient came from a good, upper-class milieu. She was a normal and psychically healthy young woman until shortly after the sudden deaths of her mother and her husband at almost the same time a few months prior to the admission. She was shocked, became depressed and then began talking vaguely about being annoyed by 'somebody' in some not defined sexual way. After a few months she appeared distinctly paranoid, was the victim of members of a 'sexual club' who did their utmost to pester her by informing her in different ways (voices?) about the white slave traffic. The patient, who considered herself to be the quintessence of feminine virtue, talked about this and a lot more in a language which made not only her family but also even hardened psychiatrists blush. Over the years she did not change much and could remain in one of the best wards.

Follow-up—In a personal interview the patient appeared natural aside from playing the role of a delicate and aristocratic lady who unfortunately had to live among coarse and vulgar women until she had gained the strength to return to life. A conversation with a brother added nothing substantially to what was already known.

Conclusion—The same as in the 2 preceding cases.
Certain schizophrenia (with psychic precipitation?).

Case 161

A 31-year-old woman married to a skilled worker and admitted because of delusional ideas.

History—A maternal uncle was psychotic (?). The patient was in every respect normal and natural prior to her illness. A few months after the death of her father she developed paranoid ideas: her husband had an affair with another woman, maybe she herself had killed her father. There were attacks of anxiety. In the hospital the patient talked about being hypnotized, somebody had put cocaine in the sugar, the eyes of her husband and children shone in a peculiar way, etc. She was discharged and readmitted a few times over the next few years, but finally had to be sent to St. Hans Hospital where she soon developed into a typical paranoid schizophrenic with grotesque delusions.

Follow-up—Contact could not be established with the autistic and hallucinated patient. An interview with the husband did not add any pertinent information.

Conclusion—The same as in the 3 preceding cases.
Certain schizophrenia, possibly precipitated by environmental stress.

The last 9 cases were schizophrenias with a spontaneous onset.

166

Case 162

A 35-year-old married skilled worker, admitted in a delusional state.

History—A brother psychotic (?). The pre-morbid psyche was normal except that the patient was an extremely sentimental fellow who always went for the sob-stuff. He was very active sexually. Following a little trouble with the police and a fine, he became distinctly paranoid, anxious, and aggressive. In the hospital the paranoid production flourished, he could stand being infected with syphilis because he was so strong, some people intended to kill him, etc. The diagnosis was simply *psychogenic psychosis*. In St. Hans Hospital he became more and more paranoid, talked a lot about sexual, including homosexual, matters and he rapidly developed a classic schizophrenic picture of the paranoid type. The crowning and ghoulish megalomanic idea was that he was 'the obsequies of Voltaire'. He died aged 41 years emaciated and without symptoms of any definite somatic disease. The spinal fluid was normal and Wassermann here and in the blood was negative.

Follow-up—It was not possible to locate any relatives, and the police could add nothing of interest to what was already known.

Conclusion—The initial diagnosis was not correct.

Certain schizophrenia.

Case 163

A 30-year-old male college student, admitted after having shown signs of being hallucinated and paranoid for some time.

History—A sister was a paranoid schizophrenic. The patient was natural except for a period with facial tics in puberty. He was very bright but his working capacity gradually diminished and he had probably been an ambulatory schizophrenic for a few years before admission. He demonstrated clear-cut ideas of reference, his professors behaved in a strange way towards him and he heard many threatening voices, mainly telling him about his lack of morality and about sexual and religious matters. In St. Hans Hospital he revealed fears of being poisoned, was the author of many wonderful inventions, went through a catatonic phase and ended up a very autistic and hallucinated person who could, however, be occupied part of the day with very simple tasks in the hospital.

Follow-up—The patient was a tall, asthenic, and dignified person with a long beard who resented any interference with his autistic circles.

Conclusion—From the very beginning the patient should have been considered a probable schizophrenic.

Certain schizophrenia.

Case 164

A 27-year-old unmarried mechanic, admitted after having caused trouble with his employer and having unveiled paranoid ideas.

History—Pre-morbidly the patient was obstinate, taciturn, honest, and straightforward. A brother was the head of the firm in which the patient worked. Without apparent provocation, the patient began to rave about

167

the brother's practice in illegal abortions. He could hear the landlord talk about these evil-doings and was admitted in this condition. He was transferred to St. Hans Hospital where his psychosis soon proved to be of an undeniably schizophrenic nature with neologisms, withdrawal of thought, hallucinations, and progressive deterioration.

Follow-up—Contact could not be established with the autistic patient. Attempts to locate any relatives were not successful.

Conclusion—Although it is easy to be wise after the event it has to be stated that from the very first the psychosis looked more like a beginning schizophrenia than a psychogenic reaction.

Certain schizophrenia.

Case 165

A 44-year-old single housekeeper, admitted because of hallucinations and delusions.

History—There was some familial psychiatric predisposition of which no details were available. The patient, who was not very bright, had always been gloomy, reticent, and inclined to asthenic-depressive reactions. She was the housekeeper to an old gentleman, a retired lawyer. In her menopause she began to have vague ideas concerning neighbours annoying her in different ways. Also, she heard peculiar noises in the house which proved that she was the victim of some nasty plot. In the state hospital she became increasingly hallucinated and paranoid and was in a short while dominated by delusions of a predominantly sexual and expansive nature: she was a countess and with child; the father of this child was only a baron. She was being poisoned by her tormentors. Periodically she soiled herself. She died, aged 49 years, of gastro-enteritis in a state of autism.

Conclusion—The same as in the previous case.

Certain schizophrenia.

Case 166

A 32-year-old woman, married to a skilled worker and admitted because of intense delusions of jealousy.

History—A brother was schizophrenic. The patient was, before her illness, a natural and out-going young woman. After several years of marriage she became, apparently without any basis in fact, increasingly jealous of her husband whose sexual appetite was great, whereas she was quite shy in that respect. During the eighteen years of hospitalization her delusions became more and more fantastic, she was clearly hallucinated and at times erethic and aggressive.

Follow-up—The patient was seen in a poor ward. She was completely autistic. In a personal interview with her mother and a daughter, who both appeared natural, nothing of particular interest could be added to what was already known. 'Psychic traumata', in particular, apart from the sexual incompatibility, could not be pointed out.

Conclusion—The same as in the 2 previous cases.

Certain schizophrenia.

168

Case 167

A 35-year-old single housekeeper, admitted after having made a nuisance of herself on account of her delusions.

History—There was some, not defined, psychiatric predisposition. The patient was pre-morbidly a noble-minded, industrious, and conscientious woman who had held several responsible posts as a housekeeper to some distinguished families. Without known psychic traumatization she began to think that some anonymous people were combining against her, her food was poisoned, she was possibly pregnant following an operation she had forgotten about (she smelled chloroform), and everything she ate was transformed by mysterious means to bananas. There were episodic states of depersonalization. Over the years in St. Hans Hospital she became more and more autistic, but she never deteriorated deeply.

Follow-up—In a personal interview it was impossible to bring the patient to talk about anything but the most trivial matters concerning her daily life. She was an efficient menial worker in the hospital. In a conversation with a cousin, the above described personality changes were corroborated.

Conclusion—The same as in the 3 previous cases.

Certain schizophrenia.

Case 168

A 24-year-old unmarried nurse, admitted because of depression and delusions.

History—The patient grew up in Russia. She was of noble descent, the daughter of a Russian doctor and a Danish mother. She did not, although in real danger, react particularly strongly to the events of the Russian revolution, the flight to Denmark and the much more humble way of life here. She was an extroverted, gay, and healthy girl, very bright and very spoiled. For some time before the admission she complained about fatigue and depression and became interested in spiritualism, hypnosis, and theosophy. All this occurred after an unhappy love affair. She also thought that the object of her tender feelings was dead. In the psychiatric ward she was distinctly psychotic, felt hypnotized (particularly when Wimmer spoke in French to her) and heard many voices talking to her in Russian and Danish about obscene topics. In St. Hans Hospital she disclosed definite schizophrenic features, in particular paranoid ideas, was a princess, already married, and she was convinced that she was living in a movie studio. She was transferred to the famous psychiatric village of Gheel in Belgium (where the family-care programme was initiated), and died there of pulmonary tuberculosis at the age of 40 years. A university professor in Copenhagen and an old girl friend, both of whom had known the patient well, supplied some of the above information.

Conclusion—The same as in the previous few cases.

Certain schizophrenia.

169

Case 169

A 41-year-old woman, married to a tailor, and admitted because of delusions.

History—The pre-morbid personality was without conspicuous traits. Shortly before the admission she became hallucinated (voices), restless, depressed, and anxious, the apartment was full of 'treacherous gases', she had been hypnotized, etc. In St. Hans Hospital any doubt about the schizophrenic nature of her illness soon vanished: she was being butchered, her body was full of snakes, and the like. She died of a cancer at the age of 55 years in a deeply demented state.

Conclusion—The same as in the last several cases.
Certain schizophrenia.

Case 170

A 43-year-old woman, married to an unskilled worker and admitted by the police because of aggressive actions directed against her husband motivated by paranoid ideas.

History—The patient had always been an erethic but good-natured individual. In her youth she was a woman of doubtful reputation, was married and soon divorced, but had been a good wife in her second marriage. She became sub-acutely paranoid with the ideas that many people, particularly policemen, 'were out to get her'. In the hospital she revealed auditory hallucinations and was sure that the police suspected her of murder. The malignant nature of her illness soon became apparent in St. Hans Hospital. She was being electrocuted, her body was full of electricity, she experienced genital sensations and heard many obscene voices. The spinal fluid and Wassermann's reaction here and in the blood were normal.

Follow-up—The patient was, at the age of 60 years, an autistic schizophrenic, only reacting in an aggressive oral way when she was addressed. A personal interview with the second husband furnished part of the information about her.

Conclusion—The same as in the last several cases.
Certain schizophrenia.

Part III

DISCUSSION AND CONCLUSIONS

INTRODUCTION

The three chapters in Part II form the clinical backbone of the present work. On the basis of the case material, certain conclusions will be formulated in Chapters 9–12 concerning the verified psychogenic psychoses. Some of these conclusions can, with a fair degree of exactness, be expressed quantitatively. Finally, Chapters 13 and 14 will deal with some general aspects of the basic issue of psychogenesis. A suggestion will be made to widen the Continental concept of psychogenesis into a universal concept, capable of embracing also reactions to stress, internal and external, in non-Western populations. An expansion of the concept along those lines is motivated by the increasing interest in and importance of comparative psychiatry and cross-cultural approaches to basic nosological problems. Also the 'choice of psychosis' and the problem of the relevance of a finalistic or teleological point of view with regard to psychogenic reactions will be discussed.

Concerning a quantitative formulation of some of the characteristics of the psychogenic psychoses three facts should be borne in mind. In the whole area of 'functional' psychoses we are dealing with rather vaguely delineated groups of clinical pictures and it is wise never to think of them as disease entities. The second fact concerns the suggestive power of numbers, percentages and statistical formulae. A small follow-up study like the present one does not lend itself well to any ambitious and subtle statistical analysis. The figures presented in Chapters 9–12 must, therefore, be looked upon as approximations to an ideal model of psychogenic psychosis. Finally, it must be remembered that all classifications of nature are arbitrary, artificial, and false. Friedell stressed that in his *Kulturgeschichte der Neuzeit* (1927–31). He also observed, however, that classifications are useful, necessary, and inevitable, motivated as they are by a passionate need in man to delineate and systematize his observations. But nature must obey necessity.

173

CHAPTER 9

TREATMENT OF THE MATERIAL AND A SURVEY OF THE RESULTS

Treatment of the Material

The assembled material was recorded and analysed by means of a punch card system. Once the laborious work of codifying the cards has been completed it permits a break-down into groups with reference to the various factors. This facilitated the tabular arrangement used here.

It is naturally difficult when dealing with a follow-up study of this sort to decide in advance what are the most significant variables. There should be as few as possible but, of course, nothing of importance should be excluded. Altogether, 130 factors were chosen for codification. They will not be listed in detail here; only the main groups, with some illustrative sub-groups added in parentheses, will be mentioned.

1. Sex.
2. Age (five-year sub-groups).
3. Hereditary predisposition (schizophrenia, other psychoses, psychopathy, neurosis, suicide, alcoholism, etc.).
4. The pre-psychotic personality ('normal', psychic deviation, sexuality, attempted suicide, intellectual capacity).
5. Socio-economic class and nationality (*cf.* Chapter 5).
6. The psychic trauma or the conflict (acute trauma or chronic traumatization, intra-psychic conflict, severity and type of trauma or conflict, trauma or conflict reflected in the content of the psychosis).
7. Temporary predispositions (alcohol, somatic illness, puberty, pregnancy, menopause).
8. Body type (pyknic, athletic, leptosomic respectively asthenic).
9. The duration of the reaction (short-lasting attack, longer lasting periods, chronic cases, recurrent and periodic psychoses).
10. The presenting syndrome (*cf.* Chapter 4).
11. The individual symptoms classified according to type and intensity (type of hallucination and delusion, intensity of depression and anxiety, etc.).

12. Psychomotor abnormalities (organized actions: fugues, criminal activity, etc., and disorganized motility: restlessness, loss of bowel control, etc.).
13. Contact with patient (good or poor).
14. Course of the disease and the result of the follow-up (cure, new attacks of psychogenic psychosis, schizophrenic development, death during the acute phase, died later, etc.).
15. Final diagnosis (supposition of psychogenic aetiology verified, psychically precipitated phases or processes, supposition of psychogenic aetiology invalidated, uncertain cases).

Survey of the Results

A natural starting point for discussion is Table 2, showing how the final diagnoses, that is the follow-up diagnoses, are distributed among the syndromes into which the original diagnoses of this material were grouped. There were three main groups, divided into eight sub-groups altogether.

Uncertain Diagnoses, Their Frequency and Causes

As there is a conspicuous number of uncertain diagnoses, they may be discussed first.

The uncertain diagnoses comprise 35 of the total 170 (20·6 per cent), a degree of error which is, however, more apparent than real, as a closer study of these 35 cases will show.

To begin with, it proved impossible to track 3 patients [*36, 99, and 133*]* and 4 had died in the initial stage of the psychoses [*45, 98, 110, and 132*]. Also 1 patient [*44*] had died at the very onset of the disease, but so detailed information had been brought to light at the follow-up that it has seemed justifiable to diagnose the psychosis as a manic phase in a manic-depressive disorder. Two patients refused to submit to re-examination [*35 and 124*]. Finally, there was 1 patient [*153*] whose disease had been unsatisfactorily described in the first place, and who died after the psychosis had lasted a couple of years. There are, thus, 10 cases where purely external factors account for the lack of reliable diagnoses. It is, therefore, in the remaining 25 cases where fairly detailed information had been forthcoming that the diagnostic procedure has failed. The original diagnostic inaccuracy of 20·6 per cent is hereby reduced to 14·7 per cent.

These 10 ineffectively examined cases will be ignored. *The total material will henceforth comprise 160 patients.*

* Italic figures in brackets refer to case histories.

TABLE 2

The Distribution of the Follow-up Diagnoses

Main groups	Sub-groups	Verified psychogenic psychoses (certain and probable diagnoses)			Other forms of the course of the disease (certain and probable diagnoses) — Schizophrenias			Manic-depressive psychoses			Epileptic psychoses (ixophrenic syndromes)			General paresis			Total number of non-psychogenic cases			Uncertain diagnoses			Sum total (the numbers in parentheses indicate the number of effectively examined cases where this differs from the total)		
		M	W	Ttl	M	W	Ttl	M	W	Ttl	M	W	Ttl	M	W	Ttl	M	W	Ttl	M	W	Ttl	M	W	Ttl
I { Emotional syndromes	Depressive syndromes	4	17	21	1	5	6	2	2	4				1		1	4	7	11		8	8	8	32 (30)	40 (38)
	Exaltations	2	1	3		3	3		1	1								4	4	1		1	3 (2)	5	8 (7)
	Total	6	18	24	1	8	9	2	3	5				1		1	4	11	15	1	8	9	11 (10)	37 (35)	48 (45)
II { Disturbances of consciousness	Dissociations of consciousness	11	13	24	1		1								1	1	1	1	2	1	2	3	13	16	29
	Deliria	4	10	14	4	5	9		3	3	2	1	3				6	9	15	3	7	10	13 (12)	26 (24)	39 (36)
	Hallucinoses		5	5		3	3											3	3		3	3		11 (10)	11 (10)
	Stupors	1	3	4	2	1	3										2	1	3		2	2	3	6 (4)	9 (7)
	Total	16	31	47	7	9	16		3	3	2	1	3		1	1	9	14	23	4	14	18	29 (28)	59 (54)	88 (82)
III { Paranoid syndromes	Without hallucinations	4	1	5	1	2	3										1	2	3	2	2	4	7	5	12
	With hallucinations	1	2	3	4	11	15										4	11	15	1	3	4	6	16 (15)	22 (21)
	Total	5	3	8	5	13	18										5	13	18	3	5	8	13	21 (20)	34 (33)
	Sum total	27	52	79	13	30	43	2	6	8	2	1	3	1	1	2	18	38	56	8	27	35	53 (51)	117 (109)	170 (160)

M = Men; W = Women; Ttl = Total.

TREATMENT OF THE MATERIAL AND RESULTS

This degree of uncertainty is fairly constant throughout all three main groups as can be seen from Table 3.

That 15 per cent of the diagnoses are deemed uncertain may, at first sight, seem surprising. They are follow-up diagnoses made at least fifteen years after the onset of the disease. A certain diagnosis might well have been expected in even a greater majority of the cases.

TABLE 3

Psychogenic, Non-Psychogenic, and Uncertain Cases Expressed as Percentages of the Total Number of Effectively Examined Cases*

Main groups	Sub-groups	Psycho-genic cases %	Non-psycho-genic cases %	Uncertain cases %
I { Emotional syndromes	Depressive syndromes	55·3	28·9	15·8
	Exaltations	42·9	57·1	0·0
	Total	53·3	33·3	12·5
II { Disturbances of consciousness	Dissociationsof consciousness	82·8	6·9	10·3
	Deliria	38·9	41·7	19·4
	Hallucinoses	50·0	30·0	20·0
	Stupors	57·1	42·9	0·0
	Total	57·3	28·0	14·6
III { Paranoid syndromes	Without hallu-cinations	41·7	25·0	33·3
	With hallu-cinations	14·3	71·4	14·2
	Total	24·2	54·5	21·2
	Sum total	49·4	35·0	15·6

* In Table 2 the material was divided according to sex. A closer examination of the table showed, however, that the verified psychogenic diagnoses, the faulty diagnoses, and the uncertain cases all appear with, practically speaking, equal frequency for men and women. In the final analysis it is therefore permissible to consider the two sexes together.

To begin with, this degree of uncertainty may be due to similar external factors as those which have already determined the exclusion of 10 cases from the material. A personal follow-up may have been

177

precluded by death or by the impossibility of contacting every surviving patient. These considerations proved, however, to be less important than might have been expected.

A long observation period, diagnostically favourable, especially in cases of slowly progressing schizophrenias, may have its drawbacks. Many patients will have died before a re-examination occurring after a lapse of fifteen to eighteen years. In this material 48 (30 per cent) of the total 160 patients had died. A supposition that the frequency of uncertain diagnoses is higher among the dead than among the living patients is natural, but it is not substantiated by analysis by the punch card system. The analysis showed that there were only 5 (or 10·6 per cent) uncertain diagnoses among the 47 patients who, surviving the acute onset of the disease, had died before the follow-up; whereas, of those that were still living at the time of the follow-up, 20 (or 17·9 per cent) of 112 diagnoses were uncertain, which is a slightly higher figure than those who had died. The fact that 26 of the 48 who had died were in mental hospitals at the time of their deaths may have contributed to a better diagnosis than was possible for the remaining 22. Information regarding this latter group could only be obtained from relatives, from the family doctor, and from similar sources. The difference between the two groups, however, is only small.

Table 1 (page 47) shows that a personal follow-up was achieved for 98 of the 112 surviving patients of the total 160. The remaining 14 patients had to be considered at second hand, but only 3 of them were classified as uncertain.

The large number of dead, together with the rather large number of living patients whom it was not possible to re-examine, cannot account for the many uncertain diagnoses, although the part played by external factors cannot reasonably be ignored. Psychiatric cases require far greater discretion and consideration, not only towards the patients themselves but also towards their relatives, than is necessary when re-examining surgical, medical, or other cases. Furthermore a single interview will not always produce a reliable impression of a psychiatric patient. It is not without satisfaction that it can be recorded that interviews, mostly harmonious, were had with 69 of the 84 patients living outside hospitals. It may be noted that in the psychogenic series (79 cases) a personal interview was obtained with 53 (19 men, 34 women).

The main reason why as many as 15 per cent of the diagnoses appear uncertain is to be sought in the nature and competency, or lack of competency, of psychiatric diagnostics at the present stage of development. One may well ask whether 15 per cent is really a high degree of uncertainty at all. It is from a desire to give the facts their due that a diagnosis is, at times, left open. Table 2 shows clearly that there are many clinical areas where the diagnoses in psychiatric reception departments is extremely uncertain. In mental hospitals the diagnoses are generally more correct owing to their being based on the protracted course of the disease, but even these favourable conditions do not prevent the appearance of a considerable number of uncertain diagnoses. Psychiatric diagnostics is also affected by the fact that many hospitals have their pet diagnoses. Many highly experienced hospital psychiatrists are of the opinion that their diagnoses of patients who have been under observation for five years or more are uncertain in 10–15 per cent of the cases. Personally, I am inclined to think that this is not a too pessimistic way of looking at the problem.

After these conjectures the diagnostic uncertainty in the present material does not seem unreasonable. The results seem to indicate that the conditions of observation have been about equal to those of chronic patients confined in mental hospitals.

Finally, it may be useful to account for the nature of the problems of differential diagnosis that attended the cases where the diagnoses were uncertain. In 15 cases [7, 37, 38, 39, 64, 93, 94, 95, 96, 116, 143, 144, 145, 154, and 155] the possibility of schizophrenic psychoses seemed strong. In 4 of these cases [37, 38, 39, and 116] there were instances of pre-schizophrenic episodes. In 3 the alternative to the psychogenic possibility was a manic-depressive psychosis [12, 74, and 152]. In 4 cases the choice lay between psychogenic reactions and organic psychoses of various forms [20, 75, 92, and 97]. Two cases [122, 123] were chronic hallucinoses and we simply know too little about their aetiology to be in a position to classify them.

Psychogenic and Non-Psychogenic Cases

An important point in Table 2 is the relationship between psychogenic and non-psychogenic cases. The formal and quantitative aspects will be discussed below. The nature of the mis-diagnoses will be debated in the subsequent paragraph.

It appears from the table that the original material contained a large number of faulty diagnoses. The follow-up proved that 56 (or 35 per cent) of the total 160 cases were, certain or probable, non-psychogenic diseases. 79 (or 49·4 per cent) of the total were certain, or almost certain, psychogenic psychoses.

In other words, the original diagnosis was allowed to stand in one-half only of the cases included in the material; in one-third it had to be revised, and in the remainder, about one-sixth, no diagnosis could be made for reasons already given.

Table 3 contains the corresponding figures for the three main groups and their sub-divisions. It shows that the wrong diagnoses are very unevenly distributed.

It appears that the relationship between the psychogenic and the non-psychogenic forms within the first two main groups is fairly equal. About 50 per cent of the original diagnoses in each group was corroborated and about 30 per cent of them was revised. These figures correspond very well with the results obtained for the material as a whole. The paranoid syndromes present a different picture entirely. One-fourth only of the diagnoses was correct, and more than one-half had to be revised. This is chiefly due to the hallucinatory forms.

The figures in the sub-division are most significant. They reveal clearly which psychotic syndromes are the trickiest to diagnose, and which are comparatively simple. The paranoid syndromes with hallucinations come out top: 15 of the 21 were wrong, only 3 were right. Paranoid syndromes without hallucinations were easier, but this was a very small group.

An analysis of the figures for the emotional forms show that there is no statistically significant difference between the psychogenic and the non-psychogenic groups, neither of the depressive syndromes nor of the elations.

The figures for disturbances of consciousness establish that there is no significant distinction between delirious and hallucinatory states. It is natural, therefore, to take these two groups together, particularly as they are, clinically and psychopathologically, closely related: hallucinatory states are turbid states with a mild impairment of consciousness and powerful hallucinations. In this way we arrive at 19 cases (or 41·3 per cent) of psychogenic forms and 18 cases (or 39·1 per cent) of non-psychogenic forms. These figures differ very clearly and very significantly from the corresponding figures for disturbances of consciousness (82·8 per cent and 6·9 per cent).

We have thus established that the dissociations of consciousness in the present material have predominantly been psychogenic diseases, whilst the deliria and the hallucinoses have often proved themselves to be non-psychogenic (predominantly schizophrenic) psychoses. As dissociations, above all, distinguish themselves from the other two forms by the fact that the latter are hallucinatory psychoses, it follows here, as for the paranoid syndromes also, that the importance hallucinations play in the problem of differential diagnosis and for prognostics must be stressed. This will be further discussed in Chapter 12.

The figures for the stupor states are on a plane with those for the deliria and hallucinoses.

TREATMENT OF THE MATERIAL AND RESULTS

The Nature of the Mis-Diagnoses

It appears conclusively from Table 2 that the problems of differentiation, where patients with presumed psychogenic psychoses are concerned, first and foremost resolve themselves into a question of psychogenic disease versus schizophrenia. In the three main groups, as also in all the sub-groups, the schizophrenias account for more than 50 per cent of the total number of mis-diagnoses. In four of the sub-groups it is the schizophrenias alone that represent the non-psychogenic diseases. Even amongst the depressive syndromes, where the cyclic depressions might have been expected to have predominated amongst the faulty diagnoses, we find 6 schizophrenias, 4 manic-depressive psychoses and 1 case of general paresis. Furthermore, atypical manic-depressive phases play a part of some importance in certain cases of turbid states of presumed psychogenic origin. The number of schizophrenic mis-diagnoses is, all told, more than five times the number of manic-depressives. Epileptic psychoses and ixophrenic syndromes do not, apparently, occupy a great place in the problem of differential diagnosis for psychogenic diseases. In this material they have only appeared amongst the delirious syndromes, and even there the number of schizophrenic mis-diagnosed cases was three times as great.

The schizophrenias account for 76·8 per cent of the total number of mis-diagnoses (43 out of 56 cases).

Two cases only of general paresis [40, 77] were originally considered to be psychogenic reactions (it will be recalled that the patient in Case 20 may also have been a paralytic), but it cannot be denied that two such wrong diagnoses mar the material more than, for instance, a many times greater number of schizophrenic mis-diagnoses.

The very important fact can thus be established that it is necessary in the 'acute' psychiatric practice to consider with the greatest care whether a seeming case of psychogenic psychosis is not in reality an initial stage of schizophrenia. Compared with the schizophrenias all other forms of psychosis play a subordinate part in the problem of differentiation.

This conclusion is, naturally, subject to a reservation, in that the present material has been chosen with a particular diagnostic bias represented by Wimmer. It is probable that both the total number of mis-diagnoses and also their distribution amongst the various non-psychogenic forms of disease vary from one department to another. Particularly would it seem that the number of schizophrenias diagnosed as psychogenic reactions may well be greater amongst Wimmer's patients than would be the case in psychiatric departments in Denmark today. Wimmer was, for a long period, greatly averse to the diagnosis of schizophrenia. That the schizophrenias in their initial stages mask

13   181

themselves as psychogenic states is due to the fact that the schizo-phrenic process engenders an excellent basis for the development of psychoplastic secondary symptoms. I refer to the conclusion to Case 106.

These facts lead us to conclude that the problems of differential diagnosis would be greatly lightened if some criteria could be set up enabling the psychogenic reactions to be distinguished from the acute schizophrenic syndromes with which they are so easily mistaken. In Chapter 12, some attempts on these lines, based on the present follow-ups, are discussed.

A short survey of the 43 cases of schizophrenias follows. The age distribution was very much the same in the schizophrenic and in the psychogenic materials. At the time of the follow-up 20 (7 men and 13 women), that is 46·5 per cent, of the 43 schizophrenic patients had died. At the same time only 17, that is 21·5 per cent, of the 79 patients with verified psychogenic reactions had died. Of the 23 surviving schizophrenics, 19 were confined to mental hospitals at the time of the follow-up, the remaining 4 were able to live outside.

CHAPTER 10

THE VERIFIED PSYCHOGENIC PSYCHOSES

I

After ascertaining which of the cases in the basic material, and how many their number, were true cases of psychogenic psychoses, we can assess fairly accurately the incidence of these diseases amongst first admissions to psychiatric reception departments. We can also calculate their characteristic sex and age distribution. On the basis of the admission figures, we can compute the disease expectancy and it is possible to formulate some impressions of the prognostics for this group of mental disorders.

Incidence and Sex Distribution

Table 4 shows the total number of first admissions to the Psychiatric Department of the Municipal Hospital in Copenhagen during the years 1924 and 1925.

TABLE 4

Total First Admissions to the Psychiatric Department of the Municipal Hospital in Copenhagen During the Years 1924 and 1925

Year	Discharged			Died during stay			Total		
	Men	Women	Total	Men	Women	Total	Men	Women	Total
1924	573	580	1,153	83	88	171	656	668	1,324
1925	518	561	1,079	75	99	174	593	660	1,253
Sum total	1,091	1,141	2,232	158	187	345	1,249	1,328	2,577

We may assume that the number of annual first admissions in the middle 1920's was about 1,300. The numbers of men and women were, practically speaking, the same.

It was seen in Table 2 that the number of verified psychogenic psychoses in the three-year period 1924–26 was 79 (27 men, 52 women).

183

The annual number of first admissions of psychogenic psychoses in the period under consideration was, therefore, 9 men and 17·3 women, 26·3 persons in all. *Verified and hospitalized psychogenic psychoses have thus amounted to 2·0 per cent of the total number of first admissions (1·4 per cent men, 2·6 per cent women).*

This suggests that hospitalized psychogenic psychoses are relatively infrequent forms of disease. At a psychiatric reception department with about 1,300 first admissions a year, corresponding to a little under 2,000 total admissions, there will be an average of 2 cases a month; of every 3 cases, 2, on an average, will be women.

In the middle 1920's the Psychiatric Department of the Municipal Hospital received only patients from Copenhagen itself. Psychiatric patients from the suburban areas were admitted to other psychiatric units. In 1925 the city had a population of 429,000 between the ages of 15 and 69 years. These are the age groups here under consideration. This means that first admissions of verified psychogenic psychoses represented a rate of 6·1 per 100,000 population (2·1 men, 4·0 women).

By way of comparison, let me refer to the corresponding figures for the non-psychotic psychogenic diseases. In 1924 the psychiatric unit of the Municipal Hospital received 88 first admissions of cases of psycho-neurosis and nervous conditions of supposedly psychogenic origin (38 men, 50 women).

The neuroses and nervous conditions thus amounted to 6·8 per cent of the total number of first admissions. Non-psychotic psychogenic reactions occurred about three times more frequently than psychotic.

The emotional syndromes in the psychotic material amounted to 30 per cent, disturbances of consciousness to 60 per cent, and the paranoid syndromes to 10 per cent of all psychogenic cases.

Non-Hospitalized Cases of Psychogenic Psychoses

It was stated above that hospitalized psychogenic psychoses are apparently relatively infrequent forms of disease. Non-hospitalized cases of psychogenic psychoses must now be considered. The figures for these cases depend very much on the nature of the different types of psychoses. It may, for instance, be safely assumed that many cases of psychogenic paranoid forms, episodic as well as chronic, are never hospitalized at all. Paranoid patients resent interference with their convictions and their private lives, besides which their behaviour often does not alarm their surroundings to the extent of instigating hospitalization. There must also be some, though perhaps not many, patients suffering from psychogenic depressions of psychotic degree who pull through at home or in convalescent homes or the like. Psychogenic disturbances of

184

consciousness, on the other hand, are usually so dramatic in their expression that it is unlikely that there are many of these cases who do not find their way into hospital; this applies, at all events, to such a hospital-minded people as the population of Copenhagen. It must, therefore, be borne in mind that the paranoid (and depressive?) syndromes, broadly speaking, probably occur with a relatively greater frequency than appears from the calculated percentages. An opinion of the absolute number of non-hospitalized cases of psychogenic psychoses cannot be substantiated; the figure can only be guessed at.

Age Distribution

A table, not reproduced here, offers an analysis of the age distribution of the material, that is to say, the age of the patients at the outbreak of their disease. It also affords a few more data on the sex distribution.

The following conclusions can be drawn: psychogenic psychoses are rare in puberty and adolescence (up to 20 years), and in the period from 20 to 24 years. But, from 25 years and onwards, they begin to appear with every increasing frequency until about 40 years, after which the curve begins to fall steeply. After 50 years, psychogenic psychoses are rare, and after 60 years they are extremely rare.

Table 11 in the *Statistical Year Book* for 1926 has the following figures: population in Copenhagen between the ages of 15 and 69 = 429,000 of which 24·2 per cent lay between 15–24 years, 36·1 per cent between 25–39 years, and 39·7 per cent between 40–69 years. It could be shown that no less than 57 per cent of all the psychogenic psychoses occurred within the 15 year period of 25–39 years, whilst the remaining 43 per cent was almost exactly divided between the other two periods. These figures make it clear that the incidence of psychogenic psychoses actually is the highest in the period from 25–39 years, they are seldom seen in the higher age groups and the figure for the period 15–24 years lies between the other two. Fremming (1947, 1951) is of the opinion that psychogenic psychoses are frequent up to the age of 60 years. It was characteristic for the period 25–39 years that there was a relatively greater number of cases amongst women. There was nothing to prove that this was due to the predominance of any particular psychogenic syndromes in this age group. In the other two groups men were relatively predominant.

A table (not reproduced) shows that the average age at the outbreak of the disease for emotional syndromes was 29 years, for disturbances of consciousness 34 years, and for paranoid syndromes 38 years. For the material as a whole the average age for the onset of the disease was 33 years and it was practically the same for men and women.

185

From what has been said here it does not follow that the vulnerability for psychic traumatization is greater amongst people from 25–39 years than amongst younger and older persons. It would rather seem that it is the risk of being exposed to psychological stress that is more frequent in this group. It is especially women who account for the greater number of cases in the period 25–39 years. It is reasonable to suppose that marital and family conflicts operating during the prime of life are mainly responsible for the particular age distribution in women.

The tendency for any special age to favour psychogenic reactions has commanded little attention in the literature; the few remarks that do appear are usually couched in very general terms. Birnhaum (1918) and Lange (1928) have only broad statements on the susceptibility of the young to such reactions and to its diminishment with increasing age. Wimmer (1916) makes no mention at all of the importance of the age factor. Goldfarb (1959) has called attention to psychiatric difficulties of the middle years:

> ... when many a person sees, or thinks he sees, his true trajectory in life and views it with disappointment, horror, or fright, without being able significantly to alter his course.

In this context it may be of interest to quote some remarks by Malzberg (1940) on the effect of age in mental illness in general:

> The probability of a mental disorder is a direct function of age. The probability is low in childhood, rises rapidly in youth and maturity, grows at a more moderate rate during the involution period and then advances rapidly to a maximum in old age. In this growth the aging process is implicated both directly and indirectly.

Much research is needed before we can attempt to answer the many complicated questions concerning psychogenesis and age.

Psychogenic Psychoses in Children

Psychogenic psychoses certainly occur in children.

Hospitalism and anaclitic depression, described by Spitz in 1945 and 1946, are the outstanding examples. These conditions are, *par excellence*, psychogenic because they are caused by a traumatic event in the true sense of the word, namely, the loss of a real object in the outside world. Whether autistic and symbiotic child psychoses in which the mother-child unit is deficient can be considered psychogenic is another matter. At the present time it is probably not possible to express any opinion about the incidence of psychogenic psychoses in childhood. In my material there was not a single case of childhood psychosis.

186

Disease Expectancy

By definition, the disease expectancy of a person is the risk of becoming ill during one's lifetime, if one lives long enough to pass the period of risk (Strömgren, 1950). The period of risk is the time during which the disease may develop. Several methods for obtaining expectancy rates in psychiatric research have been developed. Among them are Weinberg's so-called *abgekürztes Verfahren* (see Strömgren, 1935) and Strömgren's (1935, 1938, 1950) method.*

To use Weinberg's method at all it is necessary that the ages at the onset of the disease are evenly distributed about an axis traced through the centre point of the age danger zone. Strömgren's method, on the other hand, enables the calculation of the disease expectancy to be made independently of the appearance of the curve for the years of onset, a fact that is, naturally, of the utmost importance for the validity of the result in cases of uneven distributions.

In the present study Strömgren's method has been used in calculating the disease expectancy for psychogenic psychoses. The danger zone is confined to the period 15–69 years. The technical details will not be given here.

The conclusion is that the disease expectancy in the general population of Copenhagen calculated on the basis of first admissions is c. 0·3 per cent (men c. 0·2 per cent, women c. 0·4 per cent).

The figure can only be approximate. The material is too small to exclude the influence of chance oscillations.

In comparison it may be remembered that the general expectancy for schizophrenias is c. 1 per cent, for manic-depressive psychoses c. 1 per cent, and for epilepsy c. 0·3 per cent. The rate for schizophrenia can be considered universally valid whilst the rate for manic-depressive psychosis is higher than the figures quoted in other countries. This is partly because the incidence of manic-depressive illness is probably higher in many countries than expressed in the published figures for the disease expectancy, partly because manic-depressive psychoses actually occur with greater frequency in Denmark as compared with many other countries (Strömgren, 1962).

Course and Prognosis

An analysis of the material showed that about 70 per cent of cases of psychogenic psychoses recovered without psychotic relapse, whilst about 20 per cent had, sooner or later, one or more psychotic relapses of psychogenic origin; and a small number, about 5 per cent, were left

* See also Welner and Strömgren (1958).

187

with residual symptoms of varying degrees of severity; lastly, about 5 per cent developed a chronic psychogenic psychosis.

The prognosis for the psychogenic psychoses generally is, therefore, favourable, and the opinion offered by Wimmer (1916) that 'these mental diseases have a predominant tendency towards recovery' is hereby substantiated.

Cure Without Relapse

By 'cure' is meant the return to the pre-morbid personality with its more or less pronounced lability of affect, its peculiarities of temperament, and its psychoneurotic and psychosomatic symptoms. The seriousness of these anomalies, with their, on occasion, incapacitating effect, will have been apparent from the follow-ups. Some of the cured patients had, moreover, later in life, psychogenic episodes or periods that were not of psychotic degree.

Cure With Relapse

Reference to the relevant case histories shows that the relapses are largely homologous (14 of 16 cases) and, further, that the situations that provoked them were generally of a nature similar to those that had provoked the initial attack. The 14 psychoses with homologous relapses comprise 1 depression [1], 9 dissociations of consciousness [50, 54, 57, 58, 59, 61, 67, 70, and 71], 3 deliria [79, 80, and 82] and the only case of stupor that relapsed at all [129]. Only 2 patients (depressions) had relapses of a more heterologous character [3 and 9]. The patient in Case 3 was treated, in 1924, for asthenic depression. About ten years later a doubtless psychogenic paranoid episode was grafted on to the still existing asthenic-depressive syndrome. The patient in Case 9 was, in 1924, suffering from severe psychogenic depression, episodically with stuporous reactions. Subsequently, however, she had several episodes of pure and pronounced stuporous type occurring in a period of a couple of years.

The homologous relapses are often photographically true reproductions of the original attacks, especially in the dissociation group. Sometimes certain features of the original pictures may be missing and others may be added, but the type of the reaction is, none the less, unmistakenly preserved.

In this material there have, as a rule, only been single relapses, but a series of relapses, spread over a number of years, may also occur.

Chronic Psychogenic Psychoses and Cases With Severe Chronic Residual Symptoms

In these two groups we find patients in whom the acute disease is not cured but continues in a chronic psychogenic psychosis, or patients in whom, after the cessation of the acute phase of the disease, there remains more or less pronounced psychopathological traits that were not found before the onset. It is obvious that all manner of transitional forms between these two types will be found in practice. In theory, however, they can be distinguished if one desires to make a distinction: in the former the flourishing psychotic developments are preserved by psychogenic factors, in the latter the spent psychoses leave a varying number of constant, residual symptoms in their wake.

The existence of chronic psychogenic psychoses, in the meaning the expression is given here, has often been queried. But a reference to, for instance, Kretschmer's paranoid patients, speaks for the presence of such chronic, psychogenic forms of disease. The psychosis remains chronic in as much as it can persist as a living, growing component of the personality for years on end. Many individuals who are not considered 'sick' by the layman live in paranoid 'pseudo-communities' (Cameron, 1943, 1959).

Only 1 of the 4 cases regarded as chronic psychogenic psychoses can be considered to have been verified with full certainty [137]. The patient in Case 121 might equally well have been included amongst the relapsing forms. Information concerning the patients in Cases 91 and 138 was too slight to allow their inclusion amongst the chronic psychogenic forms otherwise than as a probability.

The patients in Cases 140, 149, and 150 have been classified as 'cured, with chronic residual symptoms'.

It may be concluded that the chronic psychogenic psychoses are rare forms of disease. They probably account for only a very small percentage of all psychogenic mental disorders.

Prognosis for the Different Psychogenic Syndromes

Relapses occur for the most part amongst the disturbances of consciousness, one-third of which had relapses. The dissociations had a particularly marked tendency to relapse. The figures for the depressions are small, but it is probable that relapses in this group are frequent also. The psychogenic paranoid syndromes, however, do not seem to have a tendency to recur. They alone, on the other hand, represent the imperfectly cured and the chronic forms.

Duration of the Disease

An assessment of the prognostics for the psychogenic psychoses must also include an investigation into the duration of the disease.

Attacks (few hours–one week), short phases (one week–three months) and longer phases (over three months) are represented by practically the same frequency (30, 24, and 25 cases), but the distribution of the various syndromes within these groups varies considerably. The depressions nearly always last at least one month, and are often prolonged to three months or more. The paranoid syndromes, likewise, are diseases with a protracted course, often stretching over months. It must, however, be remembered that reactive paranoid episodes of brief duration are not unusual; on occasion such syndromes are grafted on to longer lasting psychogenic depressions.

The disturbances of consciousness present an entirely different picture. Recoveries from these psychoses are made within the first week of the onset of the disease in about 60 per cent of the cases. A group of dissociations (19 cases in which there were fugues in 13) and stupor states account for the high percentage amongst these brief psychoses. Deliria and hallucinoses tend, on the other hand, to follow a more protracted course. In 5 cases the disease even continued beyond the three months' limit.

Wimmer (1916) drew attention to the extreme variability of the duration (from minutes to months) of the disturbances of consciousness, a fact that was also noted by Raecke (1901a). There is some uncertainty about the duration of the psychogenic stupor reactions. Raecke (1901b) pointed out, in his brilliant description of hysterical stupor states in prisoners, that the course often extended over weeks and months despite the fact that the patient was removed to hospital immediately after the onset of the disease. Stern (1913) described a case (Case 23 in his material) of psychogenic stupor of a year and a half's duration, but stated at the same time that such protracted psychogenic reactions must be considered unusual in the extreme. He was of the opinion that stupor forms of over a few days' duration were atypical, and a schizophrenic form of a stupor might then be present, especially where there was marked akinesis. Lückerath (1911) has described a prison stupor lasting nearly three years followed by complete cure after release.

The statements of all these authors must be taken with the reservation that either none of the patients had been re-examined or the observation time had been so brief, some years at most, that the possibility of a later malignant course of the disease cannot be excluded.

The Social Prognosis

The question of the patients' possibilities for social adjustment after recovery, respectively the cessation of the acute phase, is of particular importance in mental diseases, because these do not, as a rule, end fatally, but frequently leave the patient more or less socially incapacitated. It is obvious that where psychogenic psychoses are concerned

190

it is not, in the first place, the disease and its sequelae that are responsible for the more or less favourable social prognosis, but rather the inherent defects of the psychogenic personality.

The follow-ups of this material offer a fairly reliable indication of the social prognosis for psychogenic psychoses. A table (not reproduced) revealed that there was no significant difference in the figures for men and women, and also that there was no reason to differentiate between the various syndromes within the three main groups: 48 patients (60·8 per cent) made irreproachable social readjustments, 18 (22·8 per cent) fairly good social readjustments, while 13 (16·5 per cent) were socially incapacitated to such a degree that they were obliged to resort to financial and other aid from relations or from the community. There is a tendency for the patients with the poorest prognoses to be assembled amongst the disturbances of consciousness and the paranoid reactions.

The social prognosis for the psychogenic psychoses can hereafter be said to be favourable on the whole.

Mortality Rate

Mortality problems in psychiatry have been the subject of many studies. Malzberg (1934), Essen-Möller (1935), and Alström (1942) all found death rates amongst the important forms of psychoses considerably above the general average. Essen-Möller found, for instance, that the mortality for manic-depressives is about 1·5, for schizophrenics about 3, and for epileptics about 8 times as high as for the population as a whole.

It is of some interest to mention that Malzberg found in his group of patients with neuroses that the death rate was about 5 times that of the general population. Also, Alström established significantly higher death rates for patients with psychogenic diseases.

As already mentioned in Chapter 9, 5 of the patients included in the *basic* material of 170, died during the acute initial phase [*44, 45, 98, 110, and 132*]. The patient in Case 44 had probably been suffering from a manic-depressive psychosis. It is safe to say that of the patients in Cases 45, 98, and 110, there were only slight grounds for assuming that they had been suffering from a psychogenic disease. It is not possible to give any real opinion of the aetiology of the last case [*132*]. All the other patients survived the acute period of the disease.

Apparently, then, the lethality (by which is meant death during the disease itself) of the psychogenic psychoses is slight. A considerably higher figure than this material would seem to indicate must, however, be reckoned with in reality. To begin with, some patients suffering from severe psychogenic depression commit suicide before they are admitted

191

to a psychiatric department. This may also happen, though it is probably more seldom, to persons in whom psychogenic disturbances of consciousness and paranoid reactions develop. Patients with cloudy and delirious states are liable to meet with accidents, or to contract diseases with a possible fatal course. In many such cases the proper diagnosis will never have been made and the lethality of psychogenic psychoses is, therefore, a question that is very difficult to answer.

Concerning the post-psychotic period it has been established that 17 (6 men, 11 women) of the verified 79 psychogenic psychoses had died at some point prior to the follow-up. The cause of death in three cases was suicide [54, 56, and 79]. The remaining 14 patients had all died a natural death from causes usual in higher age groups. A statistical analysis did not substantiate the statement that the mortality rate amongst persons who have suffered from psychogenic psychoses is in significant excess of that of the population as a whole. If Malzberg's and Alström's results, referred to above, are correct, one might assume that constitutional factors are responsible for the higher death rates among persons who have suffered from psychogenic disorders. As yet, however, we know nothing certain of the existence of any correlation between types of constitution and tendencies to psychogenic reactions. In this connection it may be mentioned that leptosomic and asthenic individuals have occurred in this material with great frequency. It is a natural assumption that the pyknic-syntonic person is in possession of greater adaptive powers than is the case with the schizoid person. Let me have men about me that are fat.

CHAPTER 11

THE VERIFIED PSYCHOGENIC PSYCHOSES

II

In this chapter the following topics will be discussed: hereditary factors, pre-morbid personality, predisposing factors, the nature of the psychic trauma in the two sexes, and the psychic precipitation of schizophrenia.

Hereditary Factors

It was not possible in this investigation to obtain detailed information of familial taints.

In only 2 cases could no information be got at all, whilst in 33 patients familial predisposition for mental disease was denied. This, of course, must be taken with a grain of salt.

In 29 of the 44 cases with familial predisposition, that is nearly 75 per cent of the cases, the disposition could be tabulated under such headings as: psychopathy, psychogenic reactions, neuroses, and the like. In most cases there was a history of 'erethic', 'difficult', and 'hysterical', sometimes of sociopathic blood relatives. There were many cases of conversion symptoms, and occasional histories of genuine psychogenic psychoses often taking the form of brief cloudy states occurring in some close relation. A background of feeble-mindedness did not appear to be significant. Information of this kind was obtained in 4 cases only [2, 6, 16, and 90].

In 6 cases there was a familial schizophrenic taint, in 3 of these cases the psychoses in question could be verified as certain schizophrenias. In the other 3 it was not quite certain whether they had really been cases of schizophrenic psychoses or not. There were family histories of manic-depressive psychoses in 3 of the index cases, senile or atherosclerotic psychoses in 2, epilepsy in 1 and, lastly, undefinable psychoses in 3. In several cases, naturally, there were assorted familial taints. In these cases the most malignant disposition was considered the decisive.

There was no remarkable distribution of the various forms of familial disposition amongst the different groups into which this material has been divided, nor were there any conspicuous differences of sex.

The chief result to be deduced from the above is that in something less than one-half of the total number of cases hereditary factors for mental disease were denied by the patient and his relatives, in 20 per cent of the cases there were familial schizophrenic, manic-depressive, or other psychotic taints, and in 30 per cent of the cases a familial predisposition for 'personality disorders' was demonstrated.

The Pre-morbid Personality

There can be no doubt that psychogenic reactions chiefly strike persons whose pre-morbid personality is, in some way, psychologically deviating. As is the case for epileptic seizures, so too for the psychogenic disorders, the constitutional and acquired dispositions are inversely proportional to the environmental stress factor. Reference has already been made (page 36) to Freud's concept of complementary series. At the one extreme are found persons who are in so high a degree predisposed to psychogenic reactions that even under favourable conditions they oscillate, episodically or for longer periods, in and out of psychic states that must be called pathological. At the other extreme we find individuals whose personality is healthy and robust and who only react psychopathologically in situations with extraordinary stress; Case 78 provides an apt illustration. Presumably every single person has his breaking point beyond which he will respond psychopathologically. Overindividual reactions in persons exposed to stress, isolation, and sensory deprivation have been discussed in Chapter 1 (pages 15–17).

The personality disorders predisposing to psychogenic psychoses are probably constitutional in most cases, although environmental factors of a psychological (psychoneuroses) and an organic nature play a role.

The basis for psychopathy is still uncertain. Newkirk's (1957) findings indicate that hereditary factors probably are important. The results of electroencephalographic studies of psychopaths are contradictory. Some analytically oriented contributions (Alexander, 1930; Karpman, 1948) stress the importance of infantile experience and unconscious neurotic conflict for the development of the psychopathic personality.

That certain racial and ethnic groups may be particularly predisposed to psychogenic reactions is possible. Birnbaum (1918, 1928b), among others, has attributed an excessive amount of mental disorders to Jews. Malzberg (1959) has refuted this claim so far as psychoses are concerned. The very low incidence of alcoholic psychoses among Jews is well known. The Irish, on the other hand, have very high rates of alcoholic psychoses. We may assume that the high rates of mental disease for American Negroes is mainly due to environmental rather than to racial factors.

In the present material information concerning the pre-morbid personality was available in 77 cases. Of these, 26 (12 men, 14 women) had to be characterized as being without psychological deviations; 51 were designated 'deviating'. They fell into the following groups: 20 (6 men, 14 women) were considered psychopaths, 19 (6 men, 13 women) had both psychopathic and neurotic traits. The boundaries between these two groups must, naturally, be very vague. Finally, there were 12 cases (1 man, 11 women) that were also designated 'deviating' in which it was not possible to decide whether the psychopathological traits were primarily of constitutional origin, or whether they were acquired.

The psychopathic form that is most frequently represented is the explosive. To this form belong persons who are moody, often erethic, with a tendency to sudden paroxysms of hysterical symptoms, to wandering about in a cloudy state, and to other primitive reactions. This form has a connection with the self-assertive and the emotionally unstable psychopathic types, also frequently occurring in the present material. Depressive and asthenic psychopaths were also represented, but other types of psychopathy as described by Schneider (1942) occurred only exceptionally.

Suicide at some time prior to the psychotic episode had been attempted in 3 cases [*10, 56, and 59*]. A more or less criminal past was seen in 4 patients [*51, 58, 70, and 71*] and a history of alcoholism was forthcoming in 2 cases [*6 and 130*]. In 30 cases there was information of the sexuality of the patients and only 6 men and 7 women seemed to have achieved full genital maturity.

Unfortunately, it was not possible to cast any light on the important question of the frequency with which the different types of temperament, the syntonic, the schizoid, and the ixothymic (Kretschmer, Strömgren) appear amongst persons with psychogenic psychoses.

Body Type

With regard to the body types, the pyknic, the leptosomic or asthenic, the athletic, and the dysplastic, the investigation has produced some interesting results. Of the 53 index cases (19 men, 34 women) with whom I personally had interviews, I am inclined to characterize 30 as pyknic, leptosomic, or athletic, whilst the remaining 23 were so uncharacteristic that they could not be classified. The 30 markedly characteristic types consisted of 9 pyknics (all women), 19 leptosomics or asthenics (9 men, 10 women), and 2 athletics (both men). As the pyknic and the leptosomic types appear amongst the population of Denmark with a fairly equal frequency, about 20 per cent (Strömgren, 1942), while the athletic type is less frequent, it is remarkable to find twice as many leptosomic as pyknic persons in the material. Not least remarkable was it to discover that there was not one single man of pronounced pyknic type in the whole material. The small numbers make it necessary to accept these facts with reservation, but they do seem to lend support to the assumption expressed in the final remarks of Chapter 10.

Intelligence

Of the 66 cases in which it was possible to form some ideas of the intelligence level, only 4 [*24, 54, 60, and 70*] appeared to be intellectually retarded. This fact is in accordance with the finding that intellectual inferiority was demonstrated in the families of 4 cases only (page 193). Neustadt (1928) and Goldkuhl (1938) have attached little significance to mental deficiency as a predisposing factor for psychogenic psychoses.

Predisposing Factors

A psychogenic reaction is determined by the genic predisposition of the individual and the psychic stress factor. To these must be added a third group of determinants, namely, the widely divergent factors classed by Birnbaum (1923) as predisposing elements* (*cf*. page 22) and by Wimmer (1916) termed *concausae*.

Factors predisposing the appearance of psychogenic reactions are found, firstly, in a long list of purely exogenous noxae such as head injuries, infections, toxic states, severe physical exertion, prolonged lack of sleep, acute and chronic alcoholic conditions; secondly, in various endogenous processes, partly normal, such as puberty, menopause, etc., and partly pathological, such as hyperthyroidism. Finally, purely psychogenic factors can be predisposing: a politician in high office and deeply worried about the international situation will be particularly vulnerable to domestic stress.

In this investigation a distinction has been made between current predispositions, and factors occurring in the earlier history, of possible predisposing effect.

Predisposing factors were found in no fewer than 44 cases (17 men, 27 women). In 35 cases no such information was related. In 25 cases (6 men, 19 women) current predisposing agents were found, and in 14 cases (7 men, 7 women) there were corresponding elements in the earlier history. In 5 cases (4 men, 1 woman) both current and more remote factors were found.

---

* 'Genic predisposition' and 'predisposing elements' thus must be sharply differentiated.

The exogenous predisposing factors occurred in the following order of frequency: head injuries, 11 cases; infections, 10 cases; puberty and pregnancy, 3 cases; menopause, 8 cases; overwork, 8 cases; acute alcoholic conditions, 4 cases; other non-infectious somatic diseases named as possible predisposing factors, 4 cases.

The Nature of the Psychic Trauma in the Two Sexes

An analysis of the present material demonstrates that it is characteristic for the two sexes to react to different types of traumata.

The psychic traumata have been divided into the following seven categories: disasters and the like (7); sexual problems (23); domestic problems (17); bereavements and illnesses of near and dear (12); social conflicts (8); legal traumata (imprisonment, etc.) (2); other problems (religious, etc.) (8). (The figures in parentheses indicate the number of cases in each category).

These figures confirm Wimmer's (1916) impression that problems of a sexual nature play a conspicuous part amongst the environmental factors. Wimmer states further that sexual and domestic conflicts have a particular significance for women, while social conflicts (loss of job, lack of promotion, financial worries, and the like) primarily affect men.

The following hypothesis permits a more systematic examination of these factors as found in the present investigation: let it be supposed that three of the traumata as grouped in the present material (disasters, social, and legal problems) are of great pathogenic importance for men, while three others (sexual and domestic problems and those arising from bereavements and the illnesses of relatives) are of corresponding importance for women. It then appears that 24 men and 45 women have been affected by traumata belonging to these six categories. The hypothetically 'masculine' traumata occurred in 12 men and 5 women, the hypothetically 'feminine' in 12 men and 40 women. The incidence of 'masculine' factors in the two sexes is 12/24 (men) and 5/45 (women). The difference in frequency is thus great and it could be statistically proved that it is significant. As the qualities 'masculine' and 'feminine' factors are alternatives, the difference in frequency in the appearance of the 'feminine' ones in the two sexes is also statistically valid.

In this way it could be proved that psychogenic psychoses in women are commonly caused by sexual and domestic problems, by bereavements and by the illnesses of those near and dear; in men, on the other hand, psychogenic psychoses are commonly caused by disasters and by social and legal problems.

It must not be assumed that the vulnerability of the two sexes is entirely different with respect to these two groups of traumata. The difference is also in part due to the different degree with which the two sexes are exposed to the different sorts of traumatic situations. There is no reason to suppose that women are more resistant than men to the effects of disasters and imprisonment, but they are more rarely exposed to these experiences.

Psychic Precipitation of Schizophrenia

The importance to be attributed to environmental factors as precipitating agents of schizophrenia may conveniently be discussed here.

The whole problem of the ability of the exogenous, somatic and psychic, noxae to precipitate endogenous psychotic phases and processes is one of the most intricate in psychiatry. Theoretically and conceptually the problem has been comprehensively discussed by many German authorities. Amongst many others can be mentioned Jaspers (1913, 1923), Schneider (1919a) and, particularly, Bostroem (1929, 1931, 1933), but the root of the matter, which is the actual incidence of precipitated endogenous psychoses, remains a puzzle. Mayer-Gross (1932) in a survey in Bumke's manual, has discussed the schizophrenic aspects. He, like the majority of German psychiatrists, is inclined to attach little importance to precipitating factors, and to psychic precipitating factors least of all. His opinion is primarily based on a clinical analysis by Krauss (not published), from which it appeared that, of all the cases of schizophrenia in women treated at the Heidelberg clinic over a period of thirty years, only 28 cases might possibly have been psychically precipitated. Mayer-Gross' report of Krauss' analyses is not sufficiently documented to substantiate the theory of a predominantly spontaneous origin of the schizophrenias, but Finckh (1927), in a small clinical analysis, supports similar views, and Bratz (1928), likewise, doubts the significance of psychic precipitation and emphasizes that the problem can probably only be solved by a study of identical twins.

Twin Studies

Regarding twin studies I shall, for good reasons, limit myself to quoting the foremost authority on the subject. Kallmann (1959) writes:

> The hypothesis that the recurrence of schizophrenia follows selective patterns of distribution has been substantiated by many independent studies. In families with a clear case of schizophrenia, the morbidity risk of the given kinship is not only much higher than that of random population samples but also varies within the family itself. The observed trend is consistently toward an increased frequency of schizophrenia rather than any other type of disorder, with the magnitude of the

increase proportional to the degree of consanguinity to the schizo-phrenic relative. For instance, full sibs (11·5 to 14·3 per cent) have a higher expectancy than half-sibs (7·1 per cent), and half-sibs a higher risk than step-sibs (1·8 per cent). The highest schizophrenia rates are found in the children of two schizophrenic parents (68·1 per cent) and in the one-egg co-twins of an unselected series of schizophrenics.

The difference in concordance between two-egg (14·7 per cent) and one-egg (85·8 per cent) pairs of twins approximates a ratio of 1 to 6, *whether the twins lived together or apart.** This difference is so significant that it cannot be explained on non-genetic grounds alone.

War Experiences and Precipitation

War experiences are among the environmental factors of which we can speak with some degree of certainty. There seems to be no doubt that their effect with regard to precipitation of schizophrenias, and probably with other psychoses also, is only slight (Birnbaum, 1915–19; Sonnenberg, 1922; Mayer-Gross, 1932; Lewis, 1942 Jung, 1961). This problem has already been touched upon in Chapter 2 and in Chapter 1 it was pointed out that persons exposed to the extreme stress of the German concentration camps only rarely developed psychotic conditions. Why should we expect them to? With all due regard to the importance of constitutional factors it is perfectly acceptable to consider the pre-schizophrenic individual a 'stormy personality' (Arieti, 1955) in whom intense anxieties originating in destructive early interpersonal relation-ships constantly threaten to bring about a state of overt disequilibrium. If psychic factors do possess the ability to precipitate a latent schizo-phrenic anlage, it is reasonable to assume them to be of an order very different from the massive, conspicuous, and overindividual experiences of wars and disasters. The psychological structure of schizophrenic psychoses bears such a marked resemblance to the psychoneuroses that it is natural to expect that the ability to precipitate a latent anlage must primarily be found in situations of a strictly individual nature affecting the patient catathymically.

Psychotherapy and Precipitation

Psychotherapeutic experiences seem to indicate that schizophrenias can, on occasion, be precipitated by this particular type of interpersonal relationship. The transference can prove destructive for a weak ego whose boundaries are so defective that material from reality and from the id easily becomes mixed with the ego. Already Stekel (for ex-ample, 1930 and 1938) warned against the energetic analysis of cases (particularly obsessive-compulsive) where schizophrenic mechanisms are suspected. Kretschmer (1929) is of the same opinion with regard

---

* Italics mine (P.M.F.)

to the quite common 'bethrotal' catatonias and masturbation catatonias. Arieti (1959b) mentions that we occasionally encounter patients whose anxieties are so intense that any attempt at psychotherapy enhances their psychological disintegration. My own experience as an orthodox analyst has taught me that it is sometimes, but not often, necessary to adopt an unorthodox technique in order not to provoke such intense panic in the transference situation that overt psychosis becomes a distinct possibility. It should not be forgotten that the psychoneurotic structure can operate as a defence against underlying psychotic mechanisms and that sleeping dogs are often best left alone.

Imprisonment and Precipitation

Many authors have also observed that schizophrenias seem remarkably frequently to be precipitated by a term of imprisonment and that these prison schizophrenias have a particularly poor prognosis. In the first ten to fifteen years of the present century this question was the subject of much discussion, particularly amongst German psychiatrists led by Rüdin (1901, 1909), Siefert (1907), Birnbaum (1908), Wilmanns (1908), Aschaffenburg (1913), Kraepelin (1915), Többen (1913), and Schrøder (1913). No agreement on the question whether imprisonment can precipitate a schizophrenic anlage into overt psychosis was reached. Wilmanns was most inclined to accept the possibility of a precipitating effect, but most of the others were more sceptical, and thought that, at the most, it was a question of an exacerbation of schizophrenic symptoms already in existence.

In more recent literature there have been relatively few contributions regarding this problem. In 1940 Wilmanns considered the criminal career to be an expression of a schizoid make-up or an insidious schizophrenic process. Mayer-Gross (1932), and Mayer-Gross, Slater and Roth (1960), have expressed doubts about the power of imprisonment to precipitate psychoses. Glueck, Jr. (1962), who has an extensive experience as a psychiatrist at the Sing-Sing prison in New York, is of the opinion that the patients, here under consideration, are already psychotic or pre-psychotic when they commit their offences, and that the stress of arrest, trial, and incarceration causes an intensification of the symptomatology. This tends to be the view increasingly prevalent in prison psychiatry in the United States.

In this material 3 cases [*106, 107, and 157*, all men] in the initial stage were diagnosed as psychogenic psychoses, triggered by incarceration; the outcome in all 3 cases was schizophrenia.

CHAPTER 12

THE EARLY DIFFERENTIATION OF PSYCHO-GENIC PSYCHOSES FROM SCHIZOPHRENIAS

Repeated emphasis has already been laid on the importance of the early differentiation of psychogenic psychoses from schizophrenias. The number of schizophrenias in this material is 43, while the total number of other non-psychogenic psychoses is only 13, and in 35 cases no certain diagnosis could be made. For this reason a statistical evaluation of a number of selected symptoms has only been made for the early differentiation of psychogenic psychoses from schizophrenias.

The 79 verified psychogenic psychoses represent the hospitalized psychogenic psychoses as a whole, while the 43 cases of schizophrenia comprise material chosen for its consistency with such forms which, in their initial stages, bear a resemblance to psychogenic reactions.

A preliminary statistical evaluation showed that 5 out of 11 investigated clinical characteristics could be assumed to be of differential diagnostic relevance. They are: the psychic trauma, affect, hallucinations, duration of the disease beyond three months, and paranoid features. The 6 variables to which no statistically significant prognostic value could be attributed in this material were: hereditary predisposition, sex, age, the pre-morbid personality, anxiety, and hysterical features.

It is necessary to consider whether the different variable factors vary independently of each other or whether there is co-variation, because an investigation of the isolated factors provides no guarantee that reliable information of a particular constellation of factors in a given case will be forthcoming.

Professor Bengt Strömgren, the astronomer, described in 1946 a statistical method applicable to problems of differential diagnostics within any clinical area. The basic principle of this method lies in the adoption of alternative qualitative variations, that is, the variables under consideration are either present or absent.

With regard to the psychic trauma a distinction was made between 'severe' and 'mild' trauma. This distinction was based on the 'common sense' concept of trauma which has been discussed in Chapter 1 (pages 15–18). Concerning 'affect' the alternatives were 'pronounced affect' and 'striking lack of affect'. Obviously, such distinctions are matters of opinion. The variables 'hallucinations', 'duration of the

201

disease beyond three months', and 'paranoid features' need no particular explanation.

The result of the calculations will be given here without going into arithmetical details. First and foremost we find that the deeper analysis of the material confirms the results of the preliminary investigation, for the five factors maintain their prognostic relevance after this statistical analysis. Furthermore, it has been possible to obtain a quantitative impression of the importance to be attached to the various factors in this respect. In the calculation each of the factors is given a coefficient, and the higher the numerical value of this coefficient, the greater is the prognostic or differential diagnostic significance of the factor. Actually, we may say that each of the factors has a certain points value, and we now find that the affect is the factor that represents the highest points value. An adequate affect gives + 44 points, whereas pronounced apathy deducts 44 points. The factor next in importance is the duration of the disease; under three months gives + 34 points, duration over three months deducts 34 points. Absence of the paranoid factor gives + 27 points, whereas occurrence of the paranoid factor deducts 27 points. Finally, demonstrated massive psychic trauma represents + 17 points, absence of trauma deducts 17 points. No hallucinations means + 11, occurrence of hallucinations deducts 11 points.

Now the position is such that the higher the positive value of a case, the greater is the probability that it is a psychogenic psychosis, and, conversely, the greater the negative value, the greater the risk that the psychosis will develop in the direction of schizophrenia. Finally, in order that the delineation between psychogenic psychoses and schizophrenia may lie at 0, a constant has been inserted into the formula, a constant which has been determined at — 19. The highest points value obtainable is + 114, the lowest — 152.

The calculation is extremely simple to make in practice. Once the occurrence or absence of the particular factor has been established, its points value is given the sign + or —, according to whether its presence argues for or against a psychogenic psychosis; the values are now added together, the constant — 19 is inserted, and we have the final result. All cases with a points value over + 30 were found to be psychogenic psychoses, all those with a value under — 43, schizophrenias. In this material 71 per cent of the verified psychogenic psychoses have a points value higher than + 30, and 51 per cent of the schizophrenias under — 43. By this method, 71 or 51 per cent of the psychogenic psychoses or schizophrenias could thus have been diagnosed with certainty within the first three months after the onset of the disease. For the material as a whole the corresponding figure was 64 per cent.

For points values between 0 and + 30, 70 per cent of such cases will be psychogenic psychoses and, correspondingly, 60 per cent of the cases with values between 0 and — 43 will be schizophrenias.

The method described is merely a preliminary step towards a solution of the important and complicated problem of the early differentiation between psychogenic psychoses and schizophrenias. Its chief disadvantage lies in the fact that it deals not with measurements, but with clinical estimates. However exactly one endeavours to define the different criteria, judgments of this kind will always be matters of opinion, so that obviously the method cannot claim to being described as exact.

CHAPTER 13

PSYCHOGENESIS, COMPARATIVE PSYCHIATRY AND THE CHOICE OF PSYCHOSIS

Psychogenesis and Comparative Psychiatry

As was pointed out in Chapter 5 one of the factors limiting the representative value of the material in this study is the fact that it belongs to a definite culture. It represents psychogenic psychotic reactions in a Danish urban population in the first half of the twentieth century. In this statement is implied that psychogenic reactions are probably highly dependent on the cultural milieu in which they occur. A traumatic event, for instance the unexpected appearance of a ghost at midnight, will surely be elaborated differently by an Eskimo, an Oxford professor, a Negro from Mississippi, a call girl from New York, and a farmer from Jutland. The primitive individual, whether he be African, Asian, American, or European will react to the traumatic experience in ways very different from that of a mature and level-headed person. The primitive will respond in one of the panicky primitive ways described by Kretschmer (*cf.* page 87), whereas the emotionally higher developed will possess the power to digest the experience and to discharge the surplus of excitation in a controlled manner analogous to the working through in analysis of painful infantile experiences when the repressions are overcome.

I am in agreement with Yap (1962) who demands that the nosological categorization of psychogenic disorders be founded on a more universal basis than is the case with the existing systems of classification (*cf.* pages 5–6). This would make it possible to include certain 'exotic psychoses' under the main heading of psychogenic psychoses. The syndromes here referred to, such as latah, amok, koro, the whitico psychosis, thanatomania, and the possession syndrome, are, according to Yap, better termed 'atypical, culture-bound, psychogenic disorders'. They are certainly of psychogenic origin and they owe their atypical symptomatological peculiarities to the pathoplastic influence of specific cultural conditions.

Aside from Yap's (1951, 1952, 1960) studies a wealth of clinical material—rather unorganized from the present point of view—is to be found in the works of the 'environmentalists' (Margaret Mead and many other anthropologists). Linton has, in his monograph *Culture and Mental Disorders* (1956), pursued this important subject in a more systematic way.

Although a comparative cultural psychiatry is in the process of developing, it must be admitted that we are faced with extremely complex problems in our attempts to assess the cultural variability of psychological disorders. We do not even know if the Danes really commit suicide as frequently as many authors claim they do.

Psychogenesis and the Choice of Psychosis

In this context it is natural to mention the problem of the choice of psychosis, that is, the possible connection between the nature of the psychic trauma and the form of the pathological reaction. Does the trauma respectively conflict not only cause an abnormal reaction, a psychosis or a neurosis, but does it also condition the manner in which the reaction presents itself? Or is the form determined only by constitutional peculiarities?

It is impossible to answer these questions satisfactorily. The trauma or conflict is to a lesser degree responsible for the type of reaction in the neuroses and nervous conditions. The constitutional factor is most likely the decisive one in the creation of a hysteria, an anxiety state, or an obsessive-compulsive neurosis. Freud (1913b) was of the opinion that constitution is decisive for the choice of neurosis (*cf.* page 212).

Strömgren's Theory

We know even less about the psychogenic psychoses than we do about the milder psychogenic reaction forms. Erik Strömgren's theory on the connection between the nature of the psychic trauma and the nature of the psychogenic psychotic reaction may shed some light on this subject. I have attempted, in carrying out the follow-up study, to test the extent to which clinical experience supports the theory.

In his work on the episodic psychoses, Strömgren (1940) suggests that a change, and particularly a sudden change, in the patient's *self-image* gives rise to a paranoid development. Going along with Wernicke and Bonhoeffer the self-image is defined as the usually rather stable complex of ideas an individual has about his characteristics, abilities, and possibilities in every connection, his relationship to other people and the community, in short, his most private and intimate ideas. All of an individual's efforts, his defeats, and expectations of social and sexual success and of intellectual and ethical development belong to the self-image; we cannot be surprised that it is so intimate that most people are

205

only in rare moments completely aware of their own self-image. The self-image has been mentioned in the footnote to Case 3. It may be of some interest here to mention that already James in his *Principles of Psychology* (1890) described the 'self'. He said:

> In the widest possible sense, however, a man's self is the sum total of all that he calls his, not only his body and his psychic powers but his clothes and his house, his wife and his children, his ancestors and friends, his reputation and works, his land and horses and yacht and bank account. All these things give him the same emotions.

Emphasizing the importance of clothes for the maintenance of the self, the Anglo-American essayist Logan Pearsall Smith (1933), wrote the aphorism:

> I look at my overcoat and my hat hanging in the hall with reassurance; for although I go out of doors with one individuality to-day, when yesterday I had quite another, yet my clothes keep my various selves buttoned up together, enabling all these otherwise irreconcilable aggregates of psychological phenomena to pass themselves off as one person.

Strömgren assumes that a sudden blow to the self-image may have the most far-reaching consequences. Such a wound to the self-image takes place when an individual is exposed to a defect or a character trait of which he had had no previous knowledge. The consequence of such a fateful traumatization should, therefore, result in the development of paranoid ideas. Kretschmer's analysis of the paranoid work in his sensitive patients and his theory on the genesis of this syndrome supports the hypothesis. And in 1914 Freud observed: 'The frequent causation of paranoia by an injury to the ego, by a frustration of satisfaction within the sphere of the ego ideal. ...'

In two later works (1945, 1958), Strömgren took up the general question of the connection between the trauma and the reaction. In these he gave a complementary theory, that the two remaining groups of psychotic reaction syndromes, the emotional reactions and the disturbances of consciousness, like the paranoid syndromes, appear when the patient is exposed to psychic traumatizations of certain types. According to the theory psychogenic disturbances of consciousness are brought about by traumatic injury to the *object-image* (*Gegenstandsbewusstsein*). By this is understood the complex of ideas which comprise the individual's knowledge of all the people, objects—for instance the Empire State Building—and inter-relationships between them or, in other words, the direct opposite of the self-image. The object-image includes our knowledge of natural laws, regulations, legal as well as conventional, of people's mutual relations in the community, people's customary reactions and behaviour in certain situations and, most particularly, the habits, qualities, and characteristics of our near friends and relatives.

If the object-image is shaken, and this can be brought about in numerous ways, through the shock of natural catastrophes, railway accidents, etc., or through the completely unexpected and disappointing behaviour of those near to us, then we should find, if there is a pathological reaction, a disturbance of consciousness, for instance a clouded state.

And, finally, Strömgren believes the psychogenic emotional reaction to be a response to a so-called *simple situational conflict* which achieves a pathogenic intensity for the patient. By simple situational conflict is understood general human conflicts which are not in and of themselves surprising or disconcerting because their existence is well known and accepted by all, but which disturb the individual because he cannot avoid their emotional implications for himself. Here are included the sickness and death of relatives, economic difficulties, disappointment in expectations of advancement, etc.

Some traumata are at times simple situational conflicts and sometimes injuries to the object-image. There are also traumatic situations which can affect the self-image, the object-image, or act as simple situational conflicts, all according to the construction of the personality that experiences them. An extremely ambitious man who feels himself unusually well qualified for some high position, for example that of a general, might react to a serious disappointment in his career in different ways. His reaction will depend to a great extent on his constitutional and acquired make-up. The fact that he is passed over for the job may perhaps awaken in him a dormant suspicion that he is not so eminent a military man as he had hitherto believed himself; such an idea may lead him to project the blame for his misery on to his surroundings and to consider himself persecuted by those above him and those below him. Or perhaps the announcement of the appointment of someone else to the coveted post may throw him into a state of shock in which he may wander about the streets in a clouded state. In most cases the disappointment will lead to a more or less lengthy depressive state marked by bitterness and resentment at the capriciousness of fate. An evaluation of the personality concerned must always be taken into consideration when deciding to which of the three types of traumata the concrete situation belongs. It is impossible to classify all conceivable psychic traumata according to their objective qualities. Cultural and social circumstances, also, are important factors in deciding to what category of trauma a given situation belongs.

Bonhoeffer's Exogenous Predilection Types

Before discussing and testing the theory let us see whether Bonhoeffer's teaching on the exogenous (that is, organic or physiological) reaction types can lead us to any conclusions about the relationship between psychic noxae and reaction forms.* The objection that comes immediately to mind is that a psychic trauma is quite different in nature from an organic influence on the brain. The assumption seems justified, however, that there is a basic similarity of effect on the brain of psychic and organic insults. So far as I can see, a biological point of view must acknowledge this concordance. Every form of psychic life is biologically thinkable only as the function of nervous organs. If this view is valid then the connection between organic noxae and reaction types is of interest in helping us to evaluate the relationship between psychic trauma or conflict and the form of the psychogenic reaction. In passing, it should be mentioned that there are several authors who have supported the view that irreversible brain changes can be psychically caused (*cf.* page 28).

While Kraepelin (1881) maintained that specific organic noxae were responsible for specific forms of psychosis, for example, that every infectious disease has its characteristic psychosis, Bonhoeffer (1909, 1912, 1917) established that the majority of exogenous brain injuries, regardless of their nature, evoke only a few different types of reactions, and these are not pathognomonic for particular diseases or intoxications, but rather for whole *groups* of exogenous noxae. Incidentally, Kraepelin altered his view of this question radically in 1920.

Bonhoeffer also observed that organic noxae can lead to clinical pictures which approximate those of endogenous disorders. This is undoubtedly why Bonhoeffer cautiously contented himself with speaking of *predilection* types. Specht (1913) and Kleist (1916), in particular, maintained that constitution is far from being a negligible factor in the determination of exogenous reaction types. On the basis of self-observation, Specht described melancholiform reactions to exogenous stimuli (influenza, carbon monoxide poisoning). Kleist made similar observations on psychic disturbances in rheumatic chorea and he stressed the argument against Bonhoeffer's view created by the fact that severe cases of manic-depressive psychosis often show syndromes (for example, turbid states) indistinguishable from organic reactions.

Stertz (1928) followed up the consequence of this criticism and claimed that exogenous reactions can be differentiated into two groups.

---

* Despite its importance, this problem has not been paid much attention to in Anglo-American literature and is therefore accounted for in some detail here.

The first, which he calls *obligatory* (clouded states, deliria, amnestic and nervous-emotional syndromes), is a general human form of reaction, while the second, *facultative* (among others hallucinatory, catatonic, and psychomotor syndromes) is, on the contrary, dependent on individual, chiefly constitutional, reaction tendencies in the patient.

We now approach the question of whether there are cases in which exogenous noxae are able to produce purely constitutionally determined reactions, completely lacking in exogenous reaction-type symptoms. Bostroem (1929) gave a strong answer to this question in showing that the paralytic cerebral process can precipitate manic-depressive phases or schizophrenic pushes without displaying the slightest clinical symptom of dementia paralytica. Thus, there are cases in which the constitutional factor is the exclusive determinant of the form of psychosis and the exogenous noxae merely the precipitating factors. In this connection we must mention F. Kant's (1930) experimental study. Kant wanted to test the constitutional element in psychoses triggered by organic cerebral noxae. He chose hashish for his experiment and administered it to nine manic-depressive and ten schizophrenic women who were all in a free interval. The result was the release of the symptoms of the latent psychosis while the characteristic symptoms of hashish poisoning were far less evident. As in Bostroem's cases, the constitutional factor played the determining role.

This does not mean that Bonhoeffer's perceptions were invalid, but that they must be corrected and shaded in the light of later research. To recapitulate: psychiatric theory has moved from the form-giving qualities of the organic injury (Kraepelin) to the view which stresses partly the common human reaction tendencies (Bonhoeffer), partly and predominantly the significance of individual-constitutional factors in the determination of the form of a psychosis (Specht, Kleist, Stertz, Bostroem, Kant).

Furthermore, we have learned that the more massive the brain injury, the less individually coloured the reaction will be. This is particularly obvious in the case of irreversible brain changes: it is usually impossible to tell whether a patient suffering from a severe dementia was previously a cultured intellectual or a mental defective. In the realm of non-lesional injuries it is also true that the most severe will produce the least individual reactions: when confronted with a patient in a state of deep alcoholic intoxication it is difficult to tell whether one has the head of a department or an ordinary workman before one; the difference readily apparent in the normal state has been obliterated. Specht and Kleist have pointed out that mild infections and intoxications produce 'homonomous' and severe febrile diseases and poisoning 'heteronomous' disorders. This is also true in the case of head injuries. In general, the intensity with which the noxae affect the brain is a decisive factor for the form the reaction takes.

As it is quite uncontested that psychic traumatization can only cause the mildest of brain changes we are quite justified in the view that the psychically, even more than the organically, caused reaction takes a form that is conditioned by the individual constitutional predisposition. One may further assume that the more specialized the reaction readiness the more special the trauma must be to bring about the response. This is borne out by experience. Kretschmer's sensitive patients are the classic example of a particular personality configuration triggered into illness by a characteristic key-experience to which it is electively vulnerable.*

Thus, we can conclude that only a small number of psychogenic reactions (catastrophe reactions) are formally determined by the trauma while the majority of psychogenic disorders are conditioned by the individual's own personality. Of the latter reactions it may be said in the formal respect that some are evoked by widely varying traumata, while others demand very particular key situations for their appearance.

All of this has some bearing on Strömgren's theory. It does not claim that the particular objectively delimited nature of the traumatization always corresponds with a particular form of reaction but, on the contrary, stresses the fact that the given trauma must always be evaluated on the basis of the possibilities it has to affect a particular area of the personality.

Discussion and Evaluation of Strömgren's Theory

In the light of my material, Strömgren's theory has been substantiated so far as two reaction forms are concerned (the paranoid and the disturbances of consciousness), with specific types of traumata affecting well defined parts of the personality (self-image and object-image). However, there is no comparable area of the personality that is responsible in the emotional syndromes. One may well say that the simple situational conflict does not arouse any particular part of the personality but affects it in its entirety mainly by calling forth an emotional response.

There was sufficient information on only 56 of the 79 cases of verified psychogenic psychoses to be useful in connection with the problem of validation of Strömgren's theory.

Among the paranoid syndromes there were 6 cases [*3, 23, 120, 139, 149, and 150*]. The first 2 were paranoid episodes grafted on to depres-

* *Cf.* the criticism of Kretschmer's views, pages 175–179.

sive syndromes; the third a paranoid-hallucinatory episode in a woman with a depression of long duration. That such mechanisms also may be infused in process psychoses such as schizophrenias, is clear from cases like, for example, Case 31.

In all these 6 cases the trauma apparently had the effect proposed in the theory: injury to the patient's self-image through exposure or intimation of an inadequacy or defect, mainly a sexual-ethical one. In this difficult situation the paranoid mechanism begins to function and the blame is separated from the patient and projected on to evil-minded people or, as in Case 149, on to evil spirits who predict eternal perdition, etc. These cases appear to bear out the theory very well.

The relationship between theory and experience is somewhat less clear when we come to the emotional syndromes and the disturbances of consciousness. In going through the remaining 50 cases, 19 emotional syndromes [1–6, 9, 10, 11, 13, 14, 15, 17, 18, 19, 22, 23, 24, and 41] and 31 disturbances of consciousness [49, 50, 52–63, 65, 66, 67, 69, 71, 72, 73, 78, 81, 84, 87, 88, 117, 118, 119, 128, and 130], we can readily observe that it is very difficult to see, without an enormous amount of detailed knowledge of the pre-morbid configurations, whether the trauma represents a simple situational conflict or an injury to the object-image. I am inclined to consider the majority of cases simple situational conflicts. In only 5 cases [41, 54, 66, 73, and 78] might one have definitely expected a disturbance of consciousness sooner than a depressive reaction. These 5 were cases of intense and drastic experience: war and shipwreck, operation scenes and the like. These 5 cases actually showed disturbances of consciousness.

In the remaining 45 cases, the nature of the traumata was such that it would have been impossible to predict anything about the reaction. The traumatic experiences in these cases were normal occurrences of daily life: marital and economic difficulties, disappointments in love, grief at the death of a child or a spouse, persistent feelings of loneliness, and so forth. It could not be established that the traumatic experiences which led to a disturbance of consciousness were more acute or sudden than those which produced depressive reactions. On the other hand, I had the impression that there was an accumulation of individuals among those with disturbances of consciousness who had a tendency to primitive reactions while the depressive material was dominated by those who were constitutionally depressed or inclined to depressive reactions to every situation that was at all difficult, or individuals with apparently normal personalities to begin with.

We may thus conclude that the psychic traumata that lead to disturbances of consciousness and those that lead to depressions are objectively much the same and that the formal difference of the reactions is individually conditioned.

Strömgren's theory is founded on clinical observations. It does take into account unconscious mechanisms, particularly in the evaluation of the effect of experiential factors on the self-image. It does not, however, pay attention to the important question of the choice of defence-mechanisms in psychogenic reactions. Waelder (1951), in his paper on the theories of paranoid delusions, has suggested that denial, not projection, is the fundamental mechanism in the development of these conditions and, further, that denial plays the same part in psychotic symptom formation that repression plays in the psychoneuroses. His hypothesis that the choice of defence is decisive for the choice of type of neurosis as well as type of psychosis deserves careful attention and testing.

Amongst others Knight (1954) and Brenner (1963) have refuted the assumption—to use Knight's words—that 'neurosis is neurosis, psychosis is psychosis, and never the twain shall meet'. In Chapter 3 I adopted the same point of view. It is, therefore, natural in this context, also, to touch upon the problem of the choice of neurosis.

As mentioned on page 205, Freud claimed already in 1913 that constitution, that is, something hereditary, is decisive for the choice of neurosis. In later writings (for example, Lecture XXIII, 1916–17) disposition to neurosis is conceptualized as the result of the effects of infantile experiences on the hereditary endowment. Freud's final proposition was thus that the stage of the psychosexual, or the ego development, or both, at which the patient has become traumatically fixated determines the form of his later neurosis. Over the years many analysts have tackled the perplexing problem of 'choice of neurosis'. To mention but a few: French (1936, 1937, 1939, 1952) has suggested the working hypothesis that rational behaviour, neuroses, and dreams can be analysed into component factors that are in part common to all three. In principle this makes possible the identification of one or more variables accounting for the choice of behaviour, of neurosis, and of dream. This approach does not prejudice the observer as to the relative significance of constitutional, respectively experiential factors. Tarachow and Fink (1953) advance the hypothesis that the early loss of a parent tends to increase the difficulties of solving the problem of ambivalence and, therefore, makes the choice of obsessive-compulsive neurosis more likely than that of hysteria.

From this brief survey it will be seen that psychoanalysis has offered seemingly diametrically opposite (but not necessarily mutually exclusive) theories concerning the choice of neurosis.

CHAPTER 14

PSYCHOGENESIS, TELEOLOGY, DEPRESSION AND ANXIETY

Psychogenesis and Teleology

Much erudition has been displayed by philosophers, psychologists, and psychiatrists in discussing the principles of causality and teleology (from the Greek, *telos* = end) as they are employed in the psychological sciences. Limiting the debate to psychopathological phenomena, the question may be raised whether a neurotic or a psychotic syndrome, for instance a paranoid condition, should be looked upon as having a cause or a purpose. Naturally, no agreement between the extremists has been reached. In recent years, three Danish psychiatrists have offered their opinions. Lunn (1953) and Vanggaard (1959) are inclined to think that a deterministic and a teleological point of view are not necessarily contradictory whilst Timmermann (1960) insists that they are. The pragmatic Americans, on the whole, tend to accept the position that determinism and teleology can be reconciled and often refer to cybernetics as the science which may prove this reconciliation to be possible.

In the present context it may be appropriate to consider whether psychogenic reactions have a purposive character. It was intimated in the introduction to Chapter 7 that disturbances of consciousness and paranoid reactions must probably be considered in this way, but it may be more doubtful in the case of emotional reactions.

Disturbances of Consciousness

For many cases of disturbances of consciousness it is obvious that the reaction offers the patient substantial advantages, that is, they must be considered biologically expedient. Reference may here be made to the delirious syndromes that are not infrequent in cases of disappointment in love or bereavement, where, to be sure, the hallucinations and other psychotic contents are directly derived from the traumatic situation but in such a way that the patient in a hallucinatory wish-fulfilment has an experience diametrically opposed to the actual happening. This can be considered a traumatically induced regression to the first weeks of extra-uterine life which, according to Ferenczi, are characterized by

213

such wish-fulfilling hallucinatory experiences. Also in the normal dream we encounter this regressive phenomenon, particularly when sleep lightens (Dement and Kleitman, 1957) which happens four, five, or six times a night. The hallucinatory wish-fulfilments of the dream are guardians of sleep in that they dissipate thrusts of instinctual energy threatening to disrupt sleep.

Disturbances of consciousness are, temporarily at any rate, advantageous to the patient, a flight into the psychosis. A cloudy state gives the painful experience little opportunity of sinking in by the patient's figurative withdrawal from the scene. The problem whether turbid states governed by panic and by terrible hallucinations can be considered biologically advantageous will be discussed in the subsequent paragraph.

Many hysterical reactions are thought to be atavistic instinct or reflex mechanisms capable of mobilization under certain external, especially shocking, influences. Kretschmer (1927) has stressed this point with regard to the *Totstellreflex* (immobilization reflex). This mechanism which has been exhaustively investigated in a number of lower animals, particularly fish, is conspicuously opportune as it affords the optimal protection from a stronger and swifter foe, partly because an animal when motionless is less visible, and partly because many predatory animals only pursue a fleeing prey. It is this primitive protective apparatus that is temporarily brought into play in stuporous states often observed in persons when exposed to violent catastrophes. The fact that a stupor syndrome is no particularly appropriate mechanism for a person to employ when in an earthquake area does not gainsay the justification for the concept of the teleological character of such reactions.

Paranoid Conditions

To become paranoid may appear a rather dubious advantage under any circumstances. Jaspers has strongly emphasized, however, that the *Wahnstimmung* (delusional mood) often preceding the appearance of the paranoid syndrome is probably one of the most intolerable mental states and the termination of this horrible state with the crystallization of the paranoid ideas spells relief. To this observation should be added the psychoanalytic insight that the delusions (and hallucinations) are restitutive efforts (roughly corresponding with Bleuler's accessory symptoms) with the purpose of re-establishing contact with the world that was lost in the initial regressive psychotic phase, characterized by a break with reality, that is, with the decathexis of objects (roughly corresponding with Bleuler's autism). If this proposition is correct we have here an example of how psychoanalysis can describe in dynamic terms a psychopathological phenomenon which has been described in non-dynamic terms by traditional psychiatry.

Many of the representative German authors, for instance Gruhle (1929), Kolle (1931), and Schneider (1920, 1952), are highly sceptical of both the teleological efforts and also of the attempts to empathize with the delusional function and the delusional content. Gruhle has, especially by emphasizing the primarily abnormal and hence intuitively incomprehensible aberration from normal functioning (as opposed to abnormal content), warned against a psychological optimism which, from Maier's (1912) formulation of the catathymic concept and Kretschmer's (1918) description of the sensitive paranoics, has gained increasing prominence in the literature. Among those authors who have supported a teleological point of view, besides Maier and Kretschmer, must be mentioned Schilder (1918), Kant (1927–34), Krapf (1927), Kant (1929), and Kahn (1929). The last-mentioned author says: '*Wahn hat Sinn, Bedeutung, Zweck der Selbstwertrettung*' ('Delusions have significance, meaning, and the purpose of saving the self'). Lange (1927) is more cautious. He thinks that, provided one possesses a thorough knowledge of the personality in question, it is possible to predict, besides the content, the duration of the reaction (episode or chronic development) and its special form (expansive, sensitive, etc.) also. But the very occurrence of a paranoid reaction is taken by him to be a psychologically incomprehensible mechanism.

Analysts and analytically oriented psychiatrists insist that paranoid states can be interpreted. They see no basic differences between psychoneuroses, personality disorders, and psychotic, including paranoid, conditions. The defensive organization and the ego adaptations are, in principle, the same. This difference between academic and analytic psychiatry has already been emphasized in the introduction to Chapter 8. A cautious therapeutic optimism is clearly reflected in the writings of many analysts who devote most of their time to the treatment of psychotic patients. Psychotherapy of psychotics is perhaps being pursued with particular energy by analysts belonging to the 'neo-Freudian school' (the William Alanson White Institute of New York and the Washington School of Psychiatry) and the optimistic therapeutic attitude is mainly due to the fact that the psychosis is seen as a set of adaptive manoeuvres in individuals with intense anxieties that cannot be coped with by the employment of psychoneurotic defences. The regression in psychosis is understood to have the purpose of removing excessive anxiety and of re-establishing some kind of psychic equili-

215

brium. Arieti (1959b), who coined the term 'progressive teleologic regression' (in schizophrenia), writes:

> [Teleology] is not a denial that psychological and psychopathological phenomena are removed from physical determinism (according to which causes have effects, not purposes) but an additional affirmation that the human being, as we are able to understand him today, seems to be subjected to both mechanical and teleologic causalities.

Emotional Syndromes

It has already been mentioned that, with regard to psychogenic emotional states, it may be more difficult to sustain the principle of finality. Although positive proof is lacking there is much evidence for the assumption that the manic-depressive psychosis is caused by disturbances of a metabolic nature and not motivated by purposes. The process of mourning, on the other hand, certainly has a biological purpose, namely, slowly to overcome the actual loss of an important object in order once again to be psychologically ready to enter into a new and meaningful object relationship. Hypomanic conditions and other states of elation which are not of certain manic-depressive origin have an extremely complex psychopathological structure. Lewin (1950) has formulated some provocative ideas on the subject.

Although many depressive conditions may be caused by metabolic disturbances that have a genic basis and others (mourning) must be viewed as purposive reactions to object-losses, it is entirely legitimate to make the proposition that depression has meaning and to attempt to formulate this meaning in terms of metapsychology. By metapsychology is understood:

> . . . those psychological investigations that are not limited to conscious phenomena, and that formulate the most general assumptions of [psycho]analysis on the most abstract level of theory. Metapsychology is concerned with the substructures of personality, with the ego, the id, and the superego which are defined as units of functions. (Hartmann. 1959.)

It will prove advantageous from a clinical as well as from a conceptual point of view to discuss depression together with anxiety.

Depression and Anxiety

Man has two basic affects of unpleasure, depression and anxiety. They are ego reactions. The most sophisticated formulations concerning these two basic emotions are to be found in Bibring's paper *The Mechanism of Depression* (1953) in which he compares anxiety and depression. He states:

> According to the viewpoint adopted here, *depression represents a basic reaction* to situations of narcissistic frustration which to prevent appears to be beyond the power of the ego, just as *anxiety represents a*

basic reaction of the ego to situations of danger. . . . To clarify the status of depression still further, it may be helpful at this point to compare depression with the feeling of anxiety, particularly since the latter has been brought in close connection with the feeling of helplessness (Freud). Both are frequent—probably equally frequent—ego reactions scaling from the mildest, practically insignificant forms to the most intensive, pathological structures. Since they cannot be reduced any further, it may be justified to call them basic ego reactions. From the point of view elaborated here, anxiety and depression represent diametrically opposed basic ego responses. Anxiety as a reaction to (external or internal) danger indicates the ego's desire to survive. The ego, challenged by the danger, mobilizes the signal of anxiety and prepares for fight or flight. In depression, the opposite takes place, the ego is paralyzed because it finds itself incapable to meet the 'danger'. In extreme situations the wish to live is replaced by the wish to die.

Bibring further points out that the orally dependent type which constantly needs narcissistic supplies from the outside represents the most frequent type of predisposition to depression. This is not surprising if one takes into consideration the fact that the infant has no power over its objects and the necessary supplies it has to receive from them, and that it is entirely dependent on the benevolence of the environment for the gratification of its needs and the maintenance of its life.

According to what we know it is difficult to decide whether depression or anxiety is the primary reaction. Rapaport (1957) who, until his recent death, was the foremost authority on metapsychological problems, held the view that the anxiety reaction is the later, more complex, and more developed reaction. The anxious person is still fighting, the depressed person has lost his fighting spirit and has capitulated. It is the depressed, not the anxious, individual who often prefers death.

It is implied in these metapsychological considerations that anxiety can be looked upon as a reaction belonging to the category of teleological responses, whereas depression, although full of meaning, does not always have a purpose.

Panic and Teleology

There is general agreement that anxiety is not necessarily a pathological phenomenon. Fear and the pain of bodily illness warn us against real dangers, external and internal. Anxiety is, according to Freud's second theory (*cf.* the quotation on pages 13–14), originally the reaction to helplessness in the traumatic situation (for instance the separation from the mother) which is later reproduced when we are faced with an instinctual demand, the satisfaction of which would arouse the disapproval of external or internal (superego) authorities. Anxiety is a signal and must, therefore, be looked upon as purposive.

217

Anxiety is, according to the existentialists, the basic reaction of man to his knowledge that he exists but that he must die. It is man's prerogative.

Panic is a disequilibrium in an organism caused by overwhelming amounts of excitation which cannot be discharged through normal channels. One might conveniently distinguish three types.

Shocking external experiences actually representing a danger to life and to bodily integrity are experienced as threats to the self, including the body-ego, and are often reacted to in a panicky way.

Schizophrenic patients in the initial stage of the illness sometimes have the gruesome experience which in German psychiatry is referred to as *Weltuntergangserlebnis*. The essence of this type of panic is the threatened self-disintegration and the collapse of communication and relatedness. It is an annihilation panic, which is also observed in children who are separated from the mother (the birth of a sibling, enrolment in the nursery school, hospitalization, etc.).

Finally, we have the catathymic type of panic, triggered by an experiential factor which hits the sore spot in the personality left by an early traumatic event. The two examples mentioned on pages 15–16 may serve as illustrations.

Other classifications of panic are possible. The threat to the self may come from within and be of an instinctual nature, as when a sexual or an aggressive impulse, for instance catathymically elicited, becomes so intense that the ego experiences the distinct possibility of losing control. Typical examples are homosexual panic and rage panic. It may also come from the outside as when vitally needed narcissistic supplies are cut off in situations of separation or when life is threatened as in catastrophes and in final illness.

All attempts at classification are arbitrary and the different types of panic suggested here certainly overlap.

There are a number of different ways in which to cope with anxiety and they can be hierarchically arranged. The most primitive way to deal with anxiety is to be virtually unable to deal with it; this means that the anxiety assumes the highest possible intensity, namely, panic. A measure of control is attained when hysterical hyperkinetic mechanisms are brought into operation in the form of, usually 'headless', violent-motor-reaction types of discharge (children's temper tantrums, hysterical fits). A co-ordinated, albeit neurotic, control is obtained in the phobic reactions in which the dangerous catathymic situation is simply avoided. The mature way of handling anxiety is to tolerate it, to face the facts underlying it and to take the proper action. A model for this is the psychoanalytic situation.

Anxiety has the purpose of warning the individual experiencing it against a danger. Sometimes the psychic mechanisms employed in this process are highly effective, sometimes they are of doubtful value and sometimes it appears to the spectator that, by becoming overwhelmed by the anxiety as in a delirious state, the patient has merely fallen out of the frying pan into the fire. But the varying degrees of effectiveness with which the pathological reaction can be said to have solved the problem is no argument against the teleological view of these reactions. We must content ourselves with the resigned remark by Freud (page 14) about 'the imperfection of the psychic apparatus'. Physical pain, likewise, has a purpose and is useful, but we must regretfully admit that it also often overshoots the mark.

The Psychic Trauma and the Content of the Psychosis

While discussing the meaning of anxiety it seems appropriate once more to touch upon the relationship between the psychic trauma and the content of the psychogenic psychosis. Jaspers (*cf.* page 8) demands that the trauma must be reflected in the content of the psychogenic reaction. We have seen that this criterion is only very seldom fulfilled in disturbances of consciousness. What then, determines the content of a psychogenic disturbance of consciousness? It is tempting in some cases to interpret the immediately incomprehensible psychotic content as symbols that in reality mirror the trauma. In other cases the psychosis seemingly employs older memory material consisting mostly of memories of events in childhood which are catathymically mobilized by the trauma.

The experiences of normal psychology clearly prove that everybody commands a wide, chiefly visual, range of images capable of mobilization under unusual circumstances. Psychically normal persons sometimes have the most fantastic visual experiences when in hypnagogic states. The visions, grotesque and foreign to their personality, that normal subjects experience when in deep hypnotic trance, and which have been instructively described for instance by Schultz (1921, 1937), may also be mentioned here, besides the bizarre experiences of individuals under the influence of mescaline and LSD. Freud (1913*a*), Schilder (1918), and Storch (1922), have also made contributions to this topic. In this context, however, it is above all C. G. Jung's collective unconscious and the archetypes, populating it, that must be emphasized. What actually happens in a psychogenic delirious state, in hallucinoses, and in many schizophrenic psychoses (*cf.*, for instance, Cases 74, 123, 126, and 149) is that the ego, depleted in strength in consequence of the barrage of intense anxieties induced by the trauma, loses contact with the real world around it and is then inundated by id-impulses and by the grotesque images of man's racial past. In psychosis these impulses and images appear because the ego has been over-whelmed. The psychotic, thus, becomes a Time Traveller who travels back into the hideous and the beautiful world of the collective uncon-scious. This world of beauty and horror is not foreign to anybody. In dreams and in the twilight before sleep we can all feel awe-struck by its power.

The list of references, the name index and the subject index have been prepared in collaboration with Ellen M. Jensen, medical librarian, State Mental Hospital, Risskov, Denmark.

REFERENCES

The following abbreviations are used for manuals which are repeatedly quoted.

American Handbook of Psychiatry = S. Arieti (ed.) (1959). *American Handbook of Psychiatry*. New York; Basic Books, Inc.

Handbook of Psychiatry = G. Aschaffenburg (ed.) (1911–1929). *Handbuch der Psychiatrie*. Leipzig and Vienna; Deuticke

Handbook of Mental Disorders = O. Bumke (ed.) (1928–1939). *Handbuch der Geisteskrankheiten*. Berlin; Springer

G. W. = *Gesammelte Werke* of Sigmund Freud, ed. by Anna Freud *et al.* (1940–1952). London; Imago

St. Ed. = *The Standard Edition of the Complete Psychological Works of Sigmund Freud*, translated and edited by James Strachey (1953–). London; The Hogarth Press and the Institute of Psycho-Analysis

Names of periodicals are abbreviated according to *World Medical Periodicals*. World Medical Association 1961; 3rd ed.

Titles in parentheses indicate that the book or paper has been translated into English.

Titles in brackets indicate that the book or paper has not been translated into English.

Numbers in italics after a reference indicate the pages in this monograph on which the article or book is quoted.

Alexander, F. (1927). *Psychoanalyse der Gesamtpersönlichkeit.* Leipzig; Int. Psychoanal. Verlag. (*The Psychoanalysis of the Total Personality.* New York and Washington; Nerv. & Ment. Dis. Publ. Co. 1930.)— *34*

— (1930). 'The Neurotic Character.' *Int. J. Psycho-Anal.* **11**, 292–311. ('Der neurotische Charakter.' *Int. Z. Psychoanal.* **14**, 26–44, 1928.)— *194*

Allers, R. (1920). 'Über psychogene Störungen in sprachfremder Umgebung. Der Verfolgungswahn der sprachlich Isolierten.' [Psychogenic Disturbance in the Environment of a Foreign Language. Delusion of Persecution in the Linguistically Isolated.] *Z. ges. Neurol. Psychiat.* **60**, 281–289— *17*

Allport, G. W. (1937; 1949). *Personality. A Psychological Interpretation.* New York; Holt 1937, and London; Constable 1949— *4, 56*

Alström, C. H. (1942). *Mortality in Mental Hospitals with Especial Regard to Tuberculosis.* Copenhagen; Munksgaard— *191*

American Psychiatric Association (1952). *Diagnostic and Statistical Manual. Mental Disorders.* Washington, D.C.; American Psychiatric Association— *5, 52*

221

Arieti, S. (1955). *Interpretation of Schizophrenia.* New York; Brunner—
199
— (1959a). 'Manic-Depressive Psychosis.' *American Handbook of Psychiatry* **1**, 419–454—*26, 70*
— (1959b). 'Schizophrenia: The Manifest Symptomatology, the Psychodynamic and Formal Mechanisms.' 'Other Aspects; Psychotherapy.' *American Handbook of Psychiatry* **1**, 455–484; 485–507—*56, 200, 215*
Aschaffenburg, G. (1913). 'Degenerationspsychosen und Dementia praecox bei Kriminellen.' [Degenerative Psychoses and Dementia Praecox in Criminals.] *Z. ges. Neurol. Psychiat.* **14**, 83–96—*200*
Baelz, E. (1901). 'Über Emotionslähmung.' [On Emotional Paralysis.] *Allg. Z. Psychiat.* **58**, 717–721—*27*
Bak, R. (1939). 'Über die dynamisch-strukturellen Bedingungen des primären Beziehungswahns.' [On the Dynamic-Structural Conditions of the Primary Delusions of Reference.] *Z. ges. Neurol. Psychiat.* **166**, 342–364—*146*
— (1946). 'Masochism in Paranoia.' *Psychoanal. Quart.* **15**, 285–301—*146*
Bellak, L. (1948). *Dementia Praecox.* New York; Grune & Stratton—*74*
Benedek, Therese (1952). *Psychosexual Functions in Women.* New York; Ronald Press—*68*
Benedict, Ruth (1934). 'Anthropology and the Abnormal.' *J. gen. Psychol.* **10**, 59–80—*29*
Bergen, Mary E. (1958). 'The Effect of Severe Trauma on a Four-Year-Old Child.' *Psychoanal. Stud. Child* **13**, 407–429—*18*
Bibring, E. (1953). 'The Mechanism of Depression.' Ph. Greenacre (ed.). *Affective Disorders*, 13–49. New York; Int. Univ. Press—*216*
Birnbaum, K. (1908). *Psychosen mit Wahnbildung und wahnhafte Einbildungen bei Degenerativen.* [Psychoses with Formation of Delusions and Paranoid Imaginations in the Degenerated.] Halle; Marhold—*100, 200*
— (1910a). 'Über psychische Ursachen geistiger Störungen.' [On Psychic Causation of Mental Disturbance.] *Dtsch. med. Wschr.* **1910 I**, 884–887—*28*
— (1910b). 'Zur Frage der psychogenen Krankheitsformen.' [On the Problem of Varieties of Psychogenic Disease.] *Z. ges. Neurol. Psychiat.* **1**, 27–30—*28*
— (1911). 'Zur Frage der psychogenen Krankheitsformen. II. Beitrag.' [On the Problem of Varieties of Psychogenic Disease. Second Contribution.] *Z. ges. Neurol. Psychiat.* **7**, 404–423—*28*
— (1915–1919). 'Kriegsneurosen und -psychosen auf Grund der gegenwärtigen Kriegsbeobachtungen.' [Neuroses and Psychoses of War in the Light of Present War Observations.] *Z. ges. Neurol. Psychiat.* (*Ref.*) **11**, 321–369 (1915), **12**, 1–89 (1916), **13**, 457–533 (1917), **14**, 193–258 (1917), **16**, 1–78 (1918), **18**, 1–76 (1919)—*70, 199*
— (1918). *Psychische Verursachung seelischer Störungen und die psychisch bedingten abnormen Seelenvorgänge.* [Psychic Causation of Mental Disturbances and Psychically Conditioned Abnormal Mental Processes.] Wiesbaden; Bergmann—*28, 89, 186, 194*
— (1920). *Psychopathologische Dokumente.* [Psychopathological Documents.] Berlin; Springer—*136*

REFERENCES

Birnbaum, K. 1923). *Der Aufbau der Psychose. Grundzüge der psychia-trischen Strukturanalyse.* [The Structure of the Psychosis.] Berlin; Springer—*22, 28, 148, 196*
— (1928a). 'Der Aufbau der Psychose.' [The Structure of the Psychosis.] *Handbook of Mental Disorders* **5**, *Spec. Part 1*, 1–18—*28*
— (1928b). 'Die psychoreaktiven (psychogenen) Symptomenbildungen.' [The Psycho-Reactive (Psychogenic) Symptom Formations.] *Hand-book of Mental Disorders* **2**, *Gen. Part 2*, 92–133—*82, 89, 132, 194*
Bleuler, E. (1911). 'Dementia praecox oder Gruppe der Schizophrenien.' *Handbook of Psychiatry, Spec. Part, Section* **4**, Leipzig and Vienna; Deuticke. (Dementia Praecox or the Group of Schizophrenias. New York; Int. Univ. Press 1950.)—*25, 34, 74*
— (1919). *Das autistisch-undisziplinierte Denken in der Medizin und seine Überwindung.* [Autistic-Undisciplined Thinking in Medicine and Its Correction.] Berlin; Springer, 5th ed. by M. Bleuler, 1962—*29*
— (1937). *Lehrbuch der Psychiatrie.* [Textbook of Psychiatry.] Berlin; Springer, 6th ed. Revised ed. (10th) by M. Bleuler, 1960—*81*
Bleuler, M. (1941). *Krankheitsverlauf, Persönlichkeit und Verwandtschaft Schizophrener und ihre gegenseitigen Beziehungen.* [Course of Disease, Personality, and Kinship of Schizophrenic Patients and their Mutual Relationships.] Leipzig; Thieme—*148*
— (1943). 'Die spätschizophrenen Krankheitsbilder.' [Clinical Types of Late Schizophrenias.] *Fortschr. Neurol. Psychiat.* **15**, 259–290—*148*
— (1953). 'Eugen Bleuler's Conception of Schizophrenia—An Historical Sketch.' *Bull. Isaac Ray med. Libr.* **1**, 47–60—*34*
Bonhoeffer, K. (1907). *Klinische Beiträge zur Lehre von den Degenerations-psychosen.* [Clinical Contributions to the Problem of Degenerative Psychoses.] Halle; Marhold—*100*
— (1909). 'Zur Frage der exogenen Psychosen.' [On the Problem of Exo-genous Psychoses.]*Zbl. Nervenheilk.* **32** (*Neue Folge 20*), 499–505—*208*
— (1910). *Die symptomatischen Psychosen im Gefolge von akuten Infek-tionen und inneren Erkrankungen.* [The Symptomatic Psychoses Resulting from Acute Infections and Internal Diseases.] Leipzig and Vienna; Deuticke—*4*
— (1911). 'Wie weit kommen psychogene Krankheitszustände und Krankheitprozesse vor, die nicht der Hysterie zuzurechnen sind?' [Are There Psychogenic Pathological Conditions and Processes Which Are Not of a Hysterical Nature?] *Allg. Z. Psychiat.* **68**, 371–386—*28, 81*
— (1912). 'Die Psychosen im Gefolge von akuten Infektionen, Allge-meinerkrankungen und inneren Erkrankungen.' [The Psychoses Caused by Acute Infections, General Diseases and Internal Diseases.] *Handbook of Psychiatry, Spec. Part, Section* **3**, *1*, 1–118—*208*
— (1917). 'Die exogenen Reaktionstypen.' [The Exogenous Reaction Types.] *Arch. Psychiat. Nervenkr.* **58**, 58–70—*208*
Bostroem, A. (1929). 'Über die Auslösung endogener Psychosen durch beginnende paralytische Hirnprozesse und die Bedeutung dieses Vorgangs für die Prognose der Paralyse.' [On the Precipitation of Endogenous Psychoses by Paralytic Brain Processes and the Signifi-cance of this Process for the Prognosis of General Paralysis.] *Arch. Psychiat. Nervenkr.* **86**, 151–176—*198, 209*

223

Bostroem, A. (1931). 'Über organisch provozierte endogene Psychosen.' [On Organically Precipitated Endogenous Psychoses.] Z. ges. Neurol. Psychiat. 131, 1–6—198
— (1933). 'Zur Frage der Auslösung endogener Psychosen durch äussere Faktoren.' [On the Problem of Precipitation of Endogenous Psychoses by External Factors.] Münch. med. Wschr. 1933 I, 963–965—198
Bratz, E. (1928). '"Auslösung" der Schizophrenie und des manisch-depressiven Irreseins durch äussere Einflüsse.' ['Precipitation' of Schizophrenia and Manic-Depressive Psychosis by External Factors.] Psychiat.-neurol. Wschr. 1928 II, 387–390—198
Braun, E. (1928). 'Psychogene Reaktionen.' [Psychogenic Reactions.] Handbook of Mental Disorders 5, Spec. Part 1, 112–226—53
Brenner, C. (1963). 'The Psychopathology of the Psychoses.' Chapter in J. A. Arlow and C. Brenner. Psychoanalytic Concepts and the Structural Theory. New York; Int. Univ. Press (in press)—212
Bresowsky, M. (1933). 'Zur Diagnose und Klinik der psychogenen depressiven Reaktionen.' [Diagnosis and Clinical Aspects of the Psychogenic Depressive Reactions.] Mschr. Psychiat. Neurol. 85, 177–210—73
Breuer, J. and Freud, S. (1895). Studien über Hysterie. Leipzig and Vienna; Deuticke. ('Studies on Hysteria.' St. Ed. 2.) (Freud's contribution in G. W. 1, 75–312)—127
Bumke, O. (1928). Die gegenwärtigen Strömungen in der Psychiatrie. [Contemporary Trends in Clinical Psychiatry.] Berlin; Springer—25
— (1929). Lehrbuch der Geisteskrankheiten. [Textbook of Mental Diseases.] Munich; Bergmann, 3rd ed.—81, 132
Cameron, N. (1943). 'The Paranoid Pseudo-Community.' Amer. J. Sociol. 49, 32–38—146, 189
— (1959). 'The Paranoid Pseudo-Community Revisited.' Amer. J. Sociol. 65, 52–58—189
Cannon, W. B. (1932). The Wisdom of the Body. New York; Norton—38
Cohen, E. A. (1954). Het Duitse concentratiekamp. Een medische en psychologische studie. Amsterdam; Paris. (Human Behaviour in the Concentration Camp. London; Cape.)—16
Dement, W. and Kleitman, N. (1957). 'Cyclic Variations in EEG During Sleep and Their Relation to Eye Movements, Body Motility, and Dreaming.' Electroenceph. clin. Neurophysiol. 9, 673–690—214
Deutsch, F. (ed.) (1953). The Psychosomatic Concept in Psychoanalysis. New York; Int. Univ. Press—6
Dickens, C. (1861). Great Expectations—164
Drever, J. (1952). A Dictionary of Psychology. Harmondsworth, Middlesex; Penguin Books, Ltd.—5
Eliasberg, W. G. (1959). 'Grüsse der amerikanischen Psychiatrie.' [Salute from American Psychiatry.] E. Speer (ed.). Kritische Psychotherapie ['Critical' Psychotherapy. Papers given at the 8th Psychotherapy-Week at Lindau, Germany, 1958], 9–11. Munich; Lehmann—106
Eliot, T. S. (1932). 'Dante.' Selected Essays, 237–277. London; Faber—45
Engel, G. L. (1962). Psychological Development in Health and Disease. Philadelphia and London; Saunders—26

REFERENCES

Esquirol, E. (1838). *Des maladies mentales.* [The Mental Diseases.] Paris; Baillière, 2 Vols.—*23*

Essen-Möller, E. (1935). *Untersuchungen über die Fruchtbarkeit gewisser Gruppen von Geisteskranken.* [An Investigation of the Fertility of Certain Groups of Mental Disorders.] Copenhagen; Munksgaard—*191*

Ewald, G. (1928). 'Die Generationspsychosen des Weibes.' [Psychoses During Pregnancy and Puerperium.] *Handbook of Mental Disorders,* **7,** *Spec. Part 3,* 118–132—*68*

Eysenck, H. J. (ed.) (1960). *Experiments in Personality. Vol. 1: Psychogenetics and Psychopharmacology.* London; Routledge & Kegan Paul—*5*

Faergeman, P. M. (1941). 'Fälle psychogener Paranoia in sprachfremder Umgebung mit psychoplastisch bestimmtem, ungünstigem Verlauf.' [Cases of Psychogenic Paranoia in the Environment of a Foreign Language with Psychoplastic Determined Unfavourable Course.] *Allg. Z. Psychiat.* **117,** 10–24—*17*

— (1945). *De psykogene psykoser belyst gennem katamnestiske undersøgelser.* [The Psychogenic Psychoses. A Follow-Up Study.] Copenhagen; Munksgaard—*XI*

— (1946). 'Early Differential Diagnosis Between Psychogenic Psychosis and Schizophrenia.' *Memorial Volume to Hjalmar Helweg,* 275–279. Copenhagen; Munksgaard—*23*

Faris, R. E. L. and Dunham, H. W. (1939). *Mental Disorders in Urban Areas. An Ecological Study of Schizophrenia and Other Psychoses.* New York; Hafner, 2nd printing 1960—*45*

Ferenczi, S. (1911). 'Über die Rolle der Homosexualität in der Pathogenese der Paranoia. [On the Part Played by Homosexuality in the Pathogenesis of Paranoia.] *Jb. psychoanal. psychopath. Forsch.* **3,**101–119—*153*

— (1919). 'Sonntagsneurosen.' *Int. Z. Psychoanal.,* **5,** 46–48. ('Sunday Neuroses.' S. Ferenczi. *Further Contributions to the Theory and Technique of Psycho-Analysis,* 174–176. London; The Hogarth Press and the Institute of Psycho-Analysis, 2nd ed. 1950.)—*32*

— Abraham, K., Simmel, E. and Jones, E. (1921). *Psycho-Analysis and the War Neuroses.* London, Vienna, New York; Int. Psycho-Anal. Press—*28*

Finckh, O. (1927). 'Psychogene Initialsymptome bei Schizophrenien.' [Psychogenic Prodromal Symptoms in Schizophrenias.] *Arch. Psychiat. Nervenkr.* **81,** 152–158—*198*

Fitzgerald, F. S. (1933). *Tender is the Night.* Published in *Three Novels.* New York; Scribner, 1953—*26*

Freeman, T. (1959). 'Aspects of Defence in Neurosis and Psychosis.' *Int. J. Psycho-Anal.* **40,** 199–212—*33*

Fremming, K. H. (1947). *Sygdomsrisikoen for Sindslidelser og andre sjælelige Abnormtilstande i den danske Gennemsnitsbefolkning.* [Morbid Risk of Mental Diseases and Other Mental Abnormalities in an Average Danish Population.] Copenhagen; Munksgaard—*185*

— (1951). *The Expectation of Mental Infirmity in a Sample of the Danish Population.* London; Cassell—*185*

French, T. M. (1936). 'A Clinical Study of Learning in the Course of a Psychoanalytic Treatment.' *Psychoanal. Quart.* **5,** 148–194—*212*

French, T. M. (1937). 'Reality and the Unconscious.' *Psychoanal. Quart.* **6**, 23–61—*212*
— (1939). 'Insight and Distortion in Dreams.' *Int. J. Psycho-Anal.* **20**, 287–298—*212*
— (1952). *The Integration of Behavior. Vol. 1: Basic Postulates.* Chicago; The University of Chicago Press—*212*
Freud, Anna (1958). 'Child Observation and Prediction of Development.' *Psychoanal. Stud. Child* **13**, 92–116—*18*
Freud, S. (1900). 'Die Traumdeutung.' *G. W.* **2/3**, 1–642 ('The Interpretation of Dreams.' *St. Ed.* **4**, 1–338; **5**, 339–621.)—*24*
— (1905). 'Drei Abhandlungen zur Sexualtheorie.' *G. W.* **5**, 29–145 ('Three Essays on the Theory of Sexuality.' *St. Ed.* **7**, 130–243.)—*24*
— (1911). 'Psychoanalytische Bemerkungen über einen autobiographisch beschriebenen Fall von Paranoia (Dementia paranoides).' *G. W.* **8**, 240–320 ('Psycho-Analytic Notes on an Autobiographical Account of a Case of Paranoia (Dementia paranoides).' *St. Ed.* **12**, 9–82.)—*146, 153*
— (1913a). 'Totem und Tabu.' *G. W.* **9**, 3–194 ('Totem and Taboo.' *St. Ed.* **13**, 1–161.)—*219*
— (1913b). 'Die Disposition zur Zwangsneurose.' *G. W.* **8**, 442–452. ('The Disposition to Obsessional Neurosis.' *St. Ed.* **12**, 317–326.)—*205, 212*
— (1914). 'Zur Einführung des Narzissmus.' *G. W.* **10**, 138–170 ('On Narcissism: an Introduction.' *St. Ed.* **14**, 73–102.)—*146, 206*
— (1915). 'Mitteilung eines der psychoanalytischen Theorie widersprechenden Falles von Paranoia.' *G. W.* **10**, 234–246 ('A Case of Paranoia Running Counter to the Psycho Analytic Theory of the Disease.' *St. Ed.* **14**, 263–272.)—*146*
— (1916–1917). 'Vorlesungen zur Einführung in die Psychoanalyse.' *G. W.* **11**. ('Introductory Lectures on Psycho-Analysis.' *St. Ed.* **15**; **16**. To be published.)—*212*
— (1917). 'Trauer und Melancholie.' *G. W.* **10**, 428–446 ('Mourning and Melancholia.' *St. Ed.* **14**, 243–258.)—*9*
— (1919). 'Ein Kind wird geschlagen.' *G. W.* **12**, 197–226 ('A Child is Being Beaten.' *St. Ed.* **17**, 179–204.)—*146*
— (1920). 'Jenseits des Lustprinzips.' *G. W.* **13**, 3–69 ('Beyond the Pleasure Principle.' *St. Ed.* **18**, 7–64.)—*31, 36*
— (1922). 'Über einige neurotische Mechanismen bei Eifersucht, Paranoia und Homosexualität.' *G. W.* **13**, 195–207 ('Some Neurotic Mechanisms in Jealousy, Paranoia and Homosexuality.' *St. Ed.* **18**, 223–232.)—*34, 146, 151*
— (1923). 'Das Ich und das Es.' *G. W.* **13**, 237–289 ('The Ego and the Id.' *St. Ed.* **19**, 12–59.)—*31, 146*
— (1924a). 'Neurose und Psychose.' *G. W.* **13**, 387–391 ('Neurosis and Psychosis.' *St. Ed.* **19**, 149–153.)—*30*
— (1924b). 'Der Realitätsverlust bei Neurose und Psychose.' *G. W.* **13**, 363–368 ('The Loss of Reality in Neurosis and Psychosis.' *St. Ed.* **19**, 183–187.)—*30*
— (1926a). 'Hemmung, Symptom und Angst.' *G. W.* **14**, 113–205 ('Inhibitions, Symptoms and Anxiety.' *St. Ed.* **20**, 87–172.)—*13*

REFERENCES

Freud, S. (1926b). 'Die Frage der Laienanalyse.' *G. W.* **14**, 209–296 ('The Question of Lay Analysis.' *St. Ed.* **20**, 183–258.)—*30*
— (1930). 'Das Unbehagen in der Kultur.' *G. W.* **14**, 421–506 ('Civilization and Its Discontents.' *St. Ed.* **21**, 64–145.)—*12*
— (1937). 'Die endliche und die unendliche Analyse.' *G. W.* **16**, 59–99. ('Analysis Terminable and Interminable.' *St. Ed.* **23**. To be published.)—*37*
Friedell, E. (1927–1931). *Kulturgeschichte der Neuzeit.* Munich; Beck. (*Cultural History of the Modern Age.* New York; Knopf 1952–1954, and London; Vision 1953–1954.)—*173*
Fromm, E. (1941). *Escape from Freedom.* New York; Farrar & Rinehart, and under the title: *The Fear of Freedom.* London; Kegan Paul, 1943—*45*
Ganser, S. (1898). 'Über einen eigenartigen hysterischen Dämmerzustand.' [On a Peculiar Type of Hysterical Twilight State.] *Arch. Psychiat. Nervenkr.* **30**, 633–640—*107*
Gerö, G. (1943). 'The Idea of Psychogenesis in Modern Psychiatry and in Psychoanalysis.' *Psychoanal. Rev.* **30**, 187–211—*10*
Gerstmann, J. (1920). 'Zur Frage der Einwirkung psychischer Faktoren auf zerebrale Mechanismen und über den Begriff der "physiogenen Neurosen".' [On the Problem of the Action of Psychic Factors on Cerebral Mechanisms and on the Concept of 'Physiogenic Neuroses'.] *Wien. klin. Wschr.* **33**, 557–558—*28*
Glover, E. (1931). 'The Therapeutic Effect of Inexact Interpretation: A Contribution to the Theory of Suggestion.' *Int. J. Psycho-Anal.* **12**, 397–411—*12*
— (1932). 'A Psycho-Analytic Approach to the Classification of Mental Disorders.' *J. ment. Sci.* **78**, 819–842, and E. Glover. *On the Early Development of Mind*, 161–186. London; Imago Publ. 1956—*15*
— (1939; 1949). *Psycho-Analysis.* London and New York; Staples Press, 2nd ed. 1949—*6, 42, 146*
Glueck, B. C., Jr. (1962). Personal Communication—*200*
Goethe, J. W. (1808). *Faust. Part 1*, line 2016—*19*
Goldfarb, A. I. (1959). 'Minor Maladjustments in the Aged.' *American Handbook of Psychiatry* **1**, 378–397—*186*
Goldkuhl, E. (1938). *Psychische Insuffizienzzustände bei Oligophrenien leichteren Grades.* [Psychic States of Insufficiency in Mild Mental Retardation.] Copenhagen; Munksgaard—*196*
Greenacre, Phyllis (1945). 'Conscience in the Psychopath.' *Amer. J. Orthopsychiat.* **15**, 495–509—*13*
Griesinger, W. (1876). *Die Pathologie und Therapie der psychischen Krankheiten für Aerzte und Studirende.* [The Pathology and Therapy of Psychic Diseases.] Braunschweig; Wreden, 4th ed.—*24*
Groddeck, G. (1923). *Das Buch vom Es.* Vienna; Int. Psychoanal. Verlag. (*The Book of the It.* London; Vision 1950.)—*31*
Gruhle, H. W. (1929). 'Psychologie der Schizophrenie.' [Psychology of Schizophrenia.] J. Berze and H. W. Gruhle. *Psychologie der Schizophrenie.* Berlin; Springer—*215*
— (1932). 'Theorie der Schizophrenie.' [The Theory of Schizophrenia.] *Handbook of Mental Disorders* **9**, *Spec. Part 5*, 705–713—*27*
— (1940). *Selbstmord.* [Suicide.] Leipzig; Thieme—*27*

227

Hall, G. S. (1914). 'A Synthetic Genetic Study of Fear.' *Amer. J. Psychol.* **25,** 149–200, 321–392—*33*

Hartmann, H. (1939). 'Ich-Psychologie und Anpassungsproblem.' *Int. Z. Psychoanal. u. Imago* **24,** 62–135 (*Ego Psychology and the Problem of Adaptation.* New York; Int. Univ. Press 1958.)—*33*

— (1959). 'Psychoanalysis As a Scientific Theory.' S. Hook (ed.). *Psychoanalysis, Scientific Method and Philosophy,* 3–37. New York; New York University Press—*216*

Heinroth, J. C. A. (1818). *Lehrbuch der Störungen des Seelenlebens oder der Seelenstörungen und ihrer Behandlung.* [Textbook on the Disturbances of the Psychic Life or the Psychic Disturbances and Their Treatment.] Leipzig; Vogel, 2 Parts—*23*

Helweg, H. (1939). *Den retslige psykiatri i kort omrids.* [A Brief Outline of Forensic Psychiatry.] Copenhagen; Hagerup, 2nd ed., 1949—*29*

Helweg-Larsen, P., Hoffmeyer, H., Kieler, J., Hess Thaysen, E., Hess Thaysen, J., Thygesen, P. and Hertel Wulff, M. (1952). *Famine Disease in German Concentration Camps. Complications and Sequels.* Copenhagen; Munksgaard—*16*

Herschmann, H. (1919). 'Psychopathische Minderwertigkeit und Feldgerichtsbarkeit.' [Psychopathic Inferiority and Military Judicial Authority.] *Wien. med. Wschr.* **69,** 1419–1426—*17*

Hinsie, L. E. and Campbell, R. J. (1960). *Psychiatric Dictionary.* New York; Oxford Univ. Press, 3rd ed.—*5*

Hoch, P. and Polatin, P. (1949). 'Pseudoneurotic Forms of Schizophrenia.' *Psychiat. Quart.* **23,** 248–276—*32*

Hoche, A. (1902). *Differentialdiagnose zwischen Epilepsie und Hysterie.* [Differential Diagnosis Between Epilepsy and Hysteria.] Berlin; Hirschwald—*25*

— (1906). 'Kritisches zur psychiatrischen Formenlehre.' [A Critical Evaluation of Psychiatric Nosology.] *Neurol. Cbl.* **25,** 430–431—*25*

Hoffmann, H. (1923). 'Schizothym-Cyklothym.' [Schizothymic-Cyclothymic.] *Z. ges. Neurol. Psychiat.* **82,** 93–104—*78*

— (1926) *Das Problem des Charakteraufbaus.* [The Problem of the Structure of Character.] Berlin; Springer—*51*

Hollingshead, A. B. and Redlich, F. C. (1958). *Social Class and Mental Illness: A Community Study.* New York; Wiley, and London; Chapman & Hall—*44*

Hoskins, R. G. (1946). *The Biology of Schizophrenia.* New York; Norton—*74*

James, W. (1884). 'What is an Emotion?' *Mind* **9,** 188–205—*24*

— (1890). *The Principles of Psychology.* New York; Holt—*24, 206*

Jaspers, K. (1913; 1923; 1948; 1959). *Allgemeine Psychopathologie.* [General Psychopathology.] Berlin; Springer, 3rd ed. 1923, 5th ed. 1948, 7th ed. 1959—*8, 51, 52, 132, 155, 198*

Jung, R. (1961). 'Einleitung zur Kriegspsychiatrie.' [Introduction to War Psychiatry.] H. W. Gruhle *et al. Psychiatrie der Gegenwart* [Contemporary Psychiatry] **3,** 568–573. Berlin, Göttingen & Heidelberg; Springer—*70, 199*

Kahn, E. (1921). 'Zur Frage des schizophrenen Reaktionstypus.' [On the Problem of the Schizophrenic Reaction Type.] *Z. ges. Neurol. Psychiat.* **66,** 273–282—*78*

Kahn, E. (1927). 'Psychopathien und psychogene Reaktionen.' [Psychopathy and Psychogenic Reactions.] *Arch. Psychiat. Nervenkr.* **80,** 4–38—*57*

— (1929). 'Über Wahnbildung.' [On the Production of Delusions.] *Arch. Psychiat. Nervenkr.* **88,** 435–454—*215*

Kallmann, F. J. (1959). 'The Genetics of Mental Illness.' *American Handbook of Psychiatry,* **1,** 175–196—*5, 198*

Kant, F. (1929). 'Über die Kombination reaktiver und charakterologischer mit phasischen und prozesshaften Faktoren in der paranoischen Wahnbildung. Ein Beitrag zur Frage der "Sensitiven Beziehungspsychose".' [On the Combination of Reactive and Characterological Factors with Periodic and Process Factors in the Formation of Paranoid Delusions. A Contribution to the Problem of the 'Sensitive Psychosis of Reference'.] *Arch. Psychiat. Nervenkr.* **87,** 171–190—*215*

— (1930). 'Über Reaktionsformen im Giftrausch. Mit einem Beitrag zum Halluzinationsproblem.' [On Types of Reaction in Toxic States. With a Contribution to the Problem of Hallucinations.] *Arch. Psychiat. Nervenkr.* **91,** 694–721—*209*

Kant, O. (1927; 1930; 1933; 1934). 'Beiträge zur Wahnforschung.' [Contributions to the Study of Paranoia.] *Z. ges. Neurol. Psychiat.* **108,** 625–644 (1927); **110,** 558–579 (1927); **127,** 615–659 (1930); **146,** 599–619 (1933); **150,** 272–304 (1934)—*215*

Kardiner, A. (in coll. with H. Spiegel) (1947). *War Stress and Neurotic Illness.* New York and London; Hoeber—*28*

— (1959). 'Traumatic Neuroses of War.' *American Handbook of Psychiatry* **1,** 245–257—*28*

Karpman, Ben (1948). 'The Myth of the Psychopathic Personality.' *Amer. J. Psychiat.* **104** (March), 523–534—*194*

Katan, M. (1954). 'The Importance of the Non-Psychotic Part of the Personality in Schizophrenia.' *Int. J. Psycho-Anal.* **35,** 119–128—*33*

— (1960). 'Dream and Psychosis: Their Relationship to Hallucinatory Processes.' *Int. J. Psycho-Anal.* **41,** 341–351—*33, 132*

Kay, D. W. K. (1959). 'Observations on the Natural History and Genetics of Old Age Psychoses: A Stockholm Material (Abridged).' *Proc. Roy. Soc. Med.* **52,** 791–794—*52*

Kehrer, F. (1922). 'Erotische Wahnbildungen sexuell unbefriedigter weiblicher Wesen.' [Erotic Paranoid Productions in Sexually Unsatisfied Females.] *Arch. Psychiat. Nervenkr.* **65,** 315–385—*147, 148*

— (1930). 'Hysterie.' [Hysteria.] K. Birnbaum (ed.). *Handwörterbuch der medizinischen Psychologie* [Dictionary of Medical Psychology], 227–234. Leipzig; Thieme—*42*

Klein, Melanie (1932). *Die Psychoanalyse des Kindes.* Vienna; Int. Psychoanal. Verlag (*Psycho-Analysis of Children.* London; Hogarth Press, and New York; Norton.)—*146*

Kleist, K. (1916). *Postoperative Psychosen.* [Post-Operative Psychoses.] Berlin; Springer—*97, 208*

— (1918). 'Schreckpsychosen.' ['Terror' Psychoses.] *Allg. Z. Psychiat.* **74,** 171–172—*27, 82*

— (1926). *Episodische Dämmerzustände. Ein Beitrag zur Kenntnis der konstitutionellen Geistesstörungen.* [Episodic Twilight States. A Contribution to the Understanding of Constitutional Mental Disturbances.] Leipzig; Thieme—*39, 41, 163*

Knight, R. P. (1940). 'The Relationship of Latent Homosexuality to the Mechanism of Paranoid Delusions.' *Bull. Menninger Clin.* **4**, 149–159 —*146*

— (1954). 'Borderline State.' R. P. Knight and C. R. Friedman (eds.). *Psychoanalytic Psychiatry and Psychology,* 97–109. New York; Int. Univ. Press. *Bull. Menninger Clin.* **17**, 1–12 (1953)—*33, 212*

Kolle, K. (1931). *Die primäre Verrücktheit.* [Primary Delusions.] Leipzig; Thieme—*215*

Kraepelin, E. (1881). 'Über den Einfluss acuter Krankheiten auf die Entstehung von Geisteskrankheiten.' [On the Influence of Acute Illnesses on the Outbreak of Mental Diseases.] *Arch. Psychiat. Nervenkr.* **11**, 137–183, 295–350, 649–677—*208*

— (1883; 1896; 1927). *Psychiatrie.* Leipzig; Barth, 5th ed. 1896, 9th ed. 1927 (Clinical Psychiatry. Abstr. and adapt. from 7th ed. New York; Macmillan 1912.)—*25, 34*

— (1915). 'Der Verfolgungswahn der Schwerhörigen.' [The Delusion of Persecution in Hard-of-Hearing Persons.] *Psychiatrie.* [Psychiatry.] *Vol. 4, Part 3,* 1441–1448. 'Die psychogenen Geistesstörungen der Gefangenen.' [The Psychogenic Mental Disturbances in Prisoners.] *Ibid.,* 1502–1533. Leipzig; Barth, 8th ed.—*17, 200*

— (1920). 'Die Erscheinungsformen des Irreseins.' [Symptoms of Mental Disease.] *Z. ges. Neurol. Psychiat.* **62**, 1–29—*208*

Krapf, E. (1927). 'Paranoischer Liebes- und Verfolgungswahn mit symptomatischer Exacerbation. Ein Beitrag zur Paranoiafrage.' [Paranoid Erotic and Persecutory Delusions with Symptomatic Exacerbation. A Contribution to the Problem of Paranoia.] *Arch. Psychiat. Nervenkr.* **81**, 561–578—*215*

Kretschmer, E. (1918; 1927; 1950). *Der sensitive Beziehungswahn.* [The Sensitive Delusion of Reference.] Berlin; Springer, 2nd ed. 1927, 3rd ed. 1950—*11, 28, 56, 146, 148, 149, 215*

— 1919a). 'Über psychogene Wahnbildung bei traumatischer Hirnschwäche.' [On Psychogenic Delusional Formation in Traumatic Brain Weakness.] *Z. ges. Neurol. Psychiat.* **45**, 272–300—*89*

— (1919b). 'Gedanken über die Fortentwicklung der psychiatrischen Systematik.' [Thoughts on the Development of the System of Psychiatry.] *Z. ges. Neurol. Psychiat.* **48**, 370–377—*148*

— (1923; 1927). *Über Hysterie.* Leipzig; Thieme, 2nd ed. 1927. (*Hysteria.* Washington, D.C.; Nerv. & Ment. Dis. Publ. 1926.)—*42, 87, 214*

— (1926). *Medizinische Psychologie.* Leipzig; Thieme, 3rd ed. Stuttgart; Thieme, 1956, 11th ed. (*Textbook of Medical Psychology.* London; Oxford Univ. Press 1934.)—*87*

— (1929). 'Psychotherapie der Schizophrenie und ihrer Grenzzustände.' [Psychotherapy of Schizophrenia and Its Borderlands.] *Z. ges. Neurol. Psychiat.* **121**, 211–223—*199*

— (1931). *Körperbau und Charakter.* Berlin; Springer, 9th/10th ed. 1961, 23rd/24th ed. (*Physique and Character.* New York; Harcourt, Brace, and London; Kegan Paul, Trench, Trubner 1936, 2nd ed.)—*53*

Kris, E. (1956). 'The Recovery of Childhood Memories in Psychoanalysis.' *Psychoanal. Stud. Child* **11**, 54–88—*12, 17*

REFERENCES

Kris, Marianne (1957). 'The Use of Prediction in a Longitudinal Study.' *Psychoanal. Stud. Child* **12**, 175–189—*36*

Lange, C. (1885). *Om Sindsbevægelser. En psykofysiologisk Studie.* [*On Emotions. A Psycho-Physiological Study.*] Copenhagen; Lund—*24*

Lange, J. (1926). 'Über Melancholie.' [On Melancholia.] *Z. ges. Neurol. Psychiat.* **101**, 293–319—*52, 53, 57, 69, 71*

— (1927). 'Die Paranoiafrage.' [The Problem of Paranoia.] *Handbook of Psychiatry, Spec. Part, Section 4, 2—147, 215*

— (1928). 'Die endogenen und reaktiven Gemütserkrankungen und die manisch-depressive Konstitution.' [The Endogenous and Reactive Affective Disorders and the Manic-Depressive Constitution.] *Handbook of Mental Disorders, 6, Spec. Part 2, 1–231—40, 52, 53, 72, 82, 105, 186*

Langfeldt, G. (1939). *The Schizophreniform States.* London; Humphrey Milford, Oxford Univ. Press, and Copenhagen; Munksgaard—*78, 86*

Laughlin, H. P. (1956). *The Neuroses in Clinical Practice.* Philadelphia and London; Saunders—*6*

Lewin, B. D. (1946). 'Sleep, the Mouth and the Dream Screen.' *Psychoanal. Quart.* **15**, 419–434—*133*

— (1948). 'Inferences from the Dream Screen.' *Int. J. Psycho-Anal.* **29**, 224–231—*133*

— (1950). *The Psychoanalysis of Elation.* New York; Norton—*82, 216*

— (1953). 'Reconsideration of the Dream Screen.' *Psychoanal. Quart.* **22**, 174–199—*133*

Lewis, A. (1934). 'Melancholia; A Clinical Survey of Depressive States.' *J. ment. Sci.* **80**, 277–378—*8, 52*

— (1942). 'Incidence of Neurosis in England under War Conditions.' *Lancet* **1942** 2, 175–183—*199*

Lidz, Ruth and Lidz, T. (1950). 'Eine Interpretation der Grundideen der amerikanischen Psychiatrie.' [An Interpretation of the Fundamental Ideas in American Psychiatry.] *Nervenarzt* **21**, 490–494—*106*

Lilly, J. C. (1956). 'Mental Effects of Reduction of Ordinary Levels of Physical Stimuli on Intact, Healthy Persons.' *Psychiat. Res. Amer. psychiat. Ass.* **5**, 1–9—*17*

Linton, R. (1956). *Culture and Mental Disorders.* Ed. by G. Devereux. Springfield, Ill.; Thomas—*205*

Lückerath, M. (1911). 'Zur Differentialdiagnose zwischen Dementia praecox und Hysterie.' [Differential Diagnosis Between Dementia Praecox and Hysteria.] *Allg. Z. Psychiat.* **68**, 312–329—*190*

Lunn, V. (1953). Paranoide tilstande. [Paranoid States.] *Nord. Med.* **49**, 831–838—*213*

McLean, P. G. (1959). 'Psychiatry and Philosophy.' *American Handbook of Psychiatry, 2, 1760–1776—29*

Maier, H. W. (1912). 'Über katathyme Wahnbildung und Paranoia.' [On Catathymic Delusion Formation and Paranoia.] *Z. ges. Neurol. Psychiat.* **13**, 555–610—*15, 27, 215*

Malzberg, B. (1934). *Mortality Among Patients With Mental Disease.* Utica, N.Y.; State Hospitals Press—*191*

— (1940). *Social and Biological Aspects of Mental Disease.* Utica, N.Y.; State Hospitals Press—*186*

Malzberg, B. (1959). 'Important Statistical Data About Mental Illness.' *American Handbook of Psychiatry* **1**, 161–174—*194*

Mandiargues, A. P. de (1956). *Le Lis de Mer*. Paris; Laffont. (*The Girl Beneath the Lion*. New York; Grove Press 1958)—*12*

Margolin, S. G. (1953). 'Genetic and Dynamic Psychophysiological Determinants of Pathophysiological Processes.' F. Deutsch (ed.). *The Psychosomatic Concept in Psychoanalysis*, 3–36. New York; Int. Univ. Press—*6*

Mauz, F. (1930). *Die Prognostik der endogenen Psychosen*. [The Prognosis of the Endogenous Psychoses.] Leipzig; Thieme—*85*

Mayer-Gross, W. (1932). 'Die Schizophrenie. IV. Die Klinik.' [Clinical Part of Volume on Schizophrenia.] *Handbook of Mental Disorders*, **9**, Spec. Part 5, 293–594—*198, 199, 200*

— Slater, E. and Roth, M. (1960). *Clinical Psychiatry*. London; Cassell, 2nd ed.—*4, 17, 26, 47, 70, 107, 122, 149, 163, 164, 200*

Mendelson, M. (1960). *Psychoanalytic Concepts of Depression*. Springfield, Ill.; Thomas—*51*

Menninger, K. (1959). 'Toward a Unitary Concept of Mental Illness.' *A Psychiatrist's World. The Selected Papers of Karl Menninger*,516–528. New York; The Viking Press—*34, 38, 106*

Meyer, J.-E. (1961). 'Diagnostische Einteilungen und Diagnosensche-mata in der Psychiatrie.' [Diagnostic Classifications and Diagnostic Outlines in Psychiatry.] H. W. Gruhle *et al. Psychiatrie der Gegenwart* [Contemporary Psychiatry], **3**, 130–180. Berlin, Göttingen and Heidelberg; Springer—*6*

Miller, S. C. (1962). 'Ego-Autonomy in Sensory Deprivation, Isolation, and Stress.' *Int. J. Psycho-Anal.* **43**, 1–20—*17*

Murray, H. A. (ed.) (1938). *Explorations in Personality*. New York; Oxford Univ. Press—*4*

Neustadt, R. (1928). *Die Psychosen der Schwachsinnigen*. [Psychoses in the Mentally Retarded.] Berlin; Karger—*196*

Neve, G. (1914). *Bidrag til Spørgsmaalet om chroniske Alkoholpsykoser*. [Contributions to the Question of Chronic Alcoholic Psychoses.] Copenhagen; Gad—*121*

Newkirk, P. R. (1957). 'Psychopathic Traits Are Inheritable.' *Dis. nerv. Syst.* **18**, 52–54—*194*

Nissl, F. (1899). 'Über die sogen. functionellen Geisteskrankheiten.' [On the So-Called Functional Mental Diseases.] *Münch. med. Wschr.* **46**, 1453–1456—*24*

— (1902). 'Hysterische Symptome bei einfachen Seelenstörungen.' [Hysterical Symptoms in Simple Mental Disturbances.] *Cbl. Nervenheilk. Psychiat.* **15** (*Neue Folge 13*), 2–38—*24*

Noyes, A. P. and Kolb, L. C. (1958). *Modern Clinical Psychiatry*. Philadelphia and London; Saunders, 5th ed.—*6*

Oppenheim, H. (1915). 'Die Neurosen nach Kriegsverletzungen.' [Neuroses Following Injuries of War.] *Neurol. Cbl.* **34**, 810–813—*28*

— (1916). 'Fortgesetzte Diskussion über die traumatischen Neurosen.' [Continuation of the Discussion of Traumatic Neuroses.] *Neurol. Cbl.* **35**, 530–541—*28*

Ostow, M. (1959). 'The Biological Basis of Human Behavior.' *American Handbook of Psychiatry* **1**, 58–87—*35*

REFERENCES

Pflanz, M. (1959). 'Mitteleuropa. Gegenwärtiger Stand und Entwick-lungstendenzen der Neurosenlehre und Psychotherapie.' [Central Europe. Contemporary Viewpoints and Developmental Trends in the Theory of Neuroses and in Psychotherapy.] V. E. Frankl et al. (ed.). Handbuch der Neurosenlehre und Psychotherapie [Manual of the Theory of Neuroses], 1, 35–81. Munich and Berlin; Urban & Schwarzenberg—145

Pohlisch, K. (1927). 'Zur Pathogenese der akuten Halluzinose der Trinker.' [On the Pathogenesis of the Acute Hallucinosis in Alco-holics.] Mschr. Psychiat. Neurol. 63, 82–96—121

Popper, E. (1920). 'Der schizophrene Reaktionstypus.' [The Schizo-phrenic Reaction Type.] Z. ges. Neurol. Psychiat. 62, 194–207—78

Prichard, J. C. (1835). A Treatise on Insanity and Other Disorders Affecting the Mind. London; Sherwood, Gilbert & Piper—23

Raecke, J. (1901a). 'Beitrag zur Kenntnis des hysterischen Dämmerzu-standes.' [Contribution to the Knowledge of the Hysterical Twilight State.] Allg. Z. Psychiat. 58, 115–163—190

— (1901b). 'Hysterischer Stupor bei Strafgefangenen.' [Hysterical Stupor in Convicts.] Allg. Z. Psychiat. 58, 409–446—190

Rapaport, D. (1955). Seminars on Psychoanalytic Ego-Psychology. Vol. 3. S. C. Miller (ed.). Stockbridge, Mass.; Austen Riggs. Transcript—31

— (1957). Seminars on Advanced Metapsychology. Vol. 3: 'Affects.' S. C. Miller (ed.). Stockbridge, Mass.; Austen Riggs. Transcript—217

Reiss, E. (1910). 'Konstitutionelle Verstimmung und manisch-depres-sives Irresein.' [Depressive Constitution and Manic-Depressive Insanity.] Z. ges. Neurol. Psychiat. 2, 347–628—8, 52

Rennie, T. A. C. (1942). 'Prognosis in Manic-Depressive Psychoses.' Amer. J. Psychiat. 98, 801–814—26

Ritvo, S. (1958). Yale Report Read at Orthopsychiatric Meeting, March 1958. Report from a Longitudinal Study in Child Development, a Contribution of Psychoanalytic Treatment. Quoted from M. E. Fries (1961). 'Some Factors in the Development and Significance of Early Object Relationships.' J. Amer. psychoanal. Ass. 9, 679—36

Romano, J. (1947). H. L. Witmer (ed.). Teaching Psychotherapeutic Medicine, p. 345. New York; Commonwealth Fund—29

— (ed.) (1949). Adaptation. Ithaca, N.Y.; Cornell Univ. Press—29

Rome, H. P. and Robinson, D. B. (1959). 'Psychiatric Conditions Associated with Metabolic, Endocrine, and Nutritional Disorders.' American Handbook of Psychiatry, 2, 1260–1288—30

Ross, T. A. (1936). An Enquiry into Prognosis in the Neuroses. Cambridge; University Press—29

Roth, M. (1957). 'Interaction of Genetic and Environmental Factors in the Causation of Schizophrenia.' D. Richter (ed.). Schizophrenia. Somatic Aspects, 15–31. London, New York and Paris; Pergamon Press—26

— (1959). 'The Phenomenology of Depressive States.' Canad. psychiat. Ass. J. 4, Spec. Suppl., 32–54—52

— (1960). 'Depressive States and Their Borderlands: Classification, Diagnosis and Treatment.' Comprehens. Psychiat. 1, 135–155—52

Rüdin, E. (1901). 'Über die klinischen Formen der Gefängnispsychosen.'

[On the Clinical Types of Prison Psychoses.] *Allg. Z. Psychiat.* **58,** 447–462—*200*

Rüdin, E. (1909). *Über die klinischen Formen der Seelenstörungen bei zu lebenslänglicher Zuchthausstrafe Verurteilten.* [On the Clinical Symptoms of Mental Disease in Prisoners Condemned to a Life Sentence.] Munich; Thesis—*200*

Runge, W. (1911). 'Die Generationspsychosen des Weibes.' [Psychoses During Pregnancy and Puerperium.] *Arch. Psychiat. Nervenkr.* **48,** 545–690—*68*

Schilder, P. (1918). *Wahn und Erkenntnis.* [Delusion and Cognition.] Berlin; Springer—*215, 219*

Schipkowensky, N. (1960). *Pathologische Reaktionen der Persönlichkeit.* [Pathological Personality Reactions.] Vienna, Bonn and Berne; Maudrich—*17*

Schmideberg, Melitta (1959). 'The Borderline Patient.' *American Handbook of Psychiatry* **1,** 398–416—*33*

Schneider, K. (1919a). 'Reaktion und Auslösung bei der Schizophrenie.' [Reaction and Precipitation in Schizophrenia.] *Z. ges. Neurol. Psychiat.* **50,** 49–81—*198*

— (1919b). 'Über reaktive Manie und Angstmanie.' [On Reactive Manic States and Anxiety-Mania.] *Mschr. Psychiat. Neurol.* **46,** 176–180—*81*

— (1920). 'Zur Frage des sensitiven Beziehungswahns.' [On the Problem of the Sensitive Delusion of Reference.] *Z. ges. Neurol. Psychiat.* **59,** 51–63—*147, 215*

— (1923; 1942). *Die psychopathischen Persönlichkeiten.* Leipzig and Vienna; Deuticke, 5th ed. 1942, 9th ed. 1950. (*Psychopathic Personalities.* London; Cassell 1958.)—*53, 59, 195*

— (1927). 'Die abnormen seelischen Reaktionen.' [Abnormal Psychic Reactions.] *Handbook of Psychiatry, Spec. Part, Section* **7,** *Part 2, 1—17, 28, 39, 62, 82*

— (1932). *Probleme der klinischen Psychiatrie.* [Problems of Clinical Psychiatry.] Leipzig; Thieme—*41*

— (1952). *Über den Wahn.* [On Paranoia.] Stuttgart; Thieme—*215*

Schreber, D. P. (1903). *Denkwürdigkeiten eines Nervenkranken.* Leipzig; Mutze. (*Memoirs of my Nervous Illness.* Ed. by I. Macalpine and R. A. Hunter. London; Dawson 1955.)—*146*

Schrøder, G. E. (1913). *Fængselspsychoser og Psychoser i Fængslet.* [Imprisonment Psychoses and Psychoses in the Prison.] Copenhagen; Lund—*200*

Schultz, J. H. (1921). 'Über Schichtenbildung im hypnotischen Selbstbeobachten.' [On the Formation of Layers in Hypnotic Selfobservation.] *Mschr. Psychiat. Neurol.* **49,** 137–143—*219*

— (1930). 'Das Endgültigkeitsproblem in der Psychologie der Rückbildungsdepressionen.' [The Feeling of Inevitability in Involutional Depressions.] *Z. ges. Neurol. Psychiat.* **128,** 512–514—*8*

— (1937). *Das autogene Training.* [The Autogenic Training.] Leipzig; Thieme, 3rd ed. Stuttgart; Thieme 1960, 10th ed.—*219*

Selye, H. (1956). 'Stress and Psychiatry.' *Amer. J. Psychiat.* **113,** 423–427 —*30*

Shakespeare, W. (1600). *King Henry V,* Act 3, Scene 7. (Temple Edition.)—*14*

REFERENCES

Siefert, E. (1907). *Über die Geistesstörungen der Strafhaft mit Ausschluss der Psychosen der Untersuchungshaft und der Haftpsychosen.* [On Mental Disturbances in Prison.] Halle; Marhold—*200*

Slater, E. (1953). *Psychotic and Neurotic Illnesses in Twins.* London; Her Majesty's Stationery Office. Spec. Rep. Ser. med. Res. Coun. (Lond.), No. 278—*26*

Smith, L. P. (1933). *All Trivia.* London; Constable—*206*

Sommer, R. (1894). *Diagnostik der Geisteskrankheiten.* [Diagnostics of Mental Diseases.] Vienna; Urban & Schwarzenberg—*4*

Sonnenberg, A. (1922). 'Über die inneren und äusseren Ursachen des Jugendirreseins unter besonderer Berücksichtigung der Kriegsschädigungen.' [On the Internal and External Causes of Dementia Praecox with Special Reference to Insults of War.] *Arch. Psychiat. Nervenkr.* **64**, 13–47—*199*

Specht, G. (1913). 'Zur Frage der exogenen Schädigungstypen.' [On the Problem of the Exogenous Reaction Types.] *Z. ges. Neurol. Psychiat.* **19**, 104–116—*208*

Spinoza, B. (1677). *Ethica.* (*Ethics and De intellectus emendatione.* London; Dent, and New York; Dutton 1910; 1955.)—*24*

Spitz, R. A. (1945). 'Hospitalism. An Inquiry into the Genesis of Psychiatric Conditions in Early Childhood.' *Psychoanal. Stud. Child* **1**, 53–74—*19, 186*

— (1946). 'Anaclitic Depression. An Inquiry into the Genesis of Psychiatric Conditions in Early Childhood, II.' *Psychoanal. Stud. Child* **2**, 313–342—*19, 186*

Statistical Year Book for Copenhagen, Frederiksberg and Gjentofte (1926). Copenhagen 1927—*185*

Stekel, W. (1930). 'Die Psychologie der Zwangskrankheit.' [The Psychology of Obsessive-Compulsive Neurosis.] *Bericht über den V. allgemeinen ärztlichen Kongress für Psychotherapie* [Report on the Fifth Congress of Psychotherapy for Members of the Medical Profession] *in Baden-Baden 26. bis 29. April 1930,* 22–49. Leipzig; Hirzel—*199*

— (1938). *Die Technik der analytischen Psychotherapie.* Berne; Huber. (*Technique of Analytical Psychotherapy.* London; The Bodley Head 1950.)—*199*

Stemmermann, Anna (1907). 'Beiträge zur Kenntnis und Kasuistik der Pseudologia phantastica.' [Contributions to the Understanding of Pseudologia Fantastica and Case Material.] *Allg. Z. Psychiat.* **64**, 69–110—*60*

Stengel, E. and Cook, N. G. (1958). *Attempted Suicide. Its Social Significance and Effects.* London; Chapman & Hall—*27*

Sterba, R. (1944). 'On Christmas.' *Psychoanal. Quart.* **13**, 79–83—*32*

Stern, F. (1913). 'Beiträge zur Klinik hysterischer Situationspsychosen.' [Clinical Contributions to Hysterical Situational Psychoses.] *Arch. Psychiat. Nervenkr.* **50**, 640–787—*190*

Stertz, G. (1928). 'Die exogenen Reaktionsformen und die organischen Psychosen. Einleitung.' [The Exogenous Reaction Types and the Organic Psychoses. Introduction.] *Handbook of Mental Disorders,* **7**, Spec. Part 3, 1–13—*208*

Stierlin, E. (1909). 'Über psycho-neuropathische Folgezustände bei den Überlebenden der Katastrophe von Courrières am 10. März 1906.' [On Psycho-Neuropathic Sequelae in the Survivors of the Catastrophe at Courrières on 10 March 1906.] *Mschr. Psychiat. Neurol.* **25** (Erg.-Heft), 185–323—*27*

— (1911). 'Nervöse und psychische Störungen nach Katastrophen. Unter besonderer Berücksichtigung der Eisenbahnkatastrophe von Müllheim.' [Nervous and Psychic Disturbances Following Catastrophes with Special Reference to the Railroad Disaster at Müllheim.] *Dtsch. med. Wschr.* **37**, 2028–2035—*27*

Storch, A. (1922). *Das archaisch-primitive Erleben und Denken der Schizophrenen.* [On Archaic-Primitive Experience and Thinking in Schizophrenia.] Berlin; Springer—*219*

Strömgren, B. (1946). 'On Certain Mathematical Problems Connected With the Determination of Anthropometrical and Diagnostical Indices.' *Memorial Volume to Hjalmar Helweg*, 747–752. Copenhagen; Munksgaard—*201*

Strömgren, E. (1935). 'Zum Ersatz des Weinbergschen "abgekürzten Verfahrens".' [On the Replacement of Weinberg's "abgekürztes Verfahren'.] *Z. ges. Neurol. Psychiat.* **153**, 784–797—*187*

— (1938). *Beiträge zur psychiatrischen Erblehre.* [Contributions to Psychiatric Genetics.] Copenhagen; Munksgaard—*187*

— (1940). *Episodiske Psykoser.* [Episodic Psychoses.] Copenhagen; Munksgaard—*41, 77, 205*

— (1942). 'Om Mulighederne for en exakt Uddifferentiering af Konstitutionstyper.' [On the Possibility of an Exact Differentiation Between Constitutional Types.] *Nord. Med.* **13**, 157–162—*195*

— (1945). *Om Bevidsthedsforstyrrelser.* [On Disturbances of Consciousness.] Copenhagen; Munksgaard—*39, 87, 206*

— (1950). 'Statistical and Genetical Population Studies Within Psychiatry. Methods and Principal Results.' *Congrès International de Psychiatrie, Paris 1950*, **6**, 155–192—*187*

— (1958). 'Pathogenese der verschiedenen Formen von psychogenen Psychosen.' [Pathogenesis of the Different Types of Psychogenic Psychoses.] Memorial Volume to Ernst Kretschmer on his 70th Birthday, *Mehrdimensionale Diagnostik und Therapie* [Multidimensional Diagnostics and Therapy], 67–70. Stuttgart; Thieme—*206*

— (1962). Personal Communication—*187*

Szasz, T. (1957). *Pain and Pleasure; a Study of Bodily Feelings.* New York; Basic Books, Inc.—*102*

Tarachow, S. and Fink, M. (1953). 'Absence of a Parent as a Specific Factor Determining Choice of Neurosis: Preliminary Study.' *J. Hillside Hosp.* **2**, 67–71—*212*

Thiele, R. (1926). *Zur Kenntnis der psychischen Residuärzustände nach Encephalitis epidemica bei Kindern und Jugendlichen.* [On the Knowledge of Psychic Residual States after Epidemic Encephalitis in Children and Adolescents.] Berlin; Karger—*91*

Thompson, G. (1959). 'Acute and Chronic Alcoholic Conditions.' *American Handbook of Psychiatry*, **2**, 1203–1221—*121*

Timmermann, E. (1960). 'Vrangforestillingens beskrivelse. Med en indledning om finalistiske synsmåder.' [A Description of the

REFERENCES

Paranoid Delusion. With an Introduction on Finalistic Points of View.] *Nord. psykiat. T.* **14**, 137–146—*213*

Toch, H. H. and Hastorf, A. H. (1955). 'Homeostasis in Psychology. A Review and Critique.' *Psychiatry* **18**, 81–91—*38*

Többen, H. (1913). 'Ein Beitrag zur Psychologie der zu lebenslänglicher Zuchthausstrafe verurteilten oder begnadigten Verbrecher.' [A Contribution to the Psychology of Life Prisoners or Reprieved Criminals.] *Mschr. Kriminalpsychol. Strafrechtsreform* **9**, 449–469—*200*

Urstein, M. (1909). *Die Dementia praecox und ihre Stellung zum manisch-depressiven Irresein.* [Dementia Praecox and Its Relation to Manic-Depressive Psychosis.] Berlin and Vienna; Urban & Schwarzenberg—*78*

Vanggaard, T. (1959). 'On Objectivity and Causality in Psychiatry.' *Acta psychiat. scand.* **34**, 375–382—*213*

Waelder, R. (1951). 'The Structure of Paranoid Ideas: A Critical Survey of Various Theories.' *Int. J. Psycho-Anal.* **32**, 167–177—*33, 146, 212*

Welner, J. (1960). Personal Communication—*16*

— and Strömgren, E. (1958). 'Clinical and Genetic Studies on Benign Schizophreniform Psychoses Based on a Follow-Up.' *Acta psychiat. scand.* **33**, 377–399—*187*

Wernicke, C. (1900). *Grundriss der Psychiatrie in klinischen Vorlesungen.* [An Outline of Psychiatry in Clinical Lectures.] Leipzig; Thieme—*25, 51*

Wetzel, A. (1921). 'Über Shockpsychosen. Ergebnisse von Untersuchungen an ganz frischen Fällen.' [On Shock Psychoses. Results of Investigations of Completely Fresh Cases.] *Z. ges. Neurol. Psychiat.* **65**, 288–330—*27*

Wexler, D., Mendelson, J., Leiderman, H. and Solomon, P. (1958). 'Sensory Deprivation.' *A.M.A. Arch. Neurol. Psychiat.* **79**, 225–233—*17*

Wicksell, S. and Sondén, T. (1934). *Om självmord.* [On Suicide.] Stockholm; Bonnier—*27*

Widlocher, D. (1958). 'Psychoses réactionelles.' [Reactive Psychoses.] *Encéphale* **47**, 533, I–IX—*39*

Wigert, V. (1939). 'Några medicinska synpunkter på tillräknelighetsfrågorna.' [Medical Points of View on Sanity.] *Nord. Med.* **1**, 165–172—*29*

Wilmanns, K. (1908). *Über Gefängnispsychosen.* [On Prison Psychoses.] Halle; Marhold—*200*

— (1940). 'Über Morde im Prodromalstadium der Schizophrenie.' [On Murder in the Prodromal Stage of Schizophrenia.] *Z. ges. Neurol. Psychiat.* **170**, 583–662—*200*

Wimmer, A. (1902). *Evolutiv Paranoia.* [Evolutionary Paranoia.] Copenhagen; Lund—*7, 147*

— (1916). 'Psykogene Sindssygdomsformer.' [Psychogenic Varieties of Mental Diseases.] *St. Hans Hospital 1816–1916, Jubilee Publication*, 85–216. Copenhagen; Gad—*7, 57, 81, 89, 97, 186, 188, 190, 196, 197*

— (ed.) (1929). *Further Studies upon Chronic Epidemic Encephalitis.* Copenhagen; Lewin & Munksgaard, London; Heineman, and Leipzig; Thieme—*122*

PSYCHOGENIC PSYCHOSES

Wimmer, A. (1936). *Speciel klinisk Psykiatri for studerende og Læger.* [Special Clinical Psychiatry for Students and Physicians.] Copenhagen; Munksgaard—*17*

Wolberg, Arlene (1952). 'The "Borderline" Patient.' *Amer. J. Psychotherap.* **6**, 694–710—*32*

Wolfensberger, M. (1923). 'Der Alkoholwahnsinn (akute Halluzinose der Trinker) und seine Beziehungen zu den Schizophrenien.' [Alcoholic Paranoid Conditions (Acute Hallucinosis in Drinkers) and their Relation to the Schizophrenias.] *Z. ges. Neurol. Psychiat.* **82**, 385–418 —*121*

World Health Organisation (1957). *Manual of the International Statistical Classification of Diseases, Injuries, and Causes of Death.* 1955 Revision. Geneva—*5*

Wwedensky, I. N. (1929). 'Zur Frage der Endzustände nach reaktiven Psychosen. (Die Entwicklung postreaktiver psychischer Invalidität.)' [On the Problem of the Final Outcome of Reactive Psychoses. (The Development of Post-Reactive Psychic Disablement.)] *Z. ges. Neurol. Psychiat.* **118**, 200–216—*28*

Yap, P. M. (1951). 'Mental Diseases Peculiar to Certain Cultures: A Survey of Comparative Psychiatry.' *J. ment. Sci.* **97**, 313–327—*204*

— (1952). 'The Latah Reaction: Its Pathodynamics and Nosological Position.' *J. ment. Sci.* **98**, 515–564—*204*

— (1960). 'The Possession Syndrome: A Comparison of Hong Kong and French Findings.' *J. ment. Sci.* **106**, 114–137—*204*

— (1962). Personal Communication—*45, 204*

Zahle, V. (1940). 'Ein Fall psychogen ausgelöster Manie.' [A Case of Psychogenically Precipitated Mania.] *Mschr. Psychiat. Neurol.* **103**, 179–185—*82*

— (1951). 'On Manic-Depressive Psychosis and Neurosis.' *Acta psychiat. scand.* **26**, 95–111—*82*

Zilboorg, G. (1928). 'Malignant Psychoses Related to Childbirth.' *Amer. J. Obstet. Gynec.* **15**, 145–158—*68*

— (1929). 'The Dynamics of Schizophrenic Reactions Related to Pregnancy and Childbirth.' *Amer. J. Psychiat.* **8**, 733–767—*68*

— (1933). 'Anxiety without Affect.' *Psychoanal. Quart.* **2**, 48–67—*13*

— (1941) (in coll. with G. W. Henry). *A History of Medical Psychology.* New York; Norton—*23, 41, 145*

— (1944). 'Manic-Depressive Psychoses.' S. Lorand (ed.). *Psychoanalysis Today*, 261–273. New York; Int. Univ. Press—*45*

Zweig, S. (1943). *Schachnovelle.* Stockholm; Bermann-Fischer. (*The Royal Game.* London; Cassell, Hallam Edition, 1951.)—*16*

NAME INDEX

Abraham, Karl, 28
Alexander, Franz, 34, 194
Allers, Rudolf, 17
Allport, Gordon W., 4, 56
Alström, Carl Henry, 191, 192
Arieti, Silvano, 26, 56, 70, 199, 200, 215
Arlow, Jacob A., *see* Brenner, 212
Aschaffenburg, Gustav, 147, 200

Baelz, Erwin O., 27
Bak, Robert C., 146
Bellak, Leopold, 74
Benedek, Therese, 68
Benedict, Ruth, 29
Bergen, Mary E., 18
Bernheim, Hippolyte, 25
Bibring, Edward, 216, 217
Birnbaum, Karl, 22, 28, 70, 82, 89, 100, 132, 136, 148, 186, 194, 196, 199, 200
Bleuler, Eugen, 25, 29, 32, 34, 40, 74, 81, 138, 145, 214
Bleuler, Manfred, 34, 148
Bonhoeffer, Karl, 4, 28, 78, 81, 100, 205, 208, 209, 210
Bostroem, August, 198, 209
Bratz, Emil, 198
Braun, Ernst, 53
Brenner, Charles, 212
Bresowsky, M., 73
Breuer, Josef, 42, 127
Bumke, Oswald, 25, 81, 132, 198

Cameron, Norman, 146, 189
Campbell, Robert Jean, 5
Cannon, Walter B., 38
Charcot, Jean Martin, 25
Chrobak, Rudolf, 101
Clérambault, Gatian, 164
Cohen, Elie A., 16
Cook, Nancy G., *see* Stengel, 27

Dement, William, 214
Deutsch, Felix, 6
Dickens, Charles, 164
Drever, James, 5
Dunham, H. Warren, 45

Eliasberg, Wladimir G., 106
Eliot, Thomas S., 45
Engel, George L., 26
Esquirol, Jean E. D., 23
Essen-Möller, Erik, 191
Ewald, Gottfried, 68
Eysenck, Hans J., 5

Faergeman, Poul M., XI, 17, 23
Faris, Robert E. L., 45
Ferenczi, Sándor, 28, 32, 153, 213
Finckh, Otto, 198
Fink, Maximilian, 212
Fitzgerald, F. Scott, 26
Freeman, Thomas, 33
Fremming, Kurt H., 185
French, Thomas M., 212
Freud, Anna, 18, 19
Freud, Sigmund, 9, 12, 13, 15, 24, 25, 30, 31, 34, 35, 36, 37, 42, 102, 127, 145, 146, 151, 153, 159, 194, 205, 206, 212, 217, 219
Friedell, Egon, 173
Fromm, Erich, 45

Ganser, Siegbert, 107
Gerö, George, 6, 10, 11, 12
Gerstmann, Josef, 28
Glover, Edward, 6, 12, 15, 42, 146
Glueck, Bernard C., Jr., 200
Goethe, Johann Wolfgang v., 19
Goldfarb, Alvin I., 186
Goldkuhl, Erik, 196
Greenacre, Phyllis, 13

239

SUBJECT INDEX

243

Mental illness
age, and, 186
classifications of, survey of, (Meyer), 6*
environmental factors in, 25–26, 45, 198, 204–205
frequency of, by ethnic groups, 187, 194
Middle Ages, in, 45
middle years, in, 186
organismic approach to, 30
Reformation, and, 45
socio-economic factors, and, 44–45
unitary concept of (Menninger), 106
views on, in 19th century, 23–24
Mescaline and visions, 132, 219
Metabolic disorders, manic-depressive conditions associated with, 27, (Case 28) 72, 216
Metapsychological differences between hysterical and schizophrenic hallucinations, 132
Metapsychology
definition of, 216
structural and topographic views in, 31, see also Structural view of neurosis, psychosis and reality
Methods employed in present work, 46–47, 174–175
Middle Ages, hallucinations in, 45
Middle years, psychiatric difficulties in, 186
Mind-body dichotomy, 10, 30, 208
Mis-diagnoses in present material, 181–182, see also Psychogenic psychoses, at follow-up demonstrated to be . . .
'Mixed psychoses', 78
'Model psychoses', see Experimental psychoses
Morbidity rates, see Frequency
Mortality rate in psychogenic psychoses, 191–192
Mother-infant unit, 19, 20, (Case 21) 67–68, 186
Mothers, 'schizophrenogenic', 106
Mourning, biological purpose of, 216

Multidimensional diagnostics (Birnbaum, Kretschmer), 22*, 148
Multiple personality, 39
Murder, effect on a child of witnessing, 18–19
Mutism, akinetic (stupor), 140*

Narcissistic supplies and
depression, 217
panic, 218
Need(s)
oral, 19
primary (viscerogenic) and secondary (psychogenic) (Murray), 4–5
protection against cold, for, 19
simple gratification of, in anaclitic phase of development, 19
Neo-Freudian school, 215
Neurosis
character, total personality affected in, 32
choice of type of, and choice of defence, 212
constitution, 205, 212
dream and behaviour, basic similarities between, 212
masking psychosis, (Case 106) 127, 181–182, 199–200
pathoplastic factor in manic-depressive psychosis, as, 27
predisposing factor in psychogenic psychoses, as, 51
psychosis, and
alleged discontinuum between, 29, 30, 32, 212
continuum of, 31, 34, (Case 151) 160–161, 212, 215
organic precipitation of, (Case 21) 67–68, (Case 30) 74, 81, (Cases 85, 86) 113–114, (Case 92) 118
psychoanalytic theory of, 30–32, 33–34, 205, 212, see also Structural view of neurosis, psychosis, and reality
Sunday type of (Ferenczi), 32
war, of, 28, 36, (Case 78) 108–109